700

Adventures

by Tracy Hickman and Margaret Weis

The AD&D® game source book for continuing adventures in the world of Krynn.

TSR, Inc.
POB 756
Lake Geneva,
WI 53147

TSR, Inc.
PRODUCTS OF YOUR IMAGINATION™

TSR UK Ltd.
The Mill, Rathmore Road
Cambridge CB1 4AD
United Kingdom

Dedication

To Laura Curtis Hickman, my wife, for whom worlds were created.

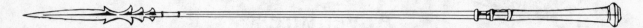

Credits

Continuity & Story: Tracy Hickman and Margaret Weis

Game Systems Design: Tracy Hickman

Editing: Mike Breault, with Jon Pickens

Proofreading: Jon Pickens, Warren Spector, and Margaret Weis

The DRAGONLANCE® Series Design Team: Tracy Hickman (Series Concept), Harold Johnson (Director of Design), Margaret Weis, Douglas Niles, Jeff Grubb, Larry Elmore, Bruce Nesmith, Mike Breault, Roger Moore, Laura Hickman, Linda Bakk, Michael Dobson, Carl Smith, Garry Spiegle.

Cover Art: Jeff Easley

Interior Illustrations: George Barr

Cartography: Karen Wynn Fonstad, and Dennis Kauth

Graphic Design: Stephanie Tabat

Typography: Kim Janke and Betty Elmore

Keyline: Stephanie Tabat and Susan Myers

Special Thanks to

Dave Cook for advice on the AD&D® game system revisions and particularly the clerics system.

Jeff Grubb for his spell constructions, long support in the DRAGONLANCE® saga, and the Gods of Krynn.

Doug Niles for his original compiling of the DRAGONLANCE saga source book and for writing almost as many DRAGONLANCE modules as I did.

And thanks to all three for bailing me out when times got tough. The work of your hands shows on every page.

Distributed to the book trade by Random House, Inc., and in Canada by Random House of Canada, Ltd.

Distributed to the toy and hobby trade by regional distributors.

Distributed in the United Kingdom by TSR UK Ltd.

©1987 TSR, Inc. All Rights Reserved.

0-88038-452-2

Printed in the U.S.A.

preface

At last...the world of Krynn!

Here you hold as much of Krynn as can be told in one book. The world of the DRAGONLANCE® saga is a vast and complex one. This book alone cannot hope to cover all of the wonder and magic of that fabled land. We have compressed as much information as we could into this volume, but it still proved to be too large a task.

To fully recreate the world of Krynn, we recommend that you read more about this world—the DRAGONLANCE modules, the *Chronicles* trilogy, the *Legends* trilogy, and the anthology series of DRAGONLANCE Tales. These not only give you a comprehensive picture of the world and its inhabitants, but they also provide rich descriptions with which to color your campaign. For more detailed maps of Krynn and many of its specific environments, we direct you to Karen Fonstad's *Atlas of Krynn*.

You can certainly enjoy this book without playing the game...but what a game it is! Those of you who are playing the DRAGONLANCE series in the AD&D® game system will, as usual, need those rule books to play the series as the epic role-playing game that it is. We have tried to avoid duplicating material that is found in those other works so as to make room for all the detail of Krynn that we possibly can. This means for you gamers that you will need to refer to other AD&D books from time to time. We assume that you have the *Dungeon Master's Guide* and the *Player's Handbook* in order to play the game. Other works, however, you may not have, such as the *Dungeoneer's Survival Guide*, *Wilderness Survival Guide*, and *Unearthed Arcana*. We have made extensive use of these reference books in detailing the world of the DRAGONLANCE saga. However, if you do not happen to have these latter works you should not worry. The series should play just fine with just your *Dungeon Master's Guide* and *Player's Handbook*.

This book is written in a different format than the other AD&D hardback books. The material that is specifically related to the AD&D game system or to running a DRAGONLANCE campaign is placed in grey boxes throughout the text. This means that the text is easier to read and the game references are readily available.

You, in all your letters, have beckoned us back to the world of Tanis, Laurana, Kitiara, Raistlin and all the rest. May we now walk that road together for a time once more, with old friends and new.

Tracy Hickman

Margaret Weis

table of contents

TABLE OF CONTENTS

the Realms Above

*"In the Cradle of the Sky,
On Silken Starshine lay
We who soon upon the Face of Krynn
would as infant mortals play."*

the universe

From the chaos born you come...the glorious brilliance of the heavens surrounds you. And the first glorious being you encounter is a wizard fumbling about in his grey cloak.

"Eh? Well! I don't seem to recall seeing you wandering about the realms of the gods before! Never had much of a memory for names. I suppose that it doesn't much matter since you don't have one yet. Oh, not to worry, not to worry, that will come in time. Everyone gets a name you know. Hard to keep our records straight here without it!

"I'm Fizban, Fizban the Fabulous, but you can call me...er, well, whatever. I guess some would call me the big guy around here, but the truth of it is a bit more complicated than that. Still, I am here to help you get on your way into the fabulous world that we have prepared for you. Tragedy and comedy, honor and mystery await you there!

"I suppose you will want to get your bearings first, eh? Not easy stepping out of the chaos and trying to make sense of the new universe, is it? Well never you fear, for you have Fizbur the Feverles...er, Fasbar the Flaver...well, I am at your side every step of the way.

"So let's...hmmmm. This crazy wizard is my favorite aspect, but I see that it is a bit difficult for you just now. Let's try something a bit more like what you would expect."

The old man's robes flare suddenly with striking rays of light. His form rises before you transformed into the shining brilliance of the greatest of benevolent dragons: Paladine.

the tale Begins
Orders of the Universe

In the beginning were the gods from Beyond.

There, before the beginning, they dwelt in joy in the presence of the High God whose children they were. It was there decreed that a new time and place would come to be. Time would there begin again, spirits would live and, in the course of time, new power would come to be.

Three were the pillars upon which this universe was forged: Good, Evil, and Neutrality. This was the great triangle upon which all the universe was brought to be.

Reorx, the Forging God, struck his hammer amidst the Chaos. Chaos slowed and the sparks from his hammer became the stars. From their light came diverse spirits of all types: some disposed to good, some to evil, and some to neutrality.

The gods began to quarrel over these spirits. The Gods of Good wanted to nurture the spirits in the paths of righteousness and share with them dominion over the universe. The Gods of Evil sought to make the spirits their slaves to do their every bidding. The Gods of Neutrality sought a balance: to give the spirits freedom to choose for themselves whether they would serve Good or Evil.

And so the All-Saints War raged among the heavens. The Good and Neutral Gods combined forces to keep Evil from a final victory. Then spoke the High God from Beyond, decreeing the Balance of the World. The Gods of Good, Evil, and Neutrality would each be allowed to bestow one gift upon the spirits.

The Gods of Good gave the spirits life and physical form. Thus, the spirits gained control over the material world and became more like the Gods themselves. The Gods of Good hoped the spirits would bring peace and order to the worlds and lead them along the path to righteousness.

The Gods of Evil decreed that these physical beings would hunger and thirst and have to work to satisfy their needs. The Gods of Evil hoped that through hunger and suffering they could subjugate the races.

The Gods of Neutrality gave the spirits the gift of free will, to choose freely between Good and Evil. Thus did they preserve the Balance.

And so the Gods created the world of Krynn as a dwelling place for the spirits. The High God decreed that each spirit could choose his own way through life. Then would come death, the passage from Krynn to the next state of existence.

the Alignments of the Gods

All of the universe stands upon the Great Triangle. This foundation has always existed and will exist down through the ages of time and until the end of the world.

At the apexes of the triangles stand the three anchors upon which the universe is built. These are known among men as Good, Evil, and Neutrality. It is into these positions that the gods align themselves in their effort to maintain progress in the universe they have brought into being.

the Place of Mortals

Many races came into being from the spirits that awoke. First were the elves, most favored by the Gods of Good. Elves are the Shapers of the world, possessing good magic to bend nature to their will. They have the longest life span of all the spirits; although they change the world, they themselves change very little.

The human race is most favored by the Gods of Neutrality, although the souls of men are coveted by the Gods of both Good and Evil. Men can choose freely between good and evil. Their shorter time in the world is spent in striving for power and knowledge. They are quick to think and to act—often without considering the consequences. Thus men give the world motion.

The race of ogres is most favored by the Gods of Evil. In the beginning, the ogres were the most beautiful of the races, but they could think only of their hungers. They were easily enslaved by their needs, and their beauty vanished as their hungers devoured them. Ogres are selfish and cruel; they delight in inflicting pain and suffering upon the weak.

The High God created the fourth class of beings: the animals. He created them with a balance of Good, Evil, and Neutrality, and they were born of the world itself. Dragons are the lords of the animal kingdom. They are free to choose among the alignments of the gods.

When the spirits awoke at the sounding of Reorx's hammer, many of them found their way into the alignments of the gods through their inherent natures. The elves were drawn naturally toward the Good alignment while the ogres were drawn to that of Evil. The animals of the world were Neutral in their aspect and came silently under the domain of the Neutral gods.

However, most wondrous were the spirits called the Maran, meaning "Free-willed." These were men who possessed the ability to choose their destinies. Not placed at any of the three poles of the gods' triangle, humans swing in the middle of the triangle from pole to pole to pole. This choice and free agency gives motion to the universe and propels it forward.

Not only does man give motion to the universe, but he also inspires the other races to action. Thus these are the most prized of all the souls that awakened.

the law of Consequence

Each of the three alignments in the universe of Krynn espouses its own philosophy. These philosophies are the roots of all moral action in the world of Krynn.

1. Good Redeems its Own: Also known as the Law of Paladine, this statement reflects the approach of all the gods of Good in their efforts to advance truth and knowledge in the universe at large. Good seeks to forward its goals and aims by redeeming and recalling the lost members of its flock and bring about the advancement of the universe by compassion and justice.

2. Evil Feeds Upon Itself: Also known as the Law of the Dark Queen, this reflects evil's belief in natural selection through the elimination of weaker beings. Chaotic Evil's objective in the universe is the supremacy of might without any moral considerations whatsoever. Lawful Evil's objectives are similar, but it seeks to attain supremacy through the rigid application of a morality of strength.

3. Both Good and Evil Must Exist in Contrast: This is known as the Law of Gilean or the Doctrine of Shadow. This is the primary position of the Neutral gods who see the diversity of both view points as balancing one another on a universal scale. Should either side dominate, Neutrals maintain, then the universe would be either all light or all dark without any contrasts to bring focus or purpose. Neutral's objective is unity in diversity.

4. The Law of Consequence: This final law was given by the High God himself to rule over all other laws. For every law and rule that is obeyed there is a reward and blessing; for every law transgressed there is a punishment. Blessings and punishments may not come about immediately, but they occur eventually.

A proper DRAGONLANCE® game bases its campaigns and its morals around these principles—promoting the power of truth over injustice, good over evil, and granting good consequences for good acts and bad consequences for evil acts.

the constellations
of krynn

Characters in krynn

Those who find their way from the heavens to their mortal existences upon the face of Krynn receive their lots in life. This is not to say that this is all that a soul may become in the world—far from it. Because of the gift of the High God to all humanity, free will brings to the circles of the world an infinite number of people and viewpoints. It is up to you to determine who you become and what you do.

Yet in the beginning you start with a certain lot in life—a classification as to who you are and what you may become. These classifications have existed since the beginning of time. Some of these character types are universal and exist not only in Krynn, but also on other worlds far from the sight and knowledge of the True Gods. Still others are unique to this world of Krynn and exist nowhere else in all the universes.

Standard Classes

While there are many more classes than are given here, these are the ones you are now free to choose. Of those classes that are common to many different universes, the following are possible for you in your sojourn in Krynn. These are types that are truly universal. Also listed are those types that are unique to the realms of Krynn—these appear in italic type.

Clerics (heathen): Clerics who worship gods other than the True Gods are considered heathen clerics in the world of Krynn. They are powerless and receive no blessings from the gods. This class of characters includes clerics from other universes who have somehow come to Krynn by chance or design from those other realms.

Druids (heathen): As with heathen clerics, this refers to that class of druid that has come from beyond Krynn. They also lose their powers upon coming to Krynn.

Holy Orders of the Stars: This title refers to the three general categories of clerics that serve the gods of this universe. These follow the lines of Good, Evil, or Neutrality. Within these three divisions are found the clerics and orders of each of the gods individually. Each order does service to its god and gains its powers dependent upon the spheres of influence which that god holds. As there are six separate gods in each of these divisions (not counting the gods of magic), there are no fewer than 18 separate True Gods who main-tain a variety of orders each. Each has its own power and sphere of influence that determines the powers that its priests have.

Fighters: Those of might and weapons. These do battle for others or for their own purposes.

Barbarians: Savages of the wilds. Though undisciplined in the ways of civilized nations, they are fierce warriors and have empathy with nature. Barbarians in Krynn generally come from the northern reaches of Ergoth and the badlands of Khur.

Rangers: Wilderness masters. These folk travel the plains of Krynn far and wide and are well versed in wilderness lore. They generally come from Nordmaar regions as well as the plains areas about Tarsis and Abanasinia.

Cavaliers: Noble Knights of kingdoms. These are always found in service of individual kingdoms and may be considered candidates for the Knights of Solamnia.

Paladins: Knights in the cause of good. Like cavaliers, these men are in single service rather than to the greater Knighthood of the Solamnic Orders. Their obedience and fealty is sworn not to a monarch but to a deity of good.

Knights of Solamnia: These are really three distinct orders grouped into one. The orders are the Knights of the Crown, Knights of the

Sword, and Knights of the Rose. A candidate for the Order of the Sword must first have attained certain fame as a Knight of the Crown in order to be accepted. A candidate for Knight of the Rose must have done likewise as a Knight of the Sword before being accepted. These Knights and their Orders of Honor have been alternately praised and reviled throughout history. They maintained a steadfast code of honor and enforced it with both might and justice throughout their long history.

Magic-Users (renegade): There are those magic-users who attempt to utilize their powers outside the moderating influence of the Orders of High Sorcery. Those who do are called magic-users by the common folk but are referred to as renegade wizards by those of the Order of High Sorcery. These are earnestly hunted down by the order to entice them to join the order or destroy them if they refuse. Renegade wizards have a short life expectancy on Krynn.

Illusionists (renegade): Renegade illusionists are those whose powers lie outside the spheres of the three moons (see page 27). They are treated the same way as renegade magic-users.

Wizards of High Sorcery: There are three types of High Sorcery Wizards: White Robe wizards, Red Robe wizards, and Black Robe wizards. They control all magic on Krynn.

Thieves (Handlers): Here is a fellow who will steal from anyone. In most Krynn societies, this type of behavior is not only condemned but punished severely. The only exceptions to this rule are the kender. These diminutive people, while embodying the traits and abilities of thieves, call themselves "handlers" since the term thief denotes one who steals for gain. Handlers, on the other hand, do not steal for personal gain, but simply out of an outrageous curiosity about everything and everyone at all times. Kender handlers are just as likely to leave something behind as to take something new. See *Kender* (page 51) for a more complete description of this race.

Thief/Acrobats: These characters not only have certain sleight-of-hand skills of thieves but also the additional capabilities of acrobatic movement.

Travelers from the Beyond

One of the many wonders in the universe is the question of where the inhabitants of Krynn come from. Are some not of Reork's forging at the beginning of time? Many have been the rumors of travelers who have crossed the void of the night sky or come by hidden paths from worlds not of Krynn.

If you find yourself face to face with one who is not of Krynn, be wary! Strangers may not understand your customs or your thinking.

Those who come to Krynn from other worlds may find more than they bargained for. The gods of Krynn have secured their world against such incursions for fear of upsetting the balance of the world. There is a 1% per day cumulative chance that a character visiting Krynn from other worlds cannot return across the void to his home world. This percentage is checked any time an attempt is made. Those failing this check remain on Krynn. This percentage never gets any higher than 98%.

Another problem is that Krynn's systems of government and finance are different from most of those in the known universes. What may be great wealth in other worlds is worth little here. The gods of Krynn are unlike those in other realms and do not readily recognize worshipers from other worlds. Renegade wizards who demonstrate power without having first passed the Test of High Sorcery (see page 34) are hunted by all members of that order in Krynn and brought before the council for justice.

Thieves who may find easy pickings elsewhere discover that law and justice in the cities of Krynn are swift and complete. Those few voyagers who have traveled from Krynn into the worlds beyond report strange things indeed. Gnomes find that there is a 105% chance of failure for their devices whenever the gods of that realm take a dislike to them.

Acceptable Character Classes

The following character classes are acceptable in a DRAGONLANCE® game campaign. They are divided into classes and subclasses. Character classes that are unique to Krynn are noted in italics.

Cleric (Heathen) *
　Druid (Heathen)*
　Holy Order of the Stars (Krynn Clerics)
Fighter
　Barbarian
　Ranger
Cavalier *
　Paladin *
　Knight of Solamnia
Magic-User *
　Illusionist *
　Wizard of High Sorcery
Thief
　Thief/Acrobat

* These classes have the following special limitations and rules in Krynn.

Clerics and Druids: Any cleric or druid who enters Krynn from another world has lost contact with his original deity. In so doing, he has become a heathen cleric.

Heathen clerics cannot cast spells or acquire them as they normally might do. The Seekers in the Haven and Solace regions of Abanasinia were clerics of this type.

Only by finding a True God who is reasonably compatible with the teachings of his former deity can a heathen cleric hope to regain his spell-casting abilities; in effect, he is converted to one of the Holy Orders of the Stars. While this may be no problem for him while he is still in Krynn (see *Messengers from the Heavens*, page 39, for details on conversion) his original deity may be upset at his actions when (and if) he returns to his original universe. This will not happen, of course, if the Krynn Order he worships is compatible with his original deity's beliefs.

Cavaliers/Paladins: These represent knights who are operating under the direction of an organization other than the Knights of Solamnia. Paladins who do not convert to one of the True Gods (as with heathen clerics) lose their special abilities and powers until they do so.

One of these characters may wish to join the Solamnic Knights while he is in Krynn, but he is not required to do so. If he joins, he must first enter the Order of the Crown as if a first-level character. He then starts a second record of his experience points for determining his level. The cavalier or paladin who joins the Knights retains his hit points, level, AC, and proficiencies at the level he had before joining the Knighthood, but these stats do not increase until his Solamnic Knight level equals his previous level. He then progresses normally as a Knight of Solamnia. Note that it is far easier for such an experienced Knight to

gain experience points and go up in levels than it is for those who are truly first level.

If the cavalier or paladin returns to his original world, he can assume either his previous experience points and level or use those he acquired as a Knight of Solamnia (whichever is higher).

Magic-Users/Illusionists: No determination of which order the magic-user will follow is made before he reaches 3d level (see *Wizards of High Sorcery*, page 27). The Wizards of High Sorcery make no clear-cut distinction between magic-users and illusionists, as opposed to the situation in many AD&D® games. What wizards are or believe is pretty much left up to them prior to 3d level.

Magic-users and illusionists from other campaigns and who are over 3d level are immediately branded as renegades. The rules for renegade wizards are found in the *Wizards of High Sorcery*. They must either join the order or be hunted by them. It is almost always a quick and tragic end for renegades unless they join the orders.

Characters of other classes revert to their major classes when they enter Krynn, with experience points equal to the mid-point of their current level. Monks, for example, become heathen clerics of equal level. There are no assassin characters in Krynn. These would become thieves.

General Limitations in Krynn

Player characters in other worlds can advance to unlimited levels, but not in Krynn. Once a player character advances beyond 18th level, the gods of Krynn feel that it is time to reassign him to some other world. Fortunately for the lovers of Krynn, advancement beyond 18th level is not mandatory. Your PC has the unique ability to refuse such advancement (and thereby stay within the world of Krynn). It is up to you.

Those few individuals who remain in the world beyond 18th level do so either by special permission of the gods or by unnatural means. The priviledged few include such beings as the Dragon Highlords of the Queen of Darkness or Raistlin. Takhisis is always out to destroy the balance of the world. This is not to say that she grants such boons without great reason. The rule is that PCs who wish to remain in Krynn must forfeit any advancement beyond 18th level regardless of class; if they advance beyond that, the gods remove them from Krynn.

What's Your Alignment?

This question comes up often in AD&D games. Alignment in Krynn has important effects that are very different from a standard AD&D campaign. The types of spells available to a magic-user or cleric and the abilities of a Knight of Solamnia are all affected by the character's alignment. In most AD&D® campaigns, the player chooses the alignment of his PC and then tries to act accordingly. Alignment in Krynn is handled differently. The alignment of a PC is determined by his actions, not the other way around.

Characters in Krynn declare their *moral alignments* (good, neutral, or evil) at the beginning of the game, though sometimes character class determines the starting alignment. For example, Knights of Solamnia who begin as Knights of the Crown have their moral alignment set for them initially as good.

DMs can use the Character Alignment Tracking chart at the back of the book (page 114) to keep track of each PC's moral alignment as it changes according to the PC's actions. Each PC's moral alignment starts at the midpoint of his chosen alignment on the chart. Each time the PC performs an action that the DM decides is outside the bounds of the PC's current alignment, the DM marks the PC's new alignment position on the chart from 1 to 3 points in the direction of the action performed.

As a character shifts alignment, he passes into a grey area between the alignments. This area warns the PC that his actions are not in line with the beliefs of his alignment. A character who enters a grey area incurs the following effects:

Attack	−1 to hit opponent
Defense	+1 to own armor class
Wizard Spells	10% fails to recall *
Cleric Spells	10% fails to recall

* When a wizard attempts to use any spell, roll 1d100. If the result is 10 or less, then the spell simply cannot be recalled and does not function. Note that the player would not know about this until the PC fails to cast a spell.

Clerics can also fail to recall a spell in the same way. In addition, clerical spells that are special to the god the cleric serves (e.g., healing spells to Mishakal) have a 20% chance of not being acquired for the day. Knights of Solamnia who have clerical spell-casting abilities are also subject to this penalty.

When a PC's alignment passes from the grey area into another alignment, shift the character's alignment to the midpoint of the new alignment. (The penalties for being in the transition area between alignments go away, but now the PC is subject to the strictures of his new alignment.) For example, if a character's alignment just passed from the grey area between good and neutral into the area of neutral, mark his alignment in the middle of the neutral area. This prevents a PC from bouncing back and forth between alignments too easily. It also makes him work hard if he wants to regain his old alignment. When a change in alignment occurs, do **not** inform the player that his PC has just changed alignment. Wait until he tries to perform an action that depends on his alignment, then tell him it doesn't work. It's up to the player to realize what happened and how to fix it.

Changes of alignment can have drastic consequences for certain character classes. Clerics who change their alignment are considered *lost* and immediately lose two levels and all their spell-casting abilities until they either repent or find another god to serve. Wizards who gain their magic by the grace of the moons of magic and who then become *renegades* (see page 36) also lose two levels. In the case of wizards, however, they revert to the robes of their new alignment and do not have to seek out new powers as do clerics. Knights of Solamnia lose position and abilities by falling from grace—they become fighters until they redeem themselves.

Of course, doing deeds that are in line with their old alignments tend to shift them back.

The special abilities and aids that each of the Orders of Knights bestows upon its members are directly dependent upon how well each Knight follows the laws of his organization.

knights of Solamnia

The Knights of Solamnia were once the greatest order of chivalry in all the history of Krynn. Now their entire way of life shifts in precarious balance between the Code of Honor and the truth of what the world has become.

the Origin of the knights

The Knights came into being nearly 2,000 years before the War of the Lance, during the Age of Dreams, rising like a phoenix from the ashes of the empire of Ergoth.

Vinas Solamnus, commander of the Ergothian Emperor's Palace Guard, set forth from the capital city of Daltigoth to squash a rebellion brewing in the northeastern reaches of the empire. However, Solamnus, a true and honorable man, found that the rebellion was well justified. Solamnus called his troops together and presented the case of the people. Any knights who believed in the cause of the rebels were entreated to stay. Those who did not were given leave to return to Daltigoth. Even though his men knew that doing so meant exile and possibly death, most chose to stay with Solamnus.

Thus began the War of Ice Tears. Although Ergoth was in the grip of the most terrible winter ever chronicled, Solamnus and his dedicated army of knights and frontier nobles marched on Daltigoth and laid siege to it. Solamnus personally led daring raids into the city. Within two months, the capital fell as a revolt of the people forced the emperor to sue for peace. As a result, the northeastern plains of Ergoth, from the Vingaard Mountains to the Estwild, gained its independence. The grateful people of that region chose Vinas as their king and named their new country Solamnia in his honor. Although it never attained any great power during the rest of that Age, Solamnia became synonymous with honesty, integrity, and fierce determination.

Vinas knew that those who followed him as rulers of Solamnia might not be as honorable as he. Thus he organized the Knights of Solamnia.

The tale of their origins is bound up in the story of the Quest of Honor that tells of Vinas Solamnus's journey in search of true honor.

The story went something along these lines.

In the year 1225 PC, following his coronation as the king of Solamnia, Vinas Solamnus was beseeched by the Lords of the Northern Reaches. They had recently broken from the tyranny of Ergoth and now looked to Solamnus to unite them. Solamnus could not see how this could be done in the light of their conflicting ideals and customs. So it was that he set off on a quest to find the answer to his dilemma. He left the united kingdoms in the hands of his lieutenants and journeyed into the wild.

After many weeks of searching and trial, he came at last to Sancrist Isle. There in that wild place he found a glade and offered supplication to the gods on a black granite stone in the center of the clearing. Three of the gods of good soon came to him: Paladine, the god of balance, justice, and defense; Kiri-Jolith, the god of just warfare; and Habbakuk, god of good nature, loyalty, and the elements.

In that glade did they outline for Vinas the model of a Knighthood that would last down the centuries. Three separate Orders would balance one another with high ideals, each patterned after the ideals of the gods who came to Vinas's aid that day. Some versions of the tale say that Vinas was also shown the downfall of the Knights; other versions tell of the Knighthood rising again and again in time of need.

As a final blessing, the gods transformed the stone before Solamnus into a pillar of translucent white crystal. This sanctified the glade and sealed the unity of these three gods in their commitment to uphold the Knighthood so long as the Knights walked in honor and worthiness.

Two other legends relating to Solamnia and the Knights come from this period of time. Bedal Brightblade was a hero said to have fought the desert nomads to a standstill, holding a pass into Solamnia singlehandedly until help came. His sword Brightblade was said to be of dwarven make and never rusted or dulled despite vigorous use. His tomb is somewhere in the far southern mountains in an unknown location. It is rumored that Bedal will return to aid Solamnia in its time of need. Sturm Brightblade, of great renown during the War of the Lance is said to be a distant descendant of this legendary figure.

Huma Dragonbane, known as the most perfect of the Knights, gathered together a group of heroes to destroy the dragons and drive them from the lands of Solamnia. Huma's legend, compiled by the great elven bard Quevalen Soth, is fragmented now. Many doubt that Huma ever really existed. But the story of the last battle between Huma

and the Queen of Darkness is still told, along with the tragic love Huma bore for a silver dragon.

Huma managed to slay the evil dragon-leader with the silver dragon's help, but in doing so he sustained a mortal wound. By some accounts, Huma died on the field of battle; others, however, say that he lingered for days in such pain that the gods themselves suffered in sympathy, inflicting terrible thunderstorms upon the land. To this day, you find people who claim that lightning and thunder strike the land in memory of Huma's agony.

Huma was buried with great reverence, and for many years those who aspired to join the Knights made pilgrimages to the tomb of Huma, which—so legend had it—was carved in the shape of a silver dragon. As the world descended into evil, the road to Huma's tomb became dark and dangerous to travel. Soon, people began to question Huma's very existence; the location of the tomb and his body were forgotten. During the War of the Lance, the Tomb was again discovered and with it the source of the special metal used to forge the fabled Dragonlances. Though the tomb was found, Huma's remains were not discovered.

Through wars with bordering states, the Third Dragon War, and Solamnia's subsequent rise to power during the Age of Might, the Knights of Solamnia remained true to the model established by their great and long-dead king.

Cataclysm to Present

The Kingpriest of Istar brought down the wrath of the gods upon Krynn, and the gods punished the people for their pride by casting a fiery mountain down on the land. The destruction and desolation caused by the disaster disrupted the world for months.

Although their land had been spared the worst of the blow, the people of Solamnia still suffered greatly during this time. Evil creatures, long banished from Krynn, returned to the land. Many of the Knights perished fighting the unknown and unspeakable horrors that ravaged the countryside.

In the end, it was the common people of Solamnia who cast the Knights into disgrace. For centuries, the Knights had kept the peace and safety of the realm. Now, in the hour of their most desperate need, it seemed that the Knights were powerless. Rumors began to spread that the Knights had foreseen the coming of the Cataclysm and had done nothing to

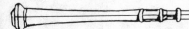 

stop it. Some Knights, it was said, actually intended to profit by the disaster and increase their land holdings.

Indeed, there was some truth to these tales but it was not the Solamnic Order's doing. Lord Soth, a Knight of the Rose who ruled in the far northeast reaches of Solamnia at Dargaard Keep had, in fact, been warned by his elven wife of the calamity that was coming.

But Soth had dark secrets to keep. He had wed the elf woman in secret though he was already married to a barren woman of human royalty. Having fathered a child by the elf woman, he then murdered his first wife and claimed that she died in childbirth. The child of the elf woman became his heir and he claimed the elf woman as his lawful wife. When warned of the impending doom of the world, Lord Soth rode forth with his loyal Knights behind him. Yet waiting for him along the way was a troop of elven clerical women who stopped him. They knew of his dark deeds and persuaded Soth to turn back in exchange for their silence.

Soth turned back and the Cataclysm took place. The elf woman and his child were consumed in a terrible fire before Soth's very throne. He returned to the keep to find the image of their bodies burned into the stone. No rug would cover it without being consumed. No brush would remove its stain. Thus did Soth sit on his throne until he, too, died but even then the gods would not grant him relief from his torment. His Knights, blind in their obedience to his will, remain with him still as skeleton warriors. The elven clerics reside there as well—banshees who sing each night to the fallen Knight of Solamnia, telling of his fallen and never-ending punishment.

The terrible deeds of this Knight did great injustice to the Knighthood as a whole. Before long, Knights were jeered in public and openly reviled. Darker acts were also committed: Knights were foully murdered, their castles and homes invaded, and their families slain or driven into exile. So it was that the Knights silently disappeared from the knowledge of men. The Knights who remained found themselves forced to roam the countryside in secret and under false names, lest they be discovered. Still, they kept their ideals and their honor, and did what they could to fight the growing evil in the world. A few Knights who found their loss of status intolerable left their homeland and settled across the waters on Sancrist Isle. To this day, a strong group of Knights exists there, while only covert organizations survive within Solamnia.

the Organization of the knighthood

The organization of the Knighthood has changed little from the Age of Might. The Great Circle of the Knighthood has long since been moved from Vingaard Keep to its current home at Whitestone Glade on Sancrist, with Castle Wistan nearby.

The Knighthood is ruled by the Lord of Knights. This position, however, has been left vacant since the time of the Cataclysm due primarily to the difficulties in calling a Grand Circle of Knights together in sufficient numbers to elect a Knight from eligible candidates. With the reestablishment of order throughout the continent of Ansalon, the day of appointment will soon be at hand. The position must be filled by one of the High Knights: either the High Warrior, the High Clerist, or the High Justice. At least 75% of the established Circles of Knights must send two representatives to vote at the Grand Circle. Once appointed, the Lord of Knights serves for life unless he is found guilty of a breach of honor by a Knightly Council.

The will of the Lord of Knights is carried out by the High Knights through their respective Orders. The High Warrior commands the Order of the Rose; the High Clerist commands the Order of the Sword; and the High Guardian commands the Order of the Crown. These are nominated and elected by members of their own Orders without influence from the other two orders. All Knightly Councils, however, must be led by a contingent of three ranking knights, one from each of the Orders of Knighthood.

Individual cells of knights exist throughout Ansalon. Some of these are in touch with the Grand Circle in Sancrist, but many still are not. These groups of Knights exist permanently in most townships and all cities throughout the continent. They are there to give aid and receive the pledge of any local Knights of Solamnia. Some of these Circles exist openly and are easy to find. Such Circles are found in Sancrist, Palanthus, and other places where the Knighthood has always been welcome. In places where the Knighthood is still viewed suspiciously (such as Nordmaar or Tarsis) or even banned (as in any lands under Dragon Highlord control), these Circles exist clandestinely and their meetings are held in secret.

Circles of knighthood

Most Knights of Solamnia are required to forfeit much of their monetary gains to the greater Knighthood and then draw according to their needs from the general coffers of the Knights of Solamnia. This is done at any of the established Circles of Knighthood.

This is not to say that such assistance is very great. Indeed, in the case of a Circle that is in the stiff grasp of the Dragon Highlords, the Circle may require more assistance from a visiting Knight than it can offer him in return.

What kind of aid awaits a Knight depends greatly upon the size of the town that he is visiting and the conditions there. Determine the modifiers for size of the town and other conditions using the Knights' Circle Modifiers table on page 128. Add these to the roll of 1d10. Then refer to the Knights' Circle table on page 128 to determine the amount and type of aid that is available at that particular Circle of Knighthood.

The results of this roll have the following effects.

Coin: This is a modifier to the amount of coinage a Knight is entitled to draw. As a Knight grows in power, he is able to draw more and more from the coffers of the Knighthood for the purposes of furthering the goals of the Orders. (But using such funds for purposes counter to the ideals of honor and the Measure is cause for questioning the honor of a knight.)

Equipment: This gives the types of weapons and armor available at that Circle.

Healing: There are three numbers listed. These represent the number of *cure light wounds*, *cure serious wounds*, and *heal* spells that are available as potions. Once used at a location, they are gone until replaced. Normally these are replaced up to these maximums at the rate of one per week, month, and year, respectively.

Ranking Authority: This lists the highest-ranking authority who governs that particular Circle. This may be important should a Knightly Council have to be called.

Note that a Knightly Council can be held anywhere, including the wild, and does not require a Circle of Knighthood to be binding or official. The Circles of Knighthood provide only an official place for such councils to be held as well as a place for assistance to Knights who are in need.

the Oath and the Measure

The organization of the Knights has not changed substantially in the last 1,800 years. The Knights subscribe to two codes: the Oath and the Measure. The Oath is simply: "Est Sularus oth Mithas" (literally, "My Honor is My Life").

The Measure is an extensive set of laws, many volumes in length, that defines what honor actually means. The Measure is complicated and exacting; only a brief summary of its laws are given here. It is important to remember that exact and unquestioned adherence to the law is the goal of the Knight. The greatest problem facing the Knights at the time of the War of the Lance was that the spirit of the Oath had left them. Only the rigid, unbending shell of the Measure remained. The Knights learned that honor does not lie in the aged and dusty codes of the Measure, but in the heart of the true Knight. Though this lesson was hard and costly and learned only slowly, it eventually promises to make the Knighthood a shining example and power in the world again.

The Oath and the Measure were compiled from the writings of Vinas Solamnus and his successors. The whole of the Measure eventually consisted of thirty-seven 300-page volumes. The following are some excerpts from the Measure.

"The Oath governs all a Knight is and does. It is his life's blood, more sacred to him than life itself."

"The Measure of a Knight is taken by how well he upholds the Oath. We judge a Knight against the Measure and by the Measure. The Measure of the Rose deals with holy wisdom among the Knights. The Measure of the Sword deals with the discipline of Honor among Knights. The Measure of the Crown deals with the disciplines of Loyalty and Obedience."

"No Knight found wanting in the Measure of any Order shall command Knights on the field of battle nor council with them until repented of his unknightly deeds."

the knights of the Crown and their Measure

The Order of the Crown exemplifies the ideals of Loyalty and Obedience in all that a Knight is and does. Loyalty is the unquestioned promise of a Knight to a higher power and authority. Loyalty is a treasure valued only when it is justly given.

Those to whom loyalty is due includes the following: the just before Habbakuk and all that is good, those oppressed by evil, and those monarchs who by decree and common consent of the Knightly Councils are in good standing with the Knighthood and deserving of its honorable loyalty and protection.

Acts befitting a Knight of the Crown include these: unquestioned obedience to those whose authority is righteously maintained in the Knightly Councils, dedication to the ideals of the Measure, loyalty to brother Knights of all orders, and all other acts that cause the strengthening of loyalty among the Knights.

Responsibilities of a Knight of the Crown: forfeiture of 10% of all wealth accrued by the Knight, service and aid to any fellow Knight who is about the business of his order and requires assistance, service to the kingdoms on the List of Loyalty as compiled by the Grand Circle of Knights.

the knights of the Sword and their Measure

The Order of the Sword combines the purest ideals of heroism and courage with the power of the gods of good. Courage is sacrifice to the ideals of honor; it is the well from which true honor draws its life. Heroism includes acts of might in defense of sacrifice and honor.

Those to whom heroism is due include the following: the weak and the oppressed, the enslaved, the poor, the falsely imprisoned, fellow Knights in need, and the defenseless.

Acts befitting a Knight of the Sword: facing evil without concern for personal suffering, accepting the challenge of combat for the honor of the Knighthood, defending the honor of the Knighthood, defending the honor of a fellow Knight in good standing, protecting the defenseless and weak.

Responsibilities of a Knight of the Sword: forfeiture to the coffers of the Knighthood of all wealth save that required for upkeep, pay homage to the gods each day (though in times of great hardship, once in a quartermonth is still a seemly practice), never decline combat with an evil opponent nor flee from such combat regardless of the strength of the enemy, protect the weak and the defenseless wherever the need arises, abstain forever from the use of Knightly powers for unrighteous reasons.

the knights of the Rose and their Measure

The Order of the Rose exemplifies honor guided by wisdom and justice.

Wisdom is the strength of honor and ability applied in the service of just causes. Justice is the heart of the Measure and the soul of a Rose Knight.

All beings regardless of their stations, positions, or beliefs have equal claim to compassion under the Measure. Deeds befitting a Knight of the Rose include the following: taking compassion on the less fortunate, sacrificing one's life for the sake of others, giving no thought to one's own safety in defense of the Knighthood, protecting the lives of fellow Knights, seeing that no life is wasted or sacrificed in vain.

Responsibilities of a Knight of the Rose: forfeiture of all wealth accrued as a Knight save for that needed for the upkeep of any principalities under the protection of the Knighthood, to honor the gods of good at all times and in all acts, to fight for justice without regard to personal safety or comfort, to never submit to any evil foe, to sacrifice all in the name of honor.

knights of the Crown

All those who wish to become Solamnic Knights must first enter into the Knighthood as squires of the Knights of the Crown. This is true regardless of what Knighthood they will eventually serve. All Knights begin here with training in the virtue of loyalty.

Candidates for the Solamnic Knighthood must be presented to a Knightly Council and be sponsored by a Knight in good standing from any of the Orders of Knighthood. After the entire group of candidates is presented, the group swears an oath to the honor of the Knighthood and to the causes of the Crown. All swear allegiance to the Order and the ideals of the Knights of Solamnia.

If there is no dissent from the Knights, and no question of honor regarding the candidates is brought forth, then all are accepted into the Knighthood as squires. Any question of honor of an individual requires that the individual be removed from the group of candidates and

be questioned separately after the rest of the candidates are accepted. If the question of honor is dismissed, then the candidate is accepted normally. If the question is found valid in the Council, then the candidate is dismissed until the question of honor is satisfied.

Knights of the Crown advance in power more quickly than the other Knights, partly due to the fact that their order is less demanding than the others. While this benefit is certainly a good one, it is also true that their special powers are quite limited.

Knights of the Crown are sworn to protect, serve, and give aid to any kingdom on the List of Loyalty. This list is maintained by the three High Knights and is updated periodically. The Knights are not required to follow the commands or laws of these kingdoms should they be out of harmony with the Code or the Measure. This rule holds true for members of all the Knighthoods.

The Order of the Crown takes its Measure from matters of loyalty and obedience to authority of the greater Knighthood through its High Councils and commanders. Examples of acts befitting the Measure of the Crown: unquestioned obedience to those whose authority is righteously maintained in the Knightly Councils, dedication to the ideals of the Measure, loyalty to brother Knights of all Orders, and all other acts that cause the strengthening of loyalty among the Knights.

knights of the crown
Game Data

Knights of the Crown are variants of cavaliers as described in *Unearthed Arcana*. While their experience point advancement is identical to that class, there are many important differences. Read the following section carefully to be sure you understand those differences.

Crown Knight Minimum Scores

Strength	10
Intelligence	7
Wisdom	10
Dexterity	8
Constitution	10
Charisma	None

Crown Knight Level Table

Level	Experience Points	Hit Dice (d10s)	Title
1	2,500	2	Squire of Crown
2	5,000	3	Defender of Crown
3	10,000	4	Knight of Crown
4	18,500	5	Scepter Knight
5	37,000	6	Shield Knight
6	85,000	7	Shield of Crown
7	140,000	8	Lord of Shields
8	220,000	9	Lord of Crown
9	300,000	10	Master Warrior
10	600,000	10 + 2	Lord Warrior
11	900,000	10 + 4	High Warrior *
12	1,200,000	10 + 6	
13	1,500,000	10 + 8	
14	1,800,000	10 + 10	
15	2,100,000	10 + 12	
16	2,400,000	10 + 14	
17	2,700,000	10 + 16	
18	3,000,000	10 + 18	

* There is only one High Warrior in each Order and he is chosen according to the Measure. All other Knights who have sufficient experience points to attain this level may do so but retain the title of Lord Warrior until such time as they are elected to take the position of High Warrior.

Proficiencies	Weapon / Nonweapon
Initial	3/2
Added	1/1 per 2 levels

Special Abilities: Unlike the cavalier or paladin, this character can use weapon specialization.

Experience Points: As for all Knights of Solamnia, experience is not awarded simply for killing monsters and taking treasure. These Knights are rewarded according to how well their deeds exemplify the creed of the Knighthood. Any Knight who performs his duties to the ends defined by the Code and the Measure will be rewarded with a 10% experience point bonus above any other bonuses he normally receives.

knights of the sword

Upon completing his squire duties in the Order of the Crown (reaching 2d level), each Knight candidate has the option of either entering that Order and continuing his allegiance to that group and its ideals or of entering into the Order of the Sword. The ambitious Knight who wishes some day to enter the Order of the Rose must first rise through the Order of the Sword before applying to the Order of the Rose.

In addition, every candidate who wishes to join the Order of the Sword must first complete a quest. According to the Measure, this test must be a witnessed deed of heroism and valor that upholds the virtues of Knightly honor and good.

When such a deed is done, the Knight must then be presented before a Knightly Council and there the tale of his deed is told. The candidate is accepted as a Knight of the Order if the tale and deed are acceptable to the presiding Lord Knight from the Order of the Sword. If no Lord Knight is present, then the highest-ranking Knight of the Sword can adjudicate so long as it is a lawful council of Knights. If no lawful council can be convened, then the matter is to be set aside until such council can be convened. Any Knight candidate who feels that he has been unjustly found wanting in his deed and tale may take the matter up before the presiding council of the Knights.

While Knights of this order have previously learned their skills during their training with the Order of the Crown, they now begin their studies in the basics of heroic honor and worship of the True Gods. The first duties and tasks of the accepted Knight candidate are learning the basic disciplines of the clerics and the requirements of the gods of good. No Knight who espouses anything but the virtues of good over evil or chaos is ever accepted into these ranks.

Although Knights of the Sword do not attain power, wealth, or position in the world as quickly as those of the Order of the Crown, they achieve these things faster than the Knights of the Rose.

After taking their initial training and demonstrating abilities and commitments to the gods of good and their ideals, a Knight of the Sword who is of royal blood may elect to enter into the Order of the Rose. In later times, the stricture about royal blood has been generally ignored (see *Knights of the Rose*).

Knights of the Sword, in addition to their

normal duties as warriors in the defense of truth and justice, often represent the power of the gods in certain limited ways. The Knights of the Sword acquire some healing powers and the abilities of foresight and prophesy. This was not always true. During the Cataclysm, the Order of the Sword lost its High Clerist and with him went the miracles which this Order once performed. While the Knights still functioned as limited clerics, their miracles where ascribed to witchcraft and sorcery—an offense against the people which was usually punished by death if the Knight was caught.

Unlike clerics, who gain their miraculous powers on a daily basis, the Knights of the Sword can only acquire their spells on a week-to-week basis as a result of a day of fasting and prayer. When a Knight joins this order, he designates a day of worship and meditation during which he supplicates the gods of good for his powers for the following week. These powers, once gained, remain with the Knight until they are expended, regardless of the amount of time that passes between the day of prayer and their use. However, as with clerics, the power goes away once used and can only be regained through another day of prayer and supplication on the appointed day of the week.

During that day, the Measure decrees that the Knight cannot take part in combat, reap financial gain, or utter harsh words to another person. The Knight cannot travel unless it is done in silence and at least three hours of the day are spent in solitude for meditation. It is said that no beast will attack the Knight on his day of meditation so long as he remains true to his vow. Those who break their vows on a day of fasting, however, have twice the normal chance for evil encounters on that day.

As a general rule, the more powerful the miracle desired, the greater the time that must be spent in meditation to receive the blessing from the gods.

The Sword Knight does not have to observe each appointed day with a full fast; this is necessary only when his need for power is great. On those occasions when the Sword Knight is not in need of any great powers, then he is only required to offer up one hour of meditation on the appointed day. He can then perform all his other duties as on any other day, so long as he performs this ceremony. The knight who does not meditate for an hour some time between dawn and dusk incurs the same wrath as those who break their fast when praying for great powers.

The Order of the Sword takes its Measure from affairs of courage and heroics. Examples

of acts befitting the Measure of the Sword: facing evil without regard to personal suffering, accepting the challenge of combat for the honor of the Knighthood, defending the honor of the Knighthood, defending the honor of a fellow Knight, protecting the defenseless and weak.

knights of the swor∂
Game ∂ata

Minimum Requirements: No character starts out as a Knight of the Sword. Characters can only attempt to enter this class after first rising to 2d level as a Knight of the Crown and having sufficient experience points to gain 3d level there. At that point, the character must speak of his intent to become a Knight of the Sword to a Knight of that order who is no less than 7th level. The candidate must also have the listed minimums in all the following statistics in order to qualify for the Order of the Sword.

Rose Knight Minimum Scores

Strength	12
Intelligence	9
Wisdom	13
Dexterity	9
Constitution	10
Charisma	None

The petitioning knight must then be brought before a Knightly Council at which a Sword Knight of no less than 7th level is one of the three presiding Knights. The Knight's name is then brought up before the Knighthood. If there is no question of honor brought up about the Knight during a Knightly Council in which his petition is heard, then the character is assigned a quest to show his worthiness and his dedication to the Order of the Sword.

The quest must include the following elements: a journey of no less than 500 miles and 30 days, three tests of the Knight's wisdom, one test of his generosity, one test of his compassion, the restoration of something that was lost, and single combat with an evil opponent of at least the same level as the candidate. The candidate must be victorious in this combat while demonstrating the ideals of honor and courage (note that this does not necessarily mean killing the foe). The knight can enlist the aid of anyone he wishes to complete the quest so long as he maintains the ideals of the Knighthood (i.e., does not fur-

ther the cause of evil). The exact form of the quest is ultimately up to the DM, but it must include these elements.

Sword Knight Advancement Table

Level	Experience Points	Hit Dice (d10s)	Title
3	12,000	4	Novice of Swords
4	24,000	5	Knight of Swords
5	45,000	6	Blade Knight
6	95,000	7	Knight Clerist
7	175,000	8	Abott of Swords
8	350,000	9	Elder of Swords
9	700,000	10	Master of Swords
10	1,050,000	10+2	Lord of Swords
11	1,400,000	10+4	Master Clerist
12	1,750,000	10+6	Lord Clerist
13	2,100,000	10+8	High Clerist *
14	2,450,000	10+10	
15	2,800,000	10+12	
16	3,150,000	10+14	
17	3,500,000	10+16	
18	3,850,000	10+18	

* The High Clerist is a position that is held by only one Knight at a time. When the need arises to choose a new High Clerist, he must be elected during a proper Knightly Council. Should any Knight attain enough experience points to rise to the level of High Clerist, he may do so but still retains the title of Lord Clerist until the High Clerist position is vacant.

Proficiencies	Weapon/Nonweapon
Initial *	3/2
Added	2/1 per 2 levels

* The initial proficiencies listed here are in addition to those proficiencies already obtained. In other words, during the Knight's training period in the Order of the Sword, he acquires three additional weapon proficiencies and two additional non-weapon proficiencies on top of any already received as a Knight of the Crown.

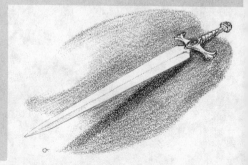

Sword Knight Spells Table *

Knight Level	Clerical Spell Level						
	1	2	3	4	5	6	7
6	1	-	-	-	-	-	-
7	2	-	-	-	-	-	-
8	2	1	-	-	-	-	-
9	3	2	-	-	-	-	-
10	4	2	-	-	-	-	-
11	4	2	1	-	-	-	-
12	5	3	1	1	-	-	-
13	6	4	1	1	1	-	-
14	7	5	2	1	1	1	-
15	8	6	3	2	1	1	1
16	9	7	3	2	2	1	1
17	9	8	4	3	3	2	1
18	9	9	5	4	3	2	1

* These are the maximum number of spells that a Knight of the Sword can have at any one time.

As mentioned earlier, a Sword Knight can only acquire his spells during his one appointed day of meditation each week. A Knight keeps his spells, once learned, until they are used. A Sword Knight requires one half hour per spell level to gain a spell. For instance, a 6th-level spell would take three hours of meditation to gain. A Knight can never meditate more than six hours during this day.

The Knights of the Sword use the spells of a cleric of Kiri-Jolith even though the most revered of the gods for the Knights is Paladine. This is primarily due to the origins of the Knighthood. While the Knights of the Sword are followers of Paladine, they do, nevertheless, take their powers from Kiri-Jolith and honor him as well.

knights of the Rose

The Knights of the Rose are the epitome of all that is good and honorable in Knighthood.

Initially, the Knights of this order were taken only from the royal houses of the land. What constituted a royal house was determined by the ruling council of Knights who would convene and hear the history and lineage of that house. If there was sufficient proof that the house was a ruling house and that its history was an honorable one, then the crest of that house was included in the Measure and those of that house were accepted. This was not something that was done often, for the Measure was strict about the require-

ments for accepting a house into the Roster of Loyalty.

Since this stricture of accepting only those of royal descent was said to have been added well after the time of Vinas Solamnus and was, in some minds, invalid as a part of the Measure, there has arisen in more recent times a more acceptable argument before the Knightly councils. Rather than represent that the Measure was in error or flawed, the argument has been made that over the course of the centuries there have been so many marriages between royal and common houses that practically everyone is somehow related to royalty. With the Cataclysm obscuring the genealogical records of the past, most acceptable candidates are not denied access to the Order of the Rose without extraordinary evidence. (Beings from off-world, however, are not accepted into the order.)

The details of how a Knight is accepted into the ranks of the Rose, however, has changed little. The Knight must be brought before a Knightly Council of the Rose. There he must relate the tale of his family and his deeds that exemplify the ideals of Knighthood and Honor tempered with leniency and wisdom. Once this tale is told, the council holds a closed session to discuss the Knight's application in light of his merits and shortcomings.

The Order of the Rose takes its Measure from deeds of wisdom and justice. Examples of deeds befitting the Measure of the Rose: taking compassion on the less fortunate, sacrificing one's life for the sake of others, giving no thought to one's own safety in defense of the Measure and its Honor, protecting the lives of fellow Knights, seeing that no life is wasted or sacrificed in vain.

knights of the Rose Game Data

Minimum Requirements: As with Knights of the Sword, characters do not start out as Knights of the Rose. Characters must first have gained two levels as Knights of the Crown, then been accepted as Knights of the Sword and earned two additional levels before they can be considered for the Order of the Rose. Once a character has earned sufficient hit points to become 4th level, he can petition the Order of the Rose to be accepted into that body. In order to be considered for the Order of the Rose, the Knight must have the following minimum characteristics:

Rose Knight Minimum Scores

Strength	15
Intelligence	10
Wisdom	13
Dexterity	12
Constitution	15
Charisma	None

The candidate must present his petition to a Rose Knight of no less than 6th level. The candidate must then be presented by that Knight to a Knightly Council at which sits a Rose Knight of no less than 9th level. If no question of honor is brought up before the Knighthood at that time, then the Knight is assigned a quest to prove his worthiness to the Knighthood.

The quest must include the following elements: a journey of no less than 500 miles and 30 days, one test of the Knight's wisdom, three tests of the Knight's generosity, three tests of the Knight's compassion, the restoration of something that was lost, and the defeat of an evil opponent of equal or higher level than the Knight. The candidate must be victorious while demonstrating the ideals of honor and courage and without killing the foes. The Knight can enlist the aid of anyone to complete the quest so long as he maintains the ideals of the Knighthood and does not further the cause of evil. The exact form of the quest is up to the DM, but it must include the preceding elements.

Rose Knight Advancement Table

Level	Experience Points	Hit Dice (d10s)	Title
4	27,000	5	Novice of Roses
5	60,000	6	Knight of Tears
6	125,000	7	Knight of Mind
7	200,000	8	Knight of Heart
8	425,000	9	Knight of Roses
9	800,000	10	Keeper of Roses
10	1,500,000	10 + 2	Master of Roses
11	2,000,000	10 + 4	Archknight
12	2,500,000	10 + 6	Lord of Roses
13	3,000,000	10 + 8	Master of Justice
14	3,500,000	10 + 10	Lord of Justice
15	4,000,000	10 + 12	High Justice *
16	4,500,000	10 + 14	
17	5,000,000	10 + 16	
18	6,000,000	10 + 18	

* There is only one High Justice at any given time. Others may attain 15th level, but their titles remain Lords of Justice.

The Knights of the Rose gain special proficiencies in weapons and combat. While they advance more slowly than other Knights (because of the great amount of training and skill required by their proficiencies), they also can advance farther than any of the other Knighthoods.

Proficiencies	Weapon/Nonweapon
Initial *	3/2
Added	2/1 per 2 levels

* The *Initial Proficiencies* listed here are in addition to those proficiencies already obtained. In other words, during the Knight's initial training period in the Order of the Rose, he acquires three additional weapons proficiencies and two additional nonweapon proficiencies on top of any already received as a Knight of the Crown and as a Knight of the Sword.

knights in Battle

Knights who take the field in defense of honor and the realm follow the order set forth by the Measure. Armies are made up of three brigades, each commanded by a Lord Knight from one of the three Orders of Knights. All armed persons operating under the protection and command of the Knights are part of one of these three brigades.

The army is commanded by a Warrior Lord, one of the three Lord Knights commanding brigades. The Warrior Lord is chosen by the majority vote of the three Lord Knight commanders; he must exemplify the highest ideals of the Knighthood. Recognition of the Warrior Lord is made openly in Knightly Council. Should a Lord Knight fall in battle, another must step forward and take his place. Should the Warrior Lord be lost, then each Lord Knight separately commands his own brigade until a Knightly Council can be called.

the knightly Council

Councils shall be convened as required by the Measure. They must include three Lord Knights, one from each of the Orders of Knights. If any order cannot provide a Lord Knight, then a Knight of that order can stand in his stead so long as there is at least one Lord Knight presiding.

Councils shall convene for the following purposes: to determine strategies of war, to assign orders for war and battle, to select the Warrior Lord prior to a battle, to hear charges of unknightly conduct, to honor those who have performed valiantly, to settle questions concerning the Measure.

The conduct of a Knightly Council follows the pattern set forth by the measure. First the Knights of each order enter and take their places in the appointed area. A table with three chairs is set opposite the entrance. The Knights of the Crown take their places to the right of the entrance, to the left of the ranking Knights, so as to signify their position as the shield and defender of honor. The Knights of the Sword take their places to the left of the entrance, to the right of the ranking Knights and thus signifying their place as the arm of might and mover of the Knighthood. The Knights of the Rose take their places to either side of the entrance and opposite the ranking Knights so as to signify that they are the heart of the Knighthood, the base upon which all else is built.

Then the three ranking Knights who will conduct the meeting enter the hall and take their places opposite the entrance. In the center of the area is a cleared space where those who are brought before the ranking Knights are heard and questioned.

A Knightly Council is Conducted as Follows:

* The code of the Knights of Solamnia ("Est Sularus oth Mithas") is recited by all before any in the hall sit. This phrase is given by the three ranking Knights in unison and then given in turn by each of the three orders of Knights present and then finally by all in unison. If the occasion is a joyful one, then the Knights' Hymn is sung at this time as well.

* News of the greater Knighthood is often not only of interest but potentially a matter of life and death for many whom the Knighthood protects. Any dispatches or proclamations regarding the Knights are read at this time. Should their news warrant a prolonged and important discussion, then the hearing of petitions may be waived.

* When the Knighthood finds itself in the throes of battle, they now discuss their orders of battle and all stratagems to be employed.

* The specific petitions that are to be discussed among the Knights at this meeting are named by cause, those mentioned (if any), and petitioner. Petitions can have one of several purposes:

Acceptance to an Order: Those who wish to enter into an order of the Knighthood are brought forward. The candidates' names are read to the ranking Knights as are the names of their Knight sponsors.

Petition for a Question of Honor: This happens when a Knight is called into question for breaking the Oath or the Measure. Those mentioned in the petition and the accused and the petitioner is the accuser.

All are allowed to speak for and against the accused. The petitioner must be present in these cases. Often witnesses from outside the order are brought in to testify. The Knightly Council hears all arguments and then dismisses the rest of the Knights as it considers arguments. Upon receiving word that the Council has completed its deliberations, all the Knights return to the hall. White roses on the table are a symbol of purging of any guilt and thus is the accused released from any question of their honor. Should black roses be present on the table upon the return of the Knights, then the Knight is held guilty and punishable for his acts. The ranking Knights in their deliberations will have decided upon the proper action for the Knight to regain his honor prior to the others returning.

Special Honors: An act of exceptional bravery or exemplary honor is brought to the attention of all the Knighthood for recognition.

Petition for War: This occurs when a general mobilization is called for. The circumstances of the petition are considered and, if the Knights present give consent, then messengers are dispatched to the Grand Circle to notify the greater Knighthood of the situation. In the meanwhile, the Knights of that council act at once in the defense of honor and good.

Petition for Aid: These are petitions brought by either Knights or outsiders who ask aid of the Knights. This does not require a general mobilization of the Knighthood. These range from situations as serious as the search for a kidnapped heir to a local kingdom to things as mundane as a few extra men to help clear a road of brush.

* Time permitting, the Knights may engage in discussions of parts of the Measure and its application to their adventures. Questions on points of the Measure are brought up at this time.

* When the ranking Knights feel that business has been finished, the council disbands until the need for another session arises.

tinkers (Gnomes)

Tinkers are gnomes and gnomes are tinkers. It is their gift and curse to be the masters or pawns of technology (depending upon whom you ask) in a world where magic is the ruling force.

You will find their story and how they came into being under the race descriptions later in this book. Here we will address ourselves to the profession of tinker.

Tinkers are the engineers of Krynn. That which has not been built, tinkers build. That which has been built, tinkers improve. They are constantly designing, building, and testing devices for a variety of applications.

Each gnome belongs to a guild that perpetuates its own peculiar branch of technology. These guilds include, but are not limited to, the following:

Hydraulics	Hydrodynamics
Aerodynamics	Thermodynamics
Chemistry	Transportation
Communication	Appliances
Kinetics	Architecture

All gnomes belong to a guild. Each guild has innumerable committees that oversee individual accomplishments (seldom) and seek to discover the cause of a system failure (often). These committees also oversee the required duties of a gnome within the structure of gnomish society.

In addition to any regular duties that a gnome has to his guild or committee, each gnome has a Lifequest. This Lifequest is to attain perfect understanding of one device. Few gnomes have ever attained this goal. Thus tinkers are the perpetually unfulfilled, never attaining that total knowledge of their devices.

Gnomish inventions are almost exclusively driven by basic mechanical devices: gears, windmills, waterwheels, pulleys, and screws. Gnomes have done elementary work in steam and chemical combustion (usually with catastrophic results), but know next to nothing about electricity. Clockwork mechanisms are a relatively recent development of gnomish society.

Moreover, their sheer love for technology often does them a disservice, for they improve technological devices to death. Simple mechanisms are scoffed at by tinkers ("Nothing so simple could possibly work!") and redundancy is the tinker watchword ("...and here we see the bell that informs us that the alarm system trouble gong has just gone off....").

tinker Class
Game Statistics

Minimum Requirements: Only gnome characters may be of the tinker class. The minimum statistics for the gnome tinker are as follows:

Tinker Minimum Scores

Strength	—
Intelligence	10/15 *
Wisdom	(12) **
Dexterity	12
Constitution	—
Charisma	—

* The number after the slash indicates that a gnome with an Intelligence of 15 or higher gains a 10% bonus to all experience points earned.

** This is a maximum score—the character cannot have a Wisdom higher than 12.

Gnome Advancement Table

Level	Experience Points	Hit Dice (d4s)	Title
1	1,250	2	Aide 5th
2	2,500	3	Aide 4th
3	5,000	4	Aide 3d
4	10,000	5	Aide 2d
5	20,000	6	Aide 1st
6	40,000	7	Mate 2d
7	60,000	8	Mate 1st
8	100,000	9	Tinker
9	140,000	10	Master Tinker
10	270,000	10 + 2	Craftsgnome
11	450,000	10 + 4	Craft Master
12	600,000	10 + 6	Head Tinker
13	800,000	10 + 8	
14	1,000,000	10 + 10	
15	1,500,000	10 + 12	Master Craftsgnome *
16	2,500,000	10 + 14	
17	4,000,000	10 + 16	
18	10,000,000	10 + 18	

* There can be only one Master Craftsgnome in any colony of gnomes at a given time. In a colony that already has a Master Crafts gnome, any gnome who has the experience points to become 15th level may do so, but he does not gain the title of Master Craftsgnome.

Proficiencies	Weapon/Nonweapon
Initial	1/5
Added	1/3 per two levels

Special Abilities: While gnomes invariably have an abundance of nonweapon proficiencies, they are abnormally poor at using them. Subtract 5 from a gnome's nonweapon proficiency when making a Proficiency Check.

Gnome Devices: Many referees view the introduction of technology into their fantasy campaigns with great misgivings. The technology of the gnomes, however, has little overall effect upon the cultures of Krynn. Dwarves care little for such innovation; elves are repelled by technology; kender cannot appreciate its use beyond their thrill of seeing it work; goblins and gully dwarves are too stupid to use it consistently. Gnomes have technology—but they are so incompetent that anything their technology can do, magic can usually do cheaper, faster, and more efficiently.

When a gnome sets out to invent something, it's a good bet that the invention will initially be at least 30 times larger than necessary, will make 10 times the noise it should, will have many totally redundant features, and will fail miserably (if not disastrously). Some tinkering will gradually reduce the less favorable aspects of the device.

The gnomes are a race of cursed engineers. They have all of the tools to create wonderful technological devices but all they turn out are impractical and dangerous mechanisms.

Players who run tinker PCs will no doubt wish to create any number of technological marvels with which to aid their party. This is the major reason to join this class and the players' creative thoughts should be allowed to run free....

But....

It is important to remember that a PC of this class is, after all, a gnome with an inherent character flaw. You must remember that while the player may be able to describe just how to build a simple, effective telegraph system, for example, his gnome player character would not build it the same way. Thus even though a player could describe with the utmost precision how to make a telegraph with some thinly wound wire and rudimentary batteries, his PC gnome would make it steam driven, operating on the basic principle of a pile driver.

Whenever a player wishes to create a technological device, he is required to design it himself with the following procedure. The DM is, of course, free to check the work and make any modifications he deems necessary.

To create a gnomish device, follow these steps:

1. DETERMINE DEVICE COMPLEXITY (SIZE): To create a technological device, you must first determine its level of complexity. On page 118 is the Gnome Device Complexity Level table that shows the various complexity values for many of the effects that gnomes commonly like to see on their devices. (The complexity rating also gives the size of the device.) Add all the complexities for all the device's effects to get the total complexity of the device.

The DM of the game, as in all things, is the final arbiter of just which effects are needed to make a device function.

Ask all of the following questions when designing a gnomish device:

● **Will it do damage, protect from damage or restrain another being?**
(If the answer is "no," go to the next question.)

Determine if it does damage or protects from damage. Refer to the Gnome Device Complexity Level table to determine Combat Complexity from the amount of damage or protection desired.

If the device is designed to restrain another being, then determine the complexity/size of the object by the HD of the creature being restrained. Count it as one complexity level for every two hit dice or levels of the target creature. Restraining an 8-hit die creature is a Complexity 4 task.

● **Does it move something or itself?**
(If the answer is "no," go to the next question.)

Determine if it moves another object (throws victim) or moves itself (flying machine). If the device throws things, then consult the column labeled "Move Vertical" on the Gnome Device Complexity Level table. If the device moves objects and itself (flies), then check the column labeled "Move Horizontal." Note that this vertical movement is straight up unless some horizontal movement effect is also included. (The numbers given in these movement columns can be either a total distance or distance per round, whichever is most appropriate.)

Size modifier: This assumes that the object being moved is size 1 or smaller (roughly the size of a small sack).

Minimum Size: Compare the size of the object to be moved with the size of the device. If the device is less than three sizes larger than the object, then the size and complexity of the device equal the size of the object plus 3. If the device merely moves itself across the ground, then no modifier is needed.

Duration: Use the following Duration

Modifiers chart to determine vertical movement complexity modifiers for the desired duration.

Duration Modifiers Chart *

Desired Duration	Dmg	Vert.	Horiz.	Environ.
Momentary	N/A	N/A	N/A	N/A
1-3 Rounds	+1	+1	N/A	N/A
4-6 Rounds	+2	+3	0	+1
7-9 Rounds	+4	+5	−1	+2
1-3 Turns	+6	+7	−2	+3
4-5 Turns	+8	+11	−3	+4
1-2 Hours	+10	+13	−4	+6
3-6 Hours	+11	+15	−5	+8
1 Day	N/A	+16	−6	+12
1 Week	N/A	N/A	−7	+14
Permanent	+15	+20	N/A	+20

* These modifiers affect only the complexity of the device, not its size.

● **Does it move something or itself any distance along the ground?**
(If the answer is "no," go to the next question.)

Determine if it moves another object (shoves a victim) or moves itself (mobile machine). If the device merely shoves or, in the case of a catapult, throws the victim over a distance, then consult the column under "Move Vertical." If the device moves with the victim, then check the column under "Move Horizontal."

Minimum size: The same restrictions on minimum size for vertical movement apply here except that the difference must be twice or less.

Duration: Use the Duration Modifiers chart to determine ground movement complexity modifiers for duration.

● **Does it alter the environment or have an area of effect?**
(If the answer is "no," go to next question.)

The amount of material altered and whether the affected region is inside the device also factor into the equation. If altering material inside the device, add 1 to Complexity per 1,000 cubic feet altered after the first 100 cubic feet. If altering an external environment, add 4 to Complexity per 1,000 cubic feet altered including the first 1,000 cubic feet.

Note that gnomish devices are often larger than the environments they alter.

● **Does it alter an existing object?**
(If the answer is "no," go to next question.)

Gnomes commonly build devices to help them build devices (a frightening thought to those familiar with gnomes). If the device takes an unfinished or partially finished object and changes it into a more finished object, then the device has this effect.

Determine the complexity difference between the original object and its final state. This is done by subtracting the complexity of the finished object from the complexity of the original object. A machine to craft raw quartz into finished lenses takes an object of complexity 20 and makes it into an object of complexity 1, a difference of 19. This means that the machine has a complexity of 19. A machine that takes glass (complexity 8) and makes it into finished lenses (complexity 1) has a complexity of 7.

Take the size of the object being refined (from the first column in the complexity table) and add that to the device's complexity rating.

● **Final design modifiers**
Each effect has a complexity rating. Often a gnome will build a device with several effects. For example: a machine to move along the ground and fire flaming metallic rocks has complexities and size ratings for both horizontal movement and damage. To determine the final complexity rating for a device, first find the highest complexity rating among the effects listed. Add 1 to that complexity for each effect beyond the one listed. In the case of the vehicle mentioned above, that is one additional effect so 1 is added to its complexity.

The size of the device greatly affects its complexity and determines whether sufficient materials are available to build it. The base size of any device is equal to its unmodified complexity rating. This means that a complexity level 20 device always starts as a size 20 device. This is not necessarily how large the device must be. The gnome may elect to make the device smaller, but this increases the complexity of the device. On the other hand, the gnome may elect to make a device bigger and thereby reduce the final complexity of the device.

Generally speaking, the larger the device, the less complicated it is (i.e., it has a better chance of working), while the smaller the device, the more complicated it is (i.e., it has a worse chance of working). This reflects the gnomish philosophy of engineering. Remember, however, larger devices require more materials to build (more expensive) and are harder to move.

The size of the design can now be altered:

Subtract 1 from the complexity for each size larger the object is built. Add 1 to the complexity for each size smaller the object is built. Note that a gnome who attempts to build a large device must also pay for the materials with which to build that device.

II. DETERMINE FINAL MODIFIERS:
How well a device is made depends largely on who made it. Just as magical swords have plus modifiers and cursed swords have minus modifiers, so too do gnomish devices. Add a +1 modifier to the device for every level of complexity the device is below the level of the gnome who made it. Give it a −1 modifier for every complexity level of the device higher than its gnome maker. Thus a 12th-level gnome who makes a level 15 netflinger would make a netflinger −3. If the same gnome made a rockpitcher with a complexity of 8, it would be a rockpitcher +4.

Gnomes love committees. They often work on devices in groups when there are enough gnomes about. This is often as harmful as it is helpful.

For every new gnome working on the device, roll 3d6 and consult the following table. Find the result of the dice roll (a number between 3 and 18) on the row corresponding to the number of gnomes present. The column that this result falls into gives the complexity modifier (see the column heading).

Gnome Crew Modifiers

Number of Gnomes *	+2	+1	Even	−1	−2
1	3	4-7	8-17	18	N/A
2	3	4-7	8-16	17-18	N/A
3-6	3	4-8	9-16	17-18	N/A
7-14	3-4	5-8	9-15	16-18	N/A
15-45	3-5	6-9	10-15	16-17	18 *
46-144	3-6	7-10	11-14	15-16	17-18 *
144+	3-8	9-12	13-14	15	16-18 **

* At least one gnome of a level equal to the device must be present in this group in order to obtain this result. If no such gnome is present in the group, then treat the result as a −1 to the complexity of the device.

** At least one gnome whose level is no less than five below the device must be present in order to obtain this result. If no such gnome is present in the group then treat the result as a −1 to the complexity of the device.

III. DETERMINE AVAILABILITY OF MATERIALS: Every gnomish device must include at least one selection from the five following component groups in order to function. It must also fit the following basic criteria:

1. It must have a number of components equal to its complexity. If the device has a final complexity of 15, then it must have 15 separate parts.

2. There must be a balance in the number of parts from the three part groups. A device may have, for example, two parts from group #1 and group #2 and three parts from group #3 but may never have three parts from group #1 and only one part from groups #2 and #3.

The components used are determined by the desires of the gnome designer. The DM must then determine if the items mentioned are obtainable in the quantities required. The size of the device also affects availability. Multiply the total costs of all components by the size of the device to determine the cost of building the mechanism. Gnomes often think up items that are far too expensive to build, so do not lose heart if your first few designs are beyond your means.

Also it must be noted that a gnome can construct any of these items from elementary materials (cut wood from trees for frames, cut gears from sheets of metal, etc.), but this doubles the construction time of the device.

Device Components and their Costs

(Cost is per size, in stl)

Part Group #1: Mechanical Transmissions

Pulleys	5
Shafts	10
Gears	20
Belts	100
Screws	500
Blades	1,000

Part Group #2: Other Transmissions

Fins (Vanes)	10
Rods (Steel)	20
Glass Rods & Panes	40
Bellows	200
Pumps	1,000
Tuning Forks	2,000

Part Group #3: Drive Sources

Counterweights	30
Coiled or Wound Springs	60
Waterwheel	100
Windmill/Coal Fire	200
Steam Pipes & Boiler	1,000
Sun Mirror	2,000

Group #4: Basic Frames

Stonework	5
Wood Frames	10
Iron Frames	20

Group #5: Mechanical Components

Clockworks *   50

* A clockwork is required for any device that has a delayed action, an automatic sequence, or has anything to do with information storage or communication.

IV. BUILD THE DEVICE: The time required to build the device depends upon its size and complexity, according to the following table. Multiple the size of the device by its complexity and then refer to the following chart.

Gnomish Device Construction Times

Size x Complex.	Time to Construct
1-3	1d10 turns
4-10	2d20 turns
11-25	2d20 hours
26-50	2d6 days
51-100	1d4 weeks
101-400	2d20 months
401+	4d12 months

Having additional gnomes does not decrease the construction time (if you have worked with gnomes, you know why).

At the end of this time, the device is finished. Note its statistics for future use.

Mass Production: Gnomes never understood the human drive for producing things in vast quantities. They believe that one learns from previous mistakes and that these lessons should be incorporated into design immediately. Thus gnomish devices are always unique. They never produce a device the same way twice and thus they cannot duplicate previous work. They may attempt a "new and improved" version of an old design, but there is no guarantee that it will work as well as it did before.

Using Gnome Devices: Every time a gnomish device is used, roll 1d20, add or subtract any modifiers listed for the device, and consult the following table.

Gnomish Invention Results Table

Complex	Success	Unpredictable	Failure
1	16+	15	14 or less
2	16+	14-15	13 or less
3	16+	13-15	12 or less
4	17+	13-16	12 or less
5	17+	12-16	11 or less
6	17+	12-16	11 or less
7	17+	11-16	10 or less
8	18+	10-17	9 or less
9	18+	9-17	8 or less
10	18+	8-17	7 or less
11	18+	7-17	6 or less
12	18+	6-17	5 or less
13	19+	6-18	5 or less
14	19+	5-18	4 or less
15	19+	4-18	3 or less
16	19+	3-18	2 or less
17	20+	3-19	2 or less
18	20+	3-19	2 or less

Success: This means that the device works as intended. It will move, inflict damage, send messages, heat food, make light, or whatever it was created to do. Each time the device works, a +1 modifier is added to the device for its next roll on this table. (If it worked once, it has a better chance of working again!)

Unpredictable: The device works, but not the way the designer originally intended. The precise effects vary, but generally consult the Gnome Mishap table on page 119. Roll 1d20 on the table and interpret the results as humorously as the situation allows.

Failure: The device totally fails to function. It can be repaired by any gnome whose level is equal to or greater than the complexity of the device. The repair time is two hours times the complexity of the device. Also, each time a device fails, a −1 modifier is subtracted from subsequent rolls on the preceding table.

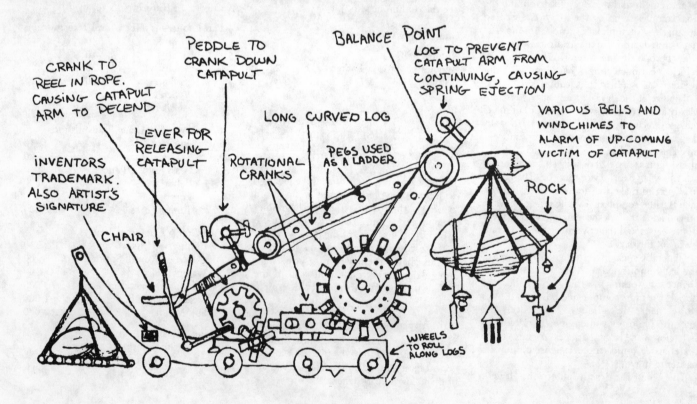

CRANK TO REEL IN ROPE. CAUSING CATAPULT ARM TO DECEND

PEDDLE TO CRANK DOWN CATAPULT

BALANCE POINT

LOG TO PREVENT CATAPULT ARM FROM CONTINUING, CAUSING SPRING EJECTION

LONG CURVED LOG

LEVER FOR RELEASING CATAPULT

VARIOUS BELLS AND WINDCHIMES TO ALARM OF UP-COMING VICTIM OF CATAPULT

INVENTORS TRADEMARK. ALSO ARTIST'S SIGNATURE

ROTATIONAL CRANKS

PEGS USED AS A LADDER

ROCK

CHAIR

WHEELS TO ROLL ALONG LOGS

hall of Gnomes Inventions

These devices are a sampling of typical gnomish inventions. We do not recommend that they be built by anyone except qualified gnomes; even then it is advised that all bystanders stand well clear of the device whenever it is either used or tested.

Netflinger

This gnomish invention was the end result of a long-term arms research project funded by the Knights of Solamnia. The weapon was supposed to render an opponent temporarily immobilized from a distance and thus allow the attacker to possibly capture the opponent unharmed. Unfortunately the ultimate effect was all too often felt by the user of the device rather than the foe.

Netflinger				
Type	Effect	Complex.	Modif.	Total
Damage	Restrain (HD8)	4	+1	5
Move Horiz	32'	4	—	4

Final Modifiers	Number	Size	Complex.
Highest Complexity	5	5	5
Additional Effects	1	—	+1
Resizing	—	−1	+2
Totals	6	4	8

Thus the netflinger is a size 4 device (roughly the size of a crossbow) with a complexity of 8. It costs 312 stl.

The netflinger, when it operates successfully, entangles any creature with 8 or less Hit Dice for a period of three melee rounds. It can do this from a distance of 32 feet. It hits automatically if it is successful, but it has various results when an unpredictable effect is rolled.

Gnomeflinger

This is the gnomish answer to stairs: an automated way to get from one place to another quickly and with relative safety. The device uses a combination of catapults of various sizes and principles as well as nets. The double-emergency backup sponge landing system is an extra option not included in the base price of the system, of course.

Gnomeflinger				
Type	Effect	Complex.	Modif.	Total
Move Vertical	800'	12	—	12

Final Modifiers	Number	Size	Complex.
Highest Complexity	12	12	12
Resizing	—	—	—
Totals		12	12

This device will toss a man-sized or smaller individual 800 feet into the air. It is size 12 (about the size of a large cottage).

flapestry

Flapestry (short for Flying Tapestry) was originally designed to send moving paintings and sound over tremendous distances.

Flapestry				
Type	Effect	Complex.	Modif.	Total
Sound	Talking	4	—	4
Light	Candlelight	4	—	4
Communicate	Direct Picture	16	—	16

Final Modifiers	Number	Size	Complex.
Highest Complexity	9	16	16
Additional effects	2	—	+2
Resizing	—	−2	+2
Totals	9	14	20

Needless to say, flapestry design is in its infancy on Krynn. A flapestry is a device the size of a three-story tower with the complexity of a time machine. Its cost is enormous, especially considering the lack of any real talented gnomes to be portrayed on the device.

Irongnome

This was originally designed as a device in which a gnome could sit and move about while deflecting any damage coming in his direction.

Irongnome				
Type	Effect	Complex.	Modif.	Total
Protection	AC 0	9	—	9
Move Horiz	400'	9	−2	7

Final Modifiers	Number	Size	Complex.
Highest Complexity	9	9	9
Additional effects	1	—	+1
Resizing	—	—	—
Totals	10	9	10

The irongnome is a moderately complex device that is barely large enough to carry its gnome driver. It is slow but has a very fine armor class rating for the protection of its occupant.

hall of gnomes inventions

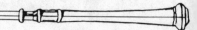

Blamblower

This was designed as a portable device that does damage to foes at a distance.

Blamblower				
Type	**Effect**	**Complex.**	**Modif.**	**Total**
Damage	2d8	7	+2	9
Move Horiz	400'	9	—	9

Final Modifiers	**Number**	**Size**	**Complex.**
Highest Complexity	9	9	9
Additional effects	1	—	+1
Resizing	—	−4	+4
Totals	10	5	14

This complex weapon is worn as a backpack and can throw a keg of volatile oil up to 400 feet away, causing 1d20 points of damage. It has six such charges before it must be rebuilt.

Whooshwagon

Original concept: a device to transport a family of gnomes over a distance.

Whooshwagon				
Type	**Effect**	**Complex.**	**Modif.**	**Total**
Move Horiz	20 miles	16	−5	11

Final Modifiers	**Number**	**Size**	**Complex.**
Highest Complexity	11	11	11
Resizing	—	−1	+1
Totals	11	10	12

This large wagon device is self propelled but only goes 20 miles in the course of a three-hour period.

Fargab

Original concept: a device to enable communication over vast distances.

Fargab				
Type	**Effect**	**Complex.**	**Modif.**	**Total**
Sound	Low voices	3	—	3
Communicate	Direct sound	13	—	13

Final Modifiers	**Number**	**Size**	**Complex.**
Highest Complexity	13	13	13
Resizing	—	−3	+3
Totals	13	10	16

This is essentially a telephone the size of a large wagon.

Gnomethink—Klackeradd

Original concept: a device to solve mathematical problems.

Gnomethink—Klackeradd				
Type	**Effect**	**Complex.**	**Modif.**	**Total**
Communicate	Calculator	12	—	12

Final Modifiers	**Number**	**Size**	**Complex.**
Highest Complexity	12	12	12
Resizing	—	+6	−6
Totals	12	18	6

This huge calculator has a computing power much lower than its size would indicate. It can add, subtract, multiply, and divide.

Blindguide

Original concept: a directional device when user cannot see.

Blindguide				
Type	**Effect**	**Complex.**	**Modif.**	**Total**
Information	Compass	3	—	3
Information	Pressure	6	—	6
Information	Clockwork	7	—	7

Final Modifiers	**Number**	**Size**	**Complex.**
Highest Complexity	7	7	7
Resizing	—	−2	+2
Totals	7	5	9

This clockwork maps the pressure changes and magnetic changes as the user travels. The clockwork keeps track of the differences and can orient the user on an x, y, z axis—assuming that everything works just right.

Stewmatic

Original concept: a device to prepare meals.

Stewmatic				
Type	**Effect**	**Complex.**	**Modif.**	**Total**
Temperature	300 deg	9	+6	15
Alter Objects	Raw to cooked	5	—	5
Information	Clockwork	7	—	7

Final Modifiers	**Number**	**Size**	**Complex.**
Highest Complexity	15	15	15
Resizing	—	−3	+3
Totals	15	12	18

This labor-saving device turns perfectly good raw vegetables and meat into an amorphous mass of steaming glop.

Of the all the orders of the world of Krynn, none are as old, as feared, or as respected as the Orders of High Sorcery. They came into being almost at the beginning of the world; their tale is that of the three Gods of Magic. The gods of magic, Solinari, Lunitari, and Nuitari, walked the face of creation before the stars settled in their places. Though they had a common love of magic, each had aspects that differed greatly from those of the others. Each also chose a different path in the universe.

They saw the other gods wheeling through the heavens and aligning themselves against one another according to their goals and philosophies. The All-Saints War was coming, as their vision and foresight had warned. The three gods feared that they too must choose. Bound by the common bond of magic, these three looked about the face of Krynn and loved it greatly.

Thus they did not join their fellow gods in the heavens, but stayed close to the world. They revolved about it, granting their powers to those who would follow their ways. Each god was granted a time to walk the face of Krynn and seek out a follower. Each found an apprentice and to each did they give the keys to the Lost Citadel—a fabulous place of wizardry that stood beyond the circles of the universe itself. Here the gods taught them the Foundations of Wizardry.

1. All wizards are brothers in their order. All orders are brothers in the power.

2. The places of High Wizardry are held in common among all orders and no sorcery is to be used there in anger against fellow wizards.

3. The world beyond the walls of the towers may bring brother against brother and order against order, but such is the way of the universe.

The Orders of Sorcery began as loosely organized groups of wizards. It was not until much later that the orders became formalized and structured. During the Age of Dreams at the onset of the First Dragonwar, the masters of each of the orders came together at the Lost Citadel and proclaimed the unity of the orders.

The Lost Citadel was a wondrous place from whence the master wizards ruled their orders in peace and harmony, far removed from the world of Krynn. Both palace and fortress, it provided a place where the powers of magic could be tempered by the wisdom of the Conclave of Wizards (see page 29).

It is important for any magic-user in Krynn to remember that a wizard's only loyalty is to magic. This is the primary reason that magic has remained in the world, despite many efforts to eliminate it.

A wizard of the Black Robes and a wizard of the White fighting on opposing sides of a war (such as the War of the Lance) would not hesitate to destroy each other. When these wizards meet on neutral ground (such as a Tower of High Sorcery), they are likely to enter into an eager discussion of magic. If attacked by an outside force seen as a threat to their magic (a renegade wizard, for example), both would join together to fight in defense of the magic.

A wealth of information on wizards, magical lore, the Towers, and the Tower guardians exists in the DRAGONLANCE® novels. Those interested in acquiring more detailed information than is provided here should draw from those works.

The Moons of Magic

Since the creation of the world, the three moons of magic have circled the globe of Krynn, bringing with them the waxing and the waning of their followers' magical powers.

Each of the three Orders of High Sorcery receives its powers from one of the moons of magic. Wizards of the White Robes get their powers from Solinari, Black Robe wizards get their power from Nuitari, and neutral Wizards get theirs from the red moon, Lunitari. It is by the position and aspect of its moon that each order gains its enhanced powers. The aspect of Nuitari has no effect on the powers of the White Robed wizards, for example. Only the moon Solinari has an effect on the wizards of the White Robes. The precise effects of the positions of the moons on the magic of Krynn is shown by the following tables. Each phase of a moon has an effect on the magic of that class of wizards.

Moon Phase Effects Table *

Moon Phase	Saving Throw	Additional Spells †	Effective Level
Low Sanction	−1	0	−1
Waning	Normal	0	Even
Waxing	Normal	+1	Even
High Sanction	+1	+2	+1 **

* A wizard of 1st through 3d level is unaffected by phases of the moons because of the low power levels involved in his spells. It is for

this reason that the tests for wizards occur at 3d level or above as this is the point at which wizards are considered to "come of age."

** Only a wizard of 6th level or higher who also has an Intelligence of 15 or above gains this benefit from the moons.

† The additional spells can be of any level the wizard can cast.

If two or more of the moons are aligned, there are bonuses to the moon phase effects given earlier. (Moons are aligned if the boxes they occupy on the Moon Tracking chart [page 28] are in a straight line from the center of the chart. For example, Lunitari on day 3 of its orbital period is aligned with Nuitari on days 6 and 7 of its period and with Solinari on days 5 and 6 of its period.)

Moon Alignment Effects Table *

Alignment	Saving Throw	Additional Spells	Effective Level
Sol. with Lun.	+1	+1	+1
Nuit. with Lun.	+1	+1	+1
Sol. with Nuit.	+1	0	Normal
All Three Moons	+2	+2	+1

* Note that all plusses on this table are cumulative with modifiers from other effects. If all the moons were to align at the time of High Sanction, then all wizards would have a +3 saving throw, +4 additional spells and +2 effective levels to their spell casting. This is known as the Night of the Eye since the moons move through the sky with a terrible aspect and cause magic to be at its peak.

Location of the Moons

The initial location of the moons is determined by rolling 1d8 for each moon and placing it in the indicated box along its orbit.

If you are playing a DRAGONLANCE campaign game, then these are the starting locations for the moons in your campaign. Hereafter, advance the moons one box per game day to keep track of their positions during the campaign. This allows your players to plan for regular changes in the lunar cycles.

moon tracking Chart

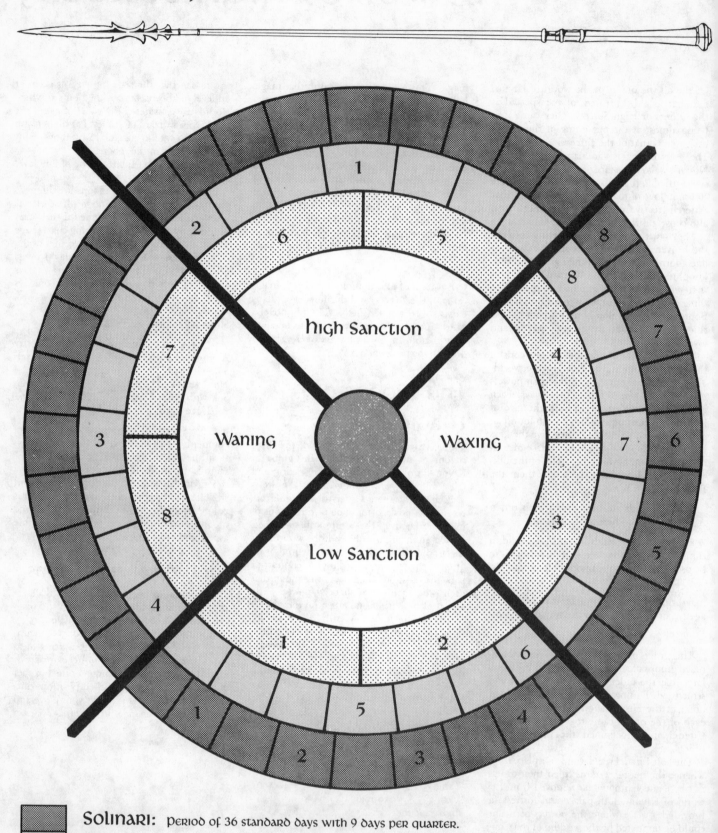

Solinari: period of 36 standard days with 9 days per quarter.

Nuitari: period of 28 standard days with 7 days per quarter.

Lunitari: period of 8 standard days with 2 days per quarter.

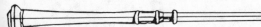

the Conclave of Wizards

The Conclave of Wizards is convened on set dates and times as dictated by the moons. The Conclave meets regularly once each Fourweek on the first day of High Sanction for the Ruling Order. The Night of the Eye is a special time when all of the orders gather together. Conclaves can also be called by the Head of the Conclave during times of grave crises that affect all orders. The Conclave does not meet when the Test is given as this is a normal function of the tower and is handled on a routine basis.

The Conclave of Wizards consists of three factions with seven representatives from each. Each of the Orders of High Sorcery is equally represented at the Conclave and each is led by a single individual selected by each order. The chosen wizard is the Master of that order. The selection process is left to each order and varies from order to order. The Black Robe representative is usually the most powerful wizard of that order. This has from time to time resulted in some rather fabulous contests of wizardry as two sorcerers vie to establish who is fit to rule their order. Such contests are invariably held beyond the boundaries of the towers. In the case of the White Robes, elections are held to determine the master of their order. The Red Robes draw lots from among the seven members of the Conclave.

The Master of the Conclave is determined by *consensus*, a spell that instantaneously determines the combined will of all the wizards of Krynn in a single matter. While not always infallible in its ability to benefit the Conclave as a whole, it still remains the method of selection for the Master of all Sorceries. The law of the Conclave is largely determined in everyday matters by the head of the Conclave and his law is final. If, however, a decision is made which is against the will of the Conclave, then a mandate may be called for in which case a *consensus* is taken of the general wizardry and a new Master of the Conclave is then determined.

the Spheres of Magic

Magic operates within spheres in Krynn. Only certain spheres are usable by the different Orders of High Sorcery; spells castable by wizards of one order may not necessarily be cast by those of another order.

The Spheres of Magic have been defined as follows:

Abjuration magics are primarily concerned with the prevention and exclusion of particular magical and nonmagical effects, situations, or individuals, and include most spells of protection, avoidance, and repellence. Examples include *protection from evil* spells, spells that *dispel magic*, and the *anti-magic shell* spells, among others. This magic is usable by those of the White Robes only.

Alteration spells modify existing conditions or individuals through the infusion of magical energy. Spells that give the recipient enhanced Strength or the ability to fly, those that transform substances (*polymorph self or others*) and spells that have general effects (*move earth* or *lower water*) are all alterations. This magic is the province of the Order of the Red Robes alone.

Conjuration/Summoning spells are a combination of two separate magics in variable quantities: The conjuration part brings additional matter from elsewhere, while the summoning portion creates a duct between the caster and some greater magical power. Spells that summon existing animals or monsters in an area, bring into being on this plane extradimensional creatures (such as elementals, for example), or use such creatures' power (such as a *wish* or *power word*) are conjuration and summoning magics. Both conjuration and summoning are usable by the Order of the Red Robes. Conjuring may be used by the White Robes as well, while summoning may be used by the Black Robes.

Divination spells are those that uncover information that is otherwise hidden under normal circumstances and include spells that detect magical effects, invisibility, and the like, those spells that predict hidden or future events, and those that place the caster in contact with powerful extradimensional creatures but do not involve direct action by those creatures. This sphere is the common ground of all Krynn magic and all wizards can use divination spells regardless of their order.

Enchantment/charm spells place a dweomer on the target individual or item that radiates a magical aura. On physical items it is normally used to invest an item with magical powers (such as *deeppockets* or *bind*), but is more commonly used to induce particular emotional or mental states in living targets (such as *animal friendship*, *forget*, and *Otto's irresistable dance*). The *magic jar* spell, which was originally listed as a possession spell, is really an enchantment/charm spell. These spells can be used by wizards of the White and Black Robes.

Evocation and **invocations** both channel magical energy, using that energy to create specific effects and types of matter. These effects include permanent features such as the wall spells, forces such as the *Bigby's hand* family of spells, and temporary effects such as *lightning bolt* or *fireball*. Invocations are dedicated to a particular powerful extradimensional being and are usually confined to clerics, while evocations involve utilizing ambient magical energy. These spheres of magic can be used by the Orders of the Red Robes and the White Robes.

Illusion/phantasm spells create a false reality. This sphere includes the bulk of the spells listed in the illusionist sub-class. Illusions alone create the apparent existence of items in the minds of the viewers, while phantasms create a shadow reality that gives these illusions the power to affect the viewer as if real. These are the province of the Red Robes and the Black Robes.

Necromantic spells involve the health, hit points, or normal functioning of a living or once-living target. Spells that increase or decrease hit points, cause or cure disease, or restore lost souls to their bodies all are necromantic spells. These are the province of the Black Robes.

A summary of magical spells divided according to level and spell type can be found on pages 126 and 127. Use this list to determine which spells are usable by the different orders of wizardry.

the towers of high Sorcery

Originally there were five Towers of High Sorcery. Built by the ancient wizards as centers for their crafts and learning, they were located in the ancient cities that later came to be called Palanthus, Wayreth, Istar, Daltigoth, and the Ruins.

The towers were all alike and yet all different. The general outline of the towers was determined by a central committee of members of all three orders (since all orders use the towers), but the supervision of the construction work was done by wizards who happened to live in the area. This resulted in the same general structure for all towers, but widely varying details and specific layouts.

The general arrangement of the towers con-

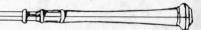

sisted of a central complex surrounded by a field or garden. This field was different for each of the five towers. The Tower at Wayreth was surrounded by a transdimensional field that allowed it to appear anywhere within 500 miles of its usual place in Wayreth Forest. The Tower in Palanthus was surrounded by the Shoikan Grove that emanated a continuous and very powerful *fear* spell. These are the two towers that are most commonly known today. Knowledge of the other three towers is hard to come by, but the properties historically ascribed to these towers' gardens were sleep (Daltigoth), forget (Istar), and passion (the Ruins). While each of these gardens held many other formidable obstacles, these were their principal attributes and defenses.

All towers are neutral zones. Fighting among the wizards is not permitted and is punishable by immediate death.

the tower of Wayreth

The Wayreth Tower's defense is the most unusual, for one does not seek out the tower, it finds you. The garden about Wayreth's Tower has different dimensions at different times and the Tower itself is said to exist without dimension, always existing where it is not. The result is that one could be walking in a forest and suddenly be trespassing within the domains of the wizards of Wayreth. Just where this tower's garden touches the world of men and elves is controlled by the wizards themselves. In this way they protect the tower from enemies of their order while still enabling wizards to enter the tower.

Access to the Wayreth Tower is the most restricted of all the Towers since the Masters of High Sorcery decide who may enter. The tower is never where it is looked for and can only be found when the wizards wish it to be so. It is impossible for a character to enter the tower though astral travel or the outer planes of existence as the tower is not connected to those planes. (Only the Tower Portals can touch on the other planes; otherwise, Raistlin would have had little difficulty in reaching the domain of the Queen of Darkness).

If the wizards want a person to enter the Wayreth Forest, he has little choice in the matter. He may wake to find himself surrounded by trees. He may try to walk away, only to find himself inexplicably walking into it. Or he may be lured inside by the magical singing of birds promising him his heart's desires. Anyone attempting to enter the forest without invitation can do so, but he better be prepared to give a good explanation of himself to the

wizards quickly. Otherwise he is attacked by the trees.

Even those invited into the forest (such as mages traveling to take the Test) are accosted by the feeling of overwhelming magic. It takes every bit of courage and will they possess to make their way to the tower itself. Wizards generally travel to the tower via magical means and do not bother to go through the forest. The exception to this would be a renegade wizard, who would not be permitted to teleport or otherwise enter the tower without permission.

The Tower of Wayreth differs from the other towers in that it contains a great central hall where the Conclave meets. This hall is huge, so large that the ceiling is lost in shadows. It is round, made of stone, and there are no decorations or enhancements of any kind. Stone chairs, created by magic, stand in a semi-circle at one side of the hall. There is light without a source in the hall; it is brightest upon the semi-circle of chairs. The entrances to this hall are magical. No one is permitted inside unless the wizards transport him here. Anyone wandering about the tower would never encounter the hall.

The black, rune-covered walls of the Tower of Wayreth were built by magic and are part of the tower's defenses. No weapon exists that can even mar the surface of these walls. Thus the Tower of Wayreth remained standing relatively untouched when the rest of the world was destroyed in Raistlin's attempt to overthrow the gods. There are no guards at the gate of the tower; there is no need. Once inside the gates, the adventurer passes through a huge courtyard paved with gray flagstone. The courtyard appears empty at first glance, but anyone walking across will suddenly realize that it is filled with people! They cannot be seen directly, only out of the corner of the eye. These are mages traveling to and from the tower, mages taking the Test, mages experimenting, etc.

An adventurer in the courtyard—if invited to the tower—is transported magically to one of the tower's many sumptuous guest rooms. These are like the most luxurious rooms of the best inns in Krynn. Uninvited guests (those who make it this far!) are either taken immediately to stand before the Conclave or to the dungeons. The dungeons of the towers are so dreadful that no report of them has reached the outside world—no one who ever went in came back alive to report on it.

A wizard entering the tower receives his own private quarters, the placement and decor of which depend on the wizard's level. Student magic-users and apprentice wizards

have their rooms on the same level as the guest chambers. High-level mages have more elegant quarters at the top of the tower. There are no locks on any doors as all wizards respect the sanctity of others' possessions.

There are libraries of spell books within the tower, plus libraries of magical scrolls and magical paraphernalia. These are under the control of the Conclave and can be given as gifts to magic-users (almost all young wizards who pass the Test are given some powerful artifact to aid them in their profession). These may also be purchased (in the case of artifacts and scrolls) or studied (in the case of spell books) with the permission of the Conclave.

Purchase prices for items would most likely be in terms of similar items rather than money. A wizard desiring to purchase a scroll would offer another scroll in exchange or some other magical object of comparable value. Thus a White Robe wizard who comes across a scroll of evil magic would not destroy it, but rather take it to the tower to trade for a scroll he can use.

Wizards can choose to be buried within the tombs of the tower, although this is not mandatory. It is rumored that those who choose to rest within the tower's walls serve their art even after their death by performing such tasks as guarding the dungeons or aiding in the Testing of young wizards. At the time of a wizard's death, all possessions and spell books are either bequeathed to an apprentice, a fellow wizard, or sent to the tower. Thus there are no magical artifacts buried in the tombs of the tower.

Adventuring in the tower can be fascinating because the DM is relatively free to do with it as he chooses. See the map of the tower (page 32) for detailed information.

the Shoikan Grove of the tower of Palanthus

The *fear* generated by the Palanthus Tower is one of the most respected visible defenses of the five. This permanent spell is of such power that only one uninvited guest has ever reached the tower—Tasslehoff Burrfoot managed to penetrate the Shoikan Grove while piloting a flying citadel over Palanthus. Wizards are generally of the opinion that the penetration was due to the fact that the citadel was a device of magic itself and the pilot of the cita-

del was, at the time of the penetration, encased in a magical field.

In the time following Raistlin's death, Dalamar, the successor to Raistlin as the Master of that Tower, laid further enchantments on the garden to extend its effects and powers into a dome that encased the tower as well as shielding it physically from any assault. Projectiles now deflect harmlessly (as would flying citadels) and the *fear* that emanates from the grove is unchallengeable.

Passage through the Shoikan Grove without a talisman requires a saving throw vs. spell with a −10 penalty, to the die roll (a difficult roll at best). A character failing this check (which must be made every five rounds the character remains in the grove) succumbs to irrational fear and blind panic, fleeing the grove in the direction from which he came.

The talismans that are given out for passage through the grove negate the penalty, but the character must still successfully make the saving throw or flee in uncontrolled panic. (See page 98 for the talismans that enable safe passage through Shoikan Grove.)

the tower of high Sorcery at Palanthus

The Tower of High Sorcery at Palanthus changes in aspect depending on when in its history it is visited.

Pre-Curse

Originally one of the most beautiful of the towers, the Tower at Palanthus was also considered one of the most powerful. Here it was that the wizards of all the orders came together to create the *dragon orbs* that were responsible for helping to defeat the Dark Queen.

Any entering the tower at this time would find it similar to the description of the Tower of Wayreth, except that this tower is equipped with a laboratory instead of a great hall. (See the description of the laboratory.)

the Curse

During the Age of Might, the wizards grew so powerful that many people feared they might take over the world. Among these was the Kingpriest of Istar, the powerful cleric of good. He turned the people against the wizards. Mobs rose up and attacked the towers.

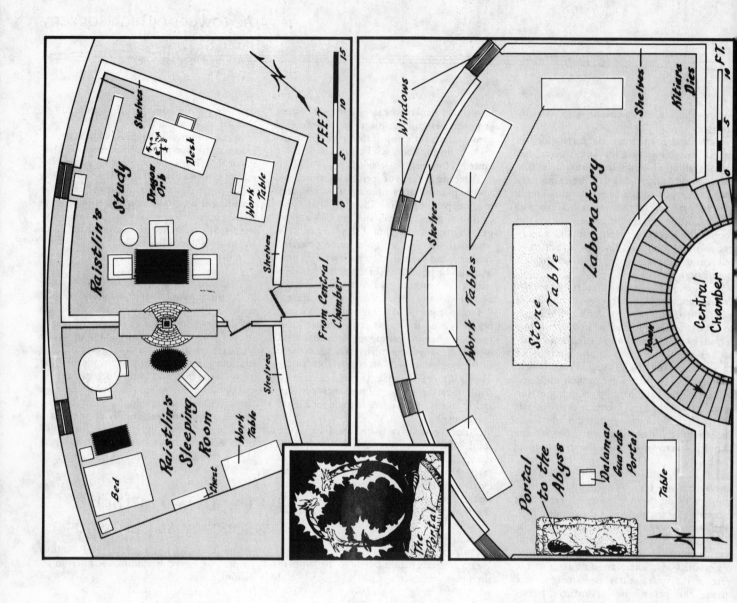

Raistlin's Study

Shelves

Dragon Orb

Desk

Work Table

Shelves

From Central Chamber

Raistlin's Sleeping Room

Work Table

Shelves

Bed

Sheet

FEET

0   5   10   15

The Portal

Windows

Shelves

Work Tables

Store Table

Laboratory

Shelves

Nitiara Dies

FT.

0   5   10

Portal to the Abyss

Dalamar Guards Portal

Table

Central Chamber

Door

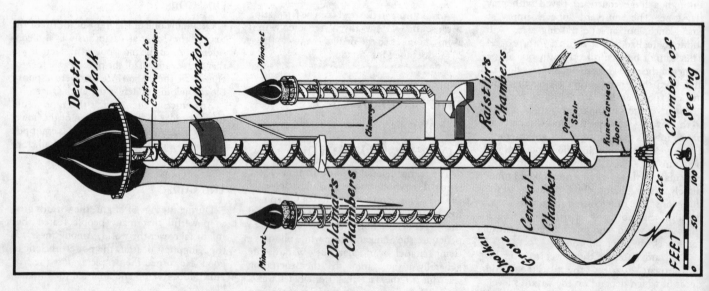

Death Walk

Entrance to Central Chamber

Laboratory

Minaret

Chimneys

Raistlin's Chambers

Open Stair

Dalamar's Chambers

Minaret

Shoiken Grove

Central Chamber

Rune-Carved Door

Gate

Chamber of Seeing

FEET

0   50   100

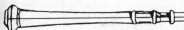 

It would have been easy for the wizards to have destroyed the people, but they knew that in so doing they would destroy the world. Rather than do this, they chose to sacrifice their own power in the world. They destroyed two of the Towers of High Sorcery—those at Daltigoth and the Ruins. They turned the Tower at Istar over to the Kingpriest and were intending to give him the Tower at Palanthus but for the terrible event that was to befall it. In return, they were allowed to retain the Tower at Wayreth, and it was here that they brought as much of their libraries and as many of their magical artifacts as was possible.

At the beginning of the ceremony to turn over the Tower of Palanthas to the Kingpriest's representative, an evil wizard—driven insane by the downfall of his art—leaped from an upper window and impaled himself upon the spikes of the tower's gate. As his blood flowed to the ground, he cast a curse upon the tower, saying that no living being would inhabit it until the Master of Past and Present returned with power.

It is unlikely that any would be able to enter the Tower during the period the curse is in effect. The only ones known to have done so were Raistlin, Caramon, and Crysania, who came here long after the Cataclysm (Raistlin mistakenly believed a Portal existed in the tower at this time).

The tower is guarded by undead of all sorts that permit an adventuring party in the tower only if Raistlin (whom they would recognize) is present.

The Tower During Raistlin's Rule

Those who enter the tower during this time are undoubtedly here by invitation and are, in any case, completely under Raistlin's control. They therefore see only what Raistlin wants them to see. This might include Raistlin's study, a luxuriously appointed room filled with books, comfortable furniture, and objects of interest from all over Krynn. A fire in the hearth dispells the chill of the tower.

The books in this room are not spell books; those are in the laboratory. These books are works of poetry and prose, books on herbal lore and anatomy, books on philosophy, and treatises on magic. The objects decorating the room are also nonmagical, being beautiful or hideous but all curious. These are mementoes Raistlin has acquired in his travels.

Dalamar's Quarters

Dalamar is Raistlin's only apprentice. Despite the fact that he is a dark elf, his quarters are very elven in design, being decorated with rugs and furniture that celebrate the beauty of nature. There are also many interesting and curious objects in these rooms, plus many magical ones and Dalamar's spell books.

The Laboratory

The laboratory is located in the top of the Tower and can be reached only after climbing a narrow stone stairway that spirals up the inner wall of the tower. Since the center of this part of the tower is hollow, one misstep on those stairs means that the person falls to his death.

Upon entering the laboratory, adventurers note that it is much larger than it could possibly be, given the size of the tower. The primary object in the room is the great stone table. Dragged from the bottom of the sea by magic, it is so large that a minotaur can lay down full length upon it. It is covered with runes to ward off any outside influences that might affect the mage's work.

Also present in this room are shelves of spell books. These include the night-blue bound spell books of Fistandantilus, plus Raistlin's own black-bound spell books. Here also are books on herbal lore and anatomy, many of them in Raistlin's own handwriting. Various magical items and artifacts are also here.

Raistlin is an expert in alchemy, so bottles and beakers of various chemicals are found both on the stone table and in other parts of the laboratory. He has also delved into the art of vivisection, and various animals and parts of animals (including humans) can be seen in jars and beakers. Several complete skeletons of animals and humans stand in the corners. Parts of skeletal remains lie about. Some of Raistlin's experimental creations live in jars or cages and take an avid interest in any newcomer who enters the lab.

At the far end, almost obscured by shadows, hangs the purple velvet curtain that hides the Portal. If these curtains are drawn, the character sees an oval doorway standing on a golden dais. It is surrounded by the dragon heads of Takhisis, the Queen of Darkness. When not activated, these heads appear to be plain gold metal, although the character may have the uncanny feeling that the eyes of the heads are watching his every move. When activated, the heads glow blue, red, black, green, and white and scream the praises of

their Dark Queen.

Characters looking into the Portal when it is not activated see only a dark void. Those looking into it when it is activated see a swirl of brilliant, blinding color, then whatever the DM wants them to see.

The Chamber of Seeing

Here dwell the Live Ones, Raistlin's failed experiments in creating life. He is unwilling to show them to anyone with the exception of Dalamar. Their task is to watch the pool that is Raistlin's window on the world. Looking into it, he can see anything that is currently happening anywhere in Krynn and can, to a certain degree, affect the actions of those he sees. He can only view the present in the pool, he cannot see either the future or the past.

The pool is quite similar in nature to the crystal he (as Fistandantilus) presented to Astinus the Historian.

The Live Ones are quite harmless, but so gruesome looking and foul smelling that any character not of evil alignment must successfully roll a Constitution Check or become violently ill. This has the effect of lowering the character's attack roll by -3 and penalizing his AC by $+3$ while he is in the Chamber of Seeing.

After Raistlin's Death

When Dalamar became Master of the Tower, he instituted many changes. Among these are opening up living quarters for additional apprentices. His most important act, however, was to shut the laboratory and seal it with a powerful curse. A lich guards the door and suffers none to pass.

Guardian Groves of the Destroyed Towers

The following are suggestions for those wishing to set a campaign in pre-Cataclysm Krynn before the other three Towers of High Sorcery were destroyed.

The towers are similar in construction to those in Palanthas and Wayreth with the exceptions noted on page 29. Each tower's guardian grove had different characteristics.

Daltigoth (sleep): All living beings enter-

ing this forest must make a successful saving throw vs. spell with a −7 penalty every five rounds they are in the forest. Those who fail fall into an enchanted sleep. The sleeping being is then transported by the wizards either into their tower or out of the forest, depending on whether or not they wish to have dealings with him.

Istar (forget): Those entering this forest must roll a successful saving throw vs. spell with a −5 penalty every five rounds they are in the forest. Failure temporarily negates all short-term memory, thus making it impossible for a person to remember from moment to moment what it is they are doing here. This effect passes once the characters leave the forest.

Ruins (passion): The character finds his own passions overwhelming him. These may be of love, hate, vengeance, etc. A saving throw vs. spell must be successfully rolled every five rounds to avoid this effect.

Early Life of a Wizard

All those who wish to join one or another of the Orders of Wizardry begin their training as children studying magic under a Master Mage (one approved by the Conclave for the teaching of young magic-users.) Magic-users can rise to the level of Initiate without formally declaring their alignment and without declaring loyalty to the Conclave. Thus a magic-user could remain an Initiate all his life, practicing only minor spells, without having to take the Test.

Those seeking greater power must travel to the Tower of Wayreth for the Test. Here they declare their alignment and are assigned to a higher level mage to serve time as apprentice wizards.

An apprentice is generally assigned to a wizard of his declared alignment, although in later days, Dalamar, wizard of the Black Robes, was known to accept Red Robes as apprentices. So also a White Robe wizard might accept a Red Robe as apprentice.

Student Magic-Users
Game Data

Minimum Requirements: Those who wish to enter into the life of wizardry in Krynn must have the following minimum game statistics:

Wizard Minimum Scores

Strength	—
Intelligence	9/15*
Wisdom	—
Dexterity	6
Constitution	—
Charisma	—

* A wizard with an Intelligence of 15 or more gains an additional 10% to all experience points earned.

Student Wizard Advancement Table

Level	Experience Points	Hit Dice (d4s)	Title
1	2,500	1	Student
2	5,000	2	Novice
3	10,000	3	Initiate *

* Wizards cannot advance higher than this without either becoming renegades or joining one of the Orders of High Sorcery.

Wizard Spells Usable by Level

Level	1	2	3	4	5	6	7	8	9
1	1	-	-	-	-	-	-	-	-
2	2	-	-	-	-	-	-	-	-
3	2	1	-	-	-	-	-	-	-

Proficiencies	Weapon/Nonweapon
Initial	1/3
Added	1/2 per 5 levels

Test of High Sorcery

The Test of High Sorcery is more than just a trial of a person's magical abilities, it also tests how that person will use the abilities he has and those he will gain. Magic is powerful in the world of Krynn and, to the wizards, the distinctions between the three different factions of wizardry are most important.

Each initiate's test is a different one, designed especially for his needs and weaknesses. Failure means death. Because magic is such a powerful force in the world, the wizards are extremely careful about who is allowed to wield this power. They are not interested in whether the power is used for good or for evil so much as they are concerned with irresponsible use of the power (one reason there are no kender magic-users!). A wizard who agrees to take the Test, therefore, literally pledges his

life to the magic. He must prove to the satisfaction of his fellow wizards that he takes magic seriously and that he will devote his life to magic.

As each Test of High Sorcery is designed for the individual, there is no specific Test detailed here—only guidelines as to how such a Test must be conducted and what the Test should include. It is up to you to design the details of the specific Test for the wizards in your campaign.

There should be at least three tests of the wizard's knowledge of magic and its use; the Test should require the casting of all of the spells known to the initiate; at least three tests that cannot be solved by magic alone; at least one combat against a character known to the initiate as an ally; at least one solo combat against an opponent who is two levels higher than the initiate.

Those attempting the Test can bring companions along, but no one who comes is guaranteed of returning alive.

One such Test offered by Dalamar allowed the initiate and his party to enter the tower freely—getting out, however, was another matter.

Changing Orders after the Test

From time to time, a wizard's actions will indicate that he is no longer a follower of the tenets of his originally chosen order. Raistlin Majere, for example, won his Red Robes in his Test but thereafter events and his own decisions brought him to the way of the Black Robes. Such changes are not without hardship.

A wizard who changes orders suffers the loss of two experience levels. This may make the wizard's spell book unusable in some instances (since the types of spells a wizard receives depend on his order, the spells in his old book may no longer be usable when he changes orders).

Also, the wizard's abilities are not affected by any moons until one game month has passed after his change (then the moon of his new order affects his abilities).

WIZARDS OF the White Robes

Wizards of the White Robes generally gain levels slower than their brothers, yet they ultimately attain higher levels than any of the other magical orders.

A White Robe wizard must follow the ways of good and keep this goal in his mind in all that he does. Acts contrary to the mandate of good can eventually result in the downfall of the wizard. One of the first indications that a wizard has lost sight of his order's goals is that his order's moon no longer affects his abilities. Also, certain spells may not work for him any more.

White Robe Wizards
Game data

Minimum Requirements: Any who wish to join the Order of the White Robes must meet all of the minimum statistics standards required of student wizards. They must also have passed the Test of High Sorcery without having committed an act contrary to the laws of good.

White Robe Advancement Table

Level	Experience Points	Hit Dice (d4s)	Title
4	20,000	4	9th Order
5	38,000	5	8th Order
6	55,000	6	7th Order
7	100,000	7	6th Order
8	200,000	8	5th Order
9	400,000	9	4th Order
10	600,000	10	3d Order
11	800,000	11	2d Order
12	1,000,000	11 + 1	1st Order
13	1,250,000	11 + 2	
14	1,500,000	11 + 3	
15	1,750,000	11 + 4	
16	2,000,000	11 + 5	
17	2,250,000	11 + 6	
18	2,500,000	11 + 7	Master *

* Only one White Robe wizard can be of Master level (see *The Conclave of Wizards* for the selection process for the White Robe Master).

Spheres of Magic Usable: A wizard of the White Robes can use the following Spheres of Magic:

Abjuration	Charm	Conjuration
Divination	Enchantment	Evocation

White Robe Spells Usable by Level

Level	1	2	3	4	5	6	7	8	9
4	3	2	-	-	-	-	-	-	-
5	4	2	1	-	-	-	-	-	-
6	4	2	2	-	-	-	-	-	-
7	4	3	2	1	-	-	-	-	-
8	4	3	3	2	-	-	-	-	-
9	4	3	3	2	1	-	-	-	-
10	4	4	3	2	2	1	-	-	-
11	4	4	4	3	3	2	1	-	-
12	4	4	4	4	4	3	2	1	-
13	5	5	5	4	4	3	2	1	-
14	5	5	5	4	4	3	2	1	-
15	5	5	5	5	5	3	2	2	1
16	5	5	5	5	5	4	2	2	1
17	5	5	5	5	5	4	3	3	2
18	5	5	5	5	5	4	3	3	3

WIZARDS OF the Red Robes

A wizard of the Red Robes gains levels faster than his White-Robed brothers, but slower than his Black-Robed counterparts. Of all the wizardries, the Red Robes have the widest range of spells available.

Red Robe Wizards
Game data

Minimum Requirements: Any who wish to join the Order of the Red Robes must meet all of the minimum statistics standards required of student wizards. They must also have passed the Test of High Sorcery without having committed an act contrary to the laws of chaos.

Red Robe Advancement Table

Level	Experience Points	Hit Dice (d4s)	Title
4	18,000	4	9th Order
5	36,000	5	8th Order
6	50,000	6	7th Order
7	90,000	7	6th Order
8	180,000	8	5th Order
9	350,000	9	4th Order
10	500,000	10	3d Order
11	700,000	11	2d Order
12	900,000	11 + 1	1st Order
13	1,100,000	11 + 2	
14	1,300,000	11 + 3	
15	1,500,000	11 + 4	
16	1,750,000	11 + 5	Master *
17	2,000,000	11 + 6	
18	2,250,000	11 + 7	

* Only one Red Robe wizard can be of Master level or above (see *The Conclave of Wizards* for the selection process for the Red Robe Master).

Spheres of Magic Usable: A wizard of the Red Robes can use the following Spheres of Magic:

Alteration	Conjuration	Divination
Illusion	Invocation	Phantasm
Summoning		

Red Robe Spells Usable by Level

Level	1	2	3	4	5	6	7	8	9
4	3	2	1	-	-	-	-	-	-
5	4	3	1	-	-	-	-	-	-
6	4	3	2	-	-	-	-	-	-
7	4	3	2	1	-	-	-	-	-
8	4	3	3	2	-	-	-	-	-
9	4	3	3	2	1	-	-	-	-
10	5	4	3	2	2	1	-	-	-
11	5	4	4	3	3	2	-	-	-
12	5	4	4	4	4	2	1	-	-
13	5	5	5	4	4	2	1	1	-
14	5	5	5	4	4	2	2	1	-
15	5	5	5	5	5	2	2	1	1
16	6	5	5	5	5	3	2	1	1
17	6	5	5	5	5	3	3	2	1
18	6	6	5	5	5	3	3	2	2

Wizards of the Black Robes

Black Robe wizards gain levels faster than either of the other two orders, yet it is in their nature to top out in levels sooner than either of the other orders.

Black Robe Wizards
Game Data

Minimum Requirements: Any who wish to join the Order of the Black Robes must meet all of the minimum statistics standards required of student wizards. They must also have passed the Test of High Sorcery without having committed an act contrary to the laws of evil.

Black Robe Wizards Advancement Table

Level	Experience Points	Hit Dice (d4s)	Title
4	17,000	4	9th Order
5	35,000	5	8th Order
6	45,000	6	7th Order
7	80,000	7	6th Order
8	135,000	8	5th Order
9	290,000	9	4th Order
10	375,000	10	Trimorte
11	500,000	11	Brother to Darkness
12	650,000	11 + 1	Blackmage
13	800,000	11 + 2	Master *
14	1,000,000	11 + 2	
15	1,200,000	11 + 3	
16	1,400,000	11 + 4	
17	1,650,000	11 + 5	
18	1,900,000	11 + 6	

* Only one Black Robe wizard can be of Master level or higher (see *The Conclave of Wizards* for the selection process for the Black Robe Master).

Spheres of Magic Usable: A wizard of the Black Robes can use the following Spheres of Magic:

Charm	Divination	Enchantment
Illusion	Necromantic	Phantasm
Summoning		

Black Robe Spells Usable by Level

Level	1	2	3	4	5	6	7	8	9
4	3	2	-	-	-	-	-	-	-
5	4	2	1	-	-	-	-	-	-
6	4	2	2	-	-	-	-	-	-
7	4	3	2	1	-	-	-	-	-
8	4	3	3	2	-	-	-	-	-
9	4	3	3	2	1	-	-	-	-
10	4	4	3	2	2	1	-	-	-
11	4	4	4	3	2	1	-	-	-
12	4	4	4	4	2	1	1	-	-
13	5	5	5	4	3	2	1	1	1
14	5	5	5	4	4	2	1	1	1
15	5	5	5	5	2	1	1	1	-
16	5	5	5	5	3	2	1	1	-
17	5	5	5	5	4	3	2	1	-
18	5	5	5	5	4	3	2	1	-

Renegade Wizards

Wizards who attempt to live outside the law of the Towers of Sorcery are known as renegade wizards. Wizards from other campaigns who do not quickly contact the heads of an order they wish to join will find themselves in the position of being considered a renegade wizard.

Renegade wizards are considered by all orders to be a menace to the balance of magic in the world. It was only by the barest of margins that Raistlin, a magic-user of extraordinary powers, retained his station in the Order of Black Robes since he was obviously intent upon defying them by entering the Abyss and challenging the gods. Why the Conclave did not order his destruction is unknown. (Most believe that it was because they feared they would not be able to stop him.) Thus they sent the dark elf apprentice wizard, Dalamar, to spy on him and eventually attempt to destroy him.

A renegade wizard who has come to the attention of the orders is invariably seen as a threat that must be either neutralized or eliminated. Each of the orders has its own way of dealing with a renegade—some orders are more benevolent than others, but all are equally effective in their methods.

Wizards who enter Krynn from other campaigns are considered renegade wizards until such time as they declare their alignment to an order.

Such wizards use the standard wizard tables found in the *DMG* and the *Player's Handbook*. It should be explained to the player, however, that the standard tables are far less favorable for a wizard than those for the orders of Krynn.

A character who starts in Krynn can opt to become a renegade after he reaches 3d level. Alternatively, a character can leave an order after having joined and become a renegade by not joining another order. Note that any wizard character leaving the Orders of High Sorcery is subject to the two-level loss penalty required of anyone who leaves an order. At that point he begins to use the magic-user tables in the *Player's Handbook*. His experience point total is altered so that he has only 1 point more than is necessary to reach his current level (after the two-level drop).

Players who run their characters as renegades from the beginning also use the AD&D® game system charts for magic-users, but they are not subject to any level penalties. An additional problem with being a renegade wizard is that there is a 50% chance that any other wizard encountered will recognize a renegade wizard. This chance is decreased by 20% if the renegade is disguised as a wizard from an order other than that of the identifying wizard.

Renegade wizards who are recognized by a wizard of another order are dealt with in ways that depend on the order of the wizard. A wizard of the White Robes will try to capture the renegade by any means at his disposal while doing the least harm. Should he fail, he will report the renegade to the nearest tower, keeping close watch on him meanwhile. He would destroy the renegade only as a last resort and then only if the renegade threatened either the balance of magic or the lives of others.

A wizard of the Red Robes will try to capture the renegade and bring him before the Conclave, if possible. If this is not possible, he would not hesitate to destroy the renegade.

A Black Robe wizard will at first attempt to win the wizard over to his side of the struggle before destroying him.

Renegade wizards who are brought before the Conclave are given a chance to join one of the Orders of High Sorcery and to abide by its laws. Those who refuse are cast out from the realms of Krynn and the circles of the world. Those who join the Orders of High Sorcery are entitled to use the better advancement tables and all of the benefits of the towers.

illusion and krynn

If, from time to time, a character comes across something that is too hard for him to believe (even in Krynn!), then the character may have cause to question whether the thing is real or merely the strange concoction of some illusionist wizard.

Disbelieving an illusion requires a period of concentration. If a character wants to disbelieve an illusion, follow these steps:

1) Ask the player how long his character will concentrate on the suspected illusion. This should be given as a number of melee rounds.

2) Determine the modifier for the disbelief check. Compare the duration of concentration time to the following table to determine a concentration modifier for the roll.

Concentration Modifiers for Illusion Disbelief

Time	Modifier
1 Round	+1
2 Rounds	+2
3 Rounds	+3
4-6 Rounds	+4
7-9 Rounds	+5
1-3 Turns	+6
4-6 Turns	+7
1+ Hours	+8

During this period of concentration, the character can perform no other actions. It is the uninterrupted period of concentration that determines the modifier. Note that the available concentration time of any character will be very limited if the illusion attacks the character.

A character who has taken damage from an illusion does not get a chance to disbelieve it.

3) Determine the Disbelief Number by adding the concentration modifier to the character's Intelligence. You may also add 1 for each other character who has successfully disbelieved during any previous round.

4) The referee secretly rolls 1d20. If the result is higher than the Disbelief Number, then the object in question looks real and its effects are as if it is real. If the number is equal to or lower, then the illusion is disbelieved.

A disbelief check can be made only once per hour by a character against any one illusion (but the character can check again whenever another character in the group makes a successful check). The illusion is either discovered by the character or else is believed. If an illusion is a group of monsters, then the check is made for the entire group, not to disbelieve

each individual monster. A successful disbelief of a group of monsters would tell which were real and which were not should illusions be interspersed with real ones. Characters who successfully disbelieve cannot be harmed by illusions.

Spells of high Sorcery
kiss of night's Guardian

(Evocation)

Level: 9	Components: V, S
Range: Touch	Casting Time: 1 seg.
Duration: 1 Passage	Saving Throw: None
Area of Effect: 1 Person	

The Master of the Tower of High Sorcery at Palanthus has the power to grant protection to anyone entering the Shoikan Grove. The Master confers this protection by means of a kiss upon the subject's forehead. To those of good or neutral alignment, the kiss seems to burn into their flesh. To those of evil alignment, the kiss will confer a pleasant, warm sensation. It leaves a scar that is visible only to the undead of the Shoikan Grove. The Kiss acts the same as the *Nightjewel* in alleviating fear and also prevents all undead in the grove from attacking the protected person. No weapons or spells can be used while under the Kiss's influence. To do so negates the spell. The Kiss's power works only for one passage through the grove.

Mindspin

(Illusion/Phantasm)

Level: 7	Components: V, S
Range: Special	Casting Time: 3 hours
Duration: Special	Saving Throw: Neg.
Area of Effect: One Person	

Mindspin takes the innermost nightmares of the subject and makes them real in a startlingly vivid illusion. These illusions most often take the form of dreamwraiths and dreamshadows as described in the *Creatures* section.

The spell has an exceedingly long casting time. This is primarily due to the need to sift through the victim's mind and distill his nightmares into a tangible form. During this time, the victim and the caster must remain undisturbed. A disturbance negates the effect

of the spell at once. A *charmed* person is not entitled to a saving throw. Otherwise, a successful saving throw by the victim can negate the spell.

The dream as woven by the spell invokes three separate layers of reality. These are referred to here as *levels* of the dream.

The *first level* of the dream alters the character's perceptions of space, time, and reality around the character's group. The terrain that is described to the PC during this section of the adventure is not the actual terrain of the area but the terrain as the PC perceives it. The PC can actually travel many miles in the real world, yet only perceive himself moving a short distance in the dream state.

The PC's perception of time is equally distorted. He may believe that only minutes have passed when, in reality, it has been days. Dreamwraiths and dreamshadows will appear among those things that are real, forcing the PC to determine which is reality and which is not. Saving throws in this level of the dream are normal and all magic works as it should.

The *second level* of the dream distorts the PC's sense of reality even further, for he no longer knows which of his companions are real and which are not. Note that dreamwraiths and dreamshadows have special magical resistances of 10% at this level of the dream.

The *third level* of the dream (the core of the dream) distorts even the PC's perceptions of himself. In addition to all the other effects of the previous two levels, at this level of the dream, all the character's strengths turn to weaknesses. Characters in melee are forced to use the attack and saving throw tables of other classes, as follows.

Clerics use thief tables.
Fighters use magic-user tables.
Magic-users use fighter tables.
Thieves use cleric tables.

In addition, due to the magical nature of the dream area, each of the following classes must take the following adjustments:

Clerics: Subtract their Wisdom from 20. Compare the result against the Adjustments for Clerics Table on page 11 of the *Player's Handbook* and use the corresponding Chance of Spell Failure for the character. On any roll requiring reference to the Matrix for Clerics Affecting Undead Table (page 75, *Dungeon Master's Guide*) use the table on the following page:

Mindspin Clerics Turning Table									
Type	1	2	3	4	5	6	7	8	9-13 14+
Skeleton	-	-	-	-	-	-	-	-	- -
Zombie	-	-	-	-	-	-	-	-	- 20
Ghoul	-	-	-	-	-	-	-	-	20 19
Shadow	-	-	-	-	-	-	-	20	19 13
Wight	-	-	-	-	-	-	20	19	16 10
Ghast	-	-	-	-	-	20	19	16	13 7
Wraith	-	-	-	-	20	19	16	13	10 4
Mummy	-	-	-	20	19	16	13	10	7 t
Spectre	-	-	20	19	16	13	10	7	4 t
Vampire	-	20	19	16	13	10	7	4	t t
Ghost	20	19	16	13	10	7	4	t	t d
Lich	19	16	13	10	7	t	t	t	d d
Special	16	13	10	7	t	t	t	d	d d

Thieves: On any roll requiring the use of the Thieves Function Table, all successes are counted as failures and all failures are successes. Otherwise, adjust the rolls normally. Simple locks are now tough opponents.

Magic-Users: Magic-users now cast spells at one level higher than normal. This is due to the magical nature of the *mindspin* spell. If this enables a magic-user to cast a spell higher than those he currently knows, he can choose any one spell from the higher level. The magic automatically gives the magic-user the illusion that he knows it. This spell has only illusionary effects, unlike the other spells the magic-user casts during the dream.

All of the effects from each level of the dream disappear if the dreamer is awakened from his sleep. It is a property of the magic that the dreamer is always present and a central figure in the dream. *Mindspin* expands at a rate of one mile per hour with a maximum range that depends on the level of the dream. The maximum distance that can be covered by the *mindspin* and its various levels depends upon the Intelligence of the character on whom the spell was cast. The first level can extend to a maximum of 20 miles times the character's Intelligence. The second level is up to one mile times the character's Intelligence. The extent of the third or core level of the dream is 20 feet times the character's Intelligence. Slightly shorter distances can be used if this best fits the existing terrain.

timeheal

(Evocation)

Level: 5	Components: V, M
Range: Touch	Casting Time: 3 seg.
Duration: Permanent	Saving Throw: Special
Area of Effect: One creature	

This spell takes the creature it is cast upon and slips its body backward in time to a point where it was in better health, thus simulating a healing ability without using clerical powers. Time is of the essence in the *timeheal* spell as the greater the amount of time, the greater the chance of failure.

Each level of the casting wizard guaranteed healing of the character's wounds for one minute previous to the casting. For example: a 9th-level wizard casting this spell is guaranteed to be able to take the wounded character back in time nine minutes to the character's condition at that time. For every minute earlier that the character must be taken back to be healed, there is a 5% cumulative chance of spell failure. Thus if the 9th-level wizard tried to use this spell to heal an adventurer wounded 20 minutes before the spell was cast, that would be 11 minutes (20 minutes minus 9 minutes for his level) further than he could guarantee success, so he would have a 55% chance (11 x 5%) that the spell fails.

Multiple *timeheals* cannot be cast to increase the time the victim can be brought back with guaranteed spell success. Thus the 9th-level wizard *cannot* cast three successive *timeheals* to bring his patient back 27 minutes and thus guarantee success (since none of the spells alone exceeded his guaranteed limit of nine minutes).

Timeheal will not recall a spirit from death and therefore is useful only if the character has at least 1 hit point remaining. A dead character who has a *timeheal* placed upon him will be healed of the appropriate damage, but will nevertheless be dead as his spirit has fled into the heavens.

timereaver

(Evocation)

Level: 9	Components: V, S, M
Range: 1″	Casting Time: 3 Turns
Duration: Permanent	Saving Throw: None
Area of Effect: 1″ radius	

The *timereaver* spell sends those within its area of effect backward or forward along the timestream of Krynn, into either Krynn's past or future. It is the spell that was used by Par-Salian to send Caramon and Tasslehoff into the past. It is also the spell that the *Scepter of Time* utilized to transport Caramon and Tasslehoff throughout the *Legends* tales.

Since the earliest days of Krynn, the wisdom of the gods has been brought to all races through the efforts of the clerics, the mortal messengers of the will of heaven.

Many have been the faces and names of these gods over the centuries. Their precise names, appearances, and demeanors have varied from land to land and people to people. Some nations have worshiped many gods and some have recognized only a few.

Yet while the names and faces of the gods may have been perceived differently from time to time and place to place, their general philosophies, laws, and powers have remained constant and recognizable. What one clan may call Thak another may call E'li, yet both were names by which Paladine was known and both peoples were equally worthy in his eyes as true worshipers.

So it is that the history of the gods, or that part of the gods' history that is known to men, depends greatly upon the culture in which the deity is recognized. With so many different cultures on Krynn, the task of sorting the truth from human fabrication and exaggeration is a difficult one. Suffice it to say that while not all worship the gods in the same way, their faith and dedication to the basic principles of their creators is accepted by the gods.

For purposes of our discourse here, however, we will be setting forth the gods as they are known among the Knights of Solamnia and as revealed by Paladine to Elistan. The basic facts seem to be confirmed by many annotated historical works compiled by Astinus of Palanthus.

There are 21 gods who are the masters of Krynn's universe. They are allied seven on each side of the triangle of good, evil, and neutrality. They are presented as three separate families of gods.

The first family, the family of Good, is that of Paladine. Mishakal is his companion and advisor. Their twin sons, Kiri-Jolith and Habbakuk, administer to their own orders of the world. Their third son was Solinari who left the circle of the family as keeper of the magic. Two other gods of good, Majere and Branchala, were adopted into the family from Beyond.

The second family, the family of Neutrality, is that of Gilean. He holds a patriarchal position in the family; he has no known companion. Zivilyn and Chislev are companions, as are Sirrion and Shinare. Both were paired before the coming from Beyond. Lunitari is the daughter of Zivilyn and Chislev. Reorx came alone from Beyond to be adopted into the family of neutrals; many are the fanciful

and tragic tales told of his existence before the creation of the world.

The third family, the family of Evil, is that of Takhisis. Her consort is Sargonnas. Zeboim is the daughter of these two and Nuitari is her twin brother. Morgion, Chemosh, and Hiddukel have been adopted into this family and were called into this universe from Beyond by Takhisis.

While these gods are not alone in the heavens, they are the only ones who are involved in the lives of the peoples of Krynn. Even though the gods take an active and impassioned interest in Krynn, they mainly allow the course of man's destiny to be shaped by the free will of mankind. The gods prefer to let their will and strength be felt through their agents rather than through direct intervention.

There are, however, several notable occasions in which the gods took a direct hand in the course of the world of Krynn.

Origins of Faith: Each religion on the face of Krynn has its own version of the origins of their faith and their god. Generally speaking, however, all of them agree that this universe was created by the gods out of chaos. Once it formed and creatures began to walk the face of Krynn, the gods instituted their faiths among their creations. Thus all learned the ways of faith in the unknowable.

Three of the gods, Solinari, Nuitari and Lunitari, forsook their former positions and, circling close above the world, brought magic in all its forms to Krynn. Their history is related with that of the wizards.

The Whitestone Glade: It was here that Paladine, Kiri-Jolith, and Habbakuk all appeared to Vinas Solamnus. They gave him the orders of the Knighthood that he would build. They left a sign as a remembrance of their visit—a great pillar of crystal.

Huma and the Lance: This legend tells of great deeds done with the gods themselves.

Takhisis was determined to impose her will upon the lands of Krynn by direct action. While she dwelt upon Krynn, she wreaked havoc with her dragons and other minions. The forces of the Knights stood in her way, but there were none among them who had the heart of a true Knight nor the courage required to stop the Queen of Darkness.

None save Huma.

Huma undertook the long, dangerous journey to Godshome, high in the Khalkist Mountains to the east of Solamnia. It was here that his *dragonlance*, forged in the mountains of Ergoth by silver dragons, was purified and endowed with special power over the Dark Queen. Huma, a knight who was barred from

the highest orders of the Knights of Solamnia, gave the fullest measure of any Knight in banishing the Queen of Darkness from the world for a time. It is still said today that the place of Godshome, should anyone find it, is one of great promise and power.

The Night of Doom: No records have ever been found concerning this night, for all who participated in it are now far removed from the knowledge of mortal man. On this night, thirteen days prior to the Cataclysm that ended the Age of Might, the true clerics of the land all disappeared. Legends have it, however, that they were taken up by the gods to protect them from the calamity that was to come.

This is not to say that all clerics were taken up—far from it. Only clerics of pure faith and good heart were taken. There were few who qualified.

Mishakal's Return: In the year 351 AC, a princess of the Abanasinian Plains was given a glorious gift. Mishakal appeared to her and gave her the Disks of Mishakal on which are written the true words of the gods and their power. It was the first manifestation of the true gods in over three centuries. From these beginnings, the message of the gods went out across the land and re-established the people's faith in the true gods.

The War of the Lance: Takhisis, the Queen of Darkness, started the War of the Lance partly as a diversion from her true intent: to find the Everman. Once the temple at Neraka was complete, then her way into the world from the Abyss would be open and she would be free to rule the world.

Opposing her, however, were the gods of good and neutrality. Paladine appeared on the face of Krynn for a time in disguise. In this way he influenced men to choose the path of good to fight the evil. All the while, Paladine tried to maintain the balance of the world and limit the gods' interference in its workings.

Gender and the Gods

While male and female genders are applied to the gods of Krynn, no mortal has ever been able to ascertain whether the gods have gender. Any determination of their gender is impossible as legends often speak about them appearing in either form at their convenience. Paladine himself, however, seems to have affirmed the relationships as described in this

section as being "as good a card toss into the hat as I have ever seen." No one is exactly sure what that means.

Thus there are occasional gender confusions and contradictions among different legends of the gods. Wizards, for example, revere the "Three Brothers" of magic (Solinari, Lunitari, and Nuitari), but the revelations of Paladine to his servant Elistan seem to indicate that Lunitari is the daughter of Gilean, not his son. The true facts of the matter are of little importance to the everyday lives of mortals on Krynn.

Obligations of Clerics

Call to the Service of the Gods: A Krynn character who wishes to enter into the service of a god must first be accepted by the god as a devotee. The character must seek the help of a cleric who is a follower of the god. If the cleric is convinced of the character's sincerity, he will teach the character the beliefs of the god and the dictates of his religion. There is occasionally a test if the cleric is not convinced of the character's sincerity in joining the clerical order of this god. Once the character is accepted, he is now a cleric of the god. His teacher gives the new cleric a Medallion of Faith (see page 92) and sends him off to preach and grow in the power of his religion.

All clerics created in Krynn start their game life possessing a Medallion of Faith. Encourage your players to create a story telling how they came to obtain their Medallions of Faith.

Clerics who come to Krynn from other worlds lose all powers until they join the order of a god as given above. Once they have joined an order, they are restored to their proper levels and powers.

The Straight and Narrow: Clerics of the DRAGONLANCE® game world enjoy many privileges bestowed on them by their gods, often more than those given clerics in other universes. However, to maintain the blessings of these privileges, each cleric of Krynn must walk the straight path as dictated by his deity. It is true that some paths are wider than others (depending upon which deity is being served), but all gods agree that the penalties for not following the precepts of one's religion are great indeed.

Acts Required: Each god requires different

acts of obedience from his clerics. These must be performed in accordance with the precepts of the religion. The following pages describe those things the known gods of Krynn require of their followers.

The Fallen: Occasionally a cleric falls from the grace of his deity. He immediately finds his powers diminished and abilities impaired.

Clerics who perform an act contrary to the tenants of their alignment have their alignment shifted (on the Character Alignment Tracking chart on page 114) by up to 3 points toward the alignment of the action performed. Clerics can fall from grace without changing the god they worship. Clerics whose alignments move away from that of their god can repent (see below) and regain their status.

Clerics who have fallen out of their god's alignment cannot cast any spells whatsoever and gain no experience while they are in this state.

Clerics who change from one religion of worship to another of the same alignment lose one level. Those who choose to worship another god of a different alignment lose two levels.

The player must declare that this is taking place. In addition, the cleric must have already proven himself worthy of this change by shifting his alignment into the appropriate alignment area through his previous actions.

At what level the novitiate is taken in by the new god depends upon the god. A cleric who has previously served another god retains his previous hit points, Hit Dice, and Armor Class. A cleric who converts from one god to another typically finds himself with two sets of levels: former level and current level. The former level is the level he was at prior to conversion to the new god, minus any modifications for alignment change. The current level refers to the level dictated by the god at the time of the conversion. In most cases, the current level is substantially lower than the former level. Where the former level of the cleric is lower than the entry level of the new religion, the cleric enters at the lower level.

When converting to a new god, the experience points of the character are set to the lowest number for the current level (or former level if lower than current level). For example, a high priestess of Takhisis who converts to Paladine would become a priestess of that order and have current experience points of 12,501. Note that she retains the hit points

and hit dice of a high priestess (and incurs the wrath of Takhisis).

In all cases, any further advancement and ability improvements occur on the table for the order the cleric currently follows. For example, the cleric mentioned above would now use the Clerics of Good table to determine all advances in level and abilities.

Repentance: Clerics who have fallen from the grace of their church lose their ability to call down miracles in the name of their gods. It is a sad fact that often through misjudgment or mortal frailty, a cleric performs some act contrary to the desires of his or her deity. When this happens, repentance is the only recourse open to the cleric.

Repentance requires acknowledgement of the wrongdoing, a sincere statement of repentance and restitution (when possible) or penance (when not).

Actions that are in accordance with the former alignment of the character will naturally move that character's alignment back to where it belongs. So it is that characters who repent are eventually forgiven and have their spells and special abilities restored to them.

Railing against the Gods: Rarely does a mortal challenge the mighty gods of Krynn. First of all, mortal characters in this world rarely attain the power necessary to engage in such combat. Secondly, the gods (with the exception of the gods of evil) rarely involve themselves directly in the affairs of mortals. Directly interfering in the affairs of Krynn is seen as meddling with an experiment in progress and thus biasing the outcome. Free will was given to men and mortals on the world so that they alone would make the world move—the meddling of the gods is viewed as rearranging the gears in a working clock.

Thus it is only on the most rare of occasions that the gods have direct contact with mortals other than through clerics or other intermediaries. Even then, these visitations usually involve only a spiritual manifestation of the god to the mortal.

For all of these reasons, mortals who wish to follow in the dark paths of Raistlin's footsteps find their task one of the most impossible in all of Krynn. Raistlin learned but one lesson: That selfish victories are hollow when all you wished to gain is laid waste in your attempt to attain it.

If one of the gods is encountered on the face

of Krynn and conflict ensues, remember that when a god of Krynn reaches 0 hit points he does not die but is cast in suffering back into his own plane of existence to rest and heal. While this may rid the world of the god's presence for a time, you can be sure that he will return with a vengeance.

Godly Spheres of Influence

The universe of the DRAGONLANCE® saga contains a pantheon of deities that oversees the world and spirits therein.

It should be no surprise that, considering the many deities in charge of the DRAGONLANCE campaign world, each god has his own area of expertise. And since every cleric obtains his powers from a single deity, the powers available to the cleric depend upon the specialty of his deity.

The listings of the gods in this section contain familiar game data, but also give three new categories of godly statistics: Spheres of Influence, Specials, and Additionals. These groupings define the range of spells that can be obtained through worship of each deity.

On pages 120-125 of this book, there is a listing of clerical spells. The spells listed there are grouped into categories that reflect their nature. These categories include All, Animal, Astral, Charm, Combat, Creation, Divination, Elemental, Guardianship, Healing, Necromancy, Plants, Protection, Stellar, Summoning, and Weather.

Spells in the Sphere of "All" can be cast by any cleric regardless of whom he worships. Note, however, that there may be certain restrictions on the way that some clerics can cast these spells. For example, clerics of good can cast only the true form of the *light* spell and cannot cast its reverse, *darkness*. On the other hand, clerics of evil can cast only *darkness*.

Deity Descriptions

Special Bonuses: These are bonus abilities the god's clerics gain for following the god.

Spheres: gives the general categories of spells that clerics of that deity can learn and cast each day.

The names of the gods are listed with notations under them concerning the abilities and spells they grant to their clerics. These notations are interpreted as follows:

Specials: These are the spells the deity grants his followers in addition to any other spells they normally obtain. These special powers are not counted against the normal spells acquired for the day and can be cast even if the cleric is not yet of sufficient level to cast the spell normally.

Additionals: These are spells that, while outside the deity's spheres of influence, are still part of the powers the god grants to his clerics.

When a character becomes a cleric, he must select which god he will follow. When he selects his spells, he can only choose those spells offered by his deity (he also gains the benefit of the specials).

Holy Orders of the Stars

Game Data

All clerics of the DRAGONLANCE saga must meet the same minimum requirements regardless of their alignment or the religion they espouse.

Minimum Requirements: Clerics may be of any of Krynn's races except gnomes (who, while they revere Reorx, see no need for a formalized religion other than their work).

Holy Orders of Stars Minimum Scores

Strength	—
Intelligence	—
Wisdom	9/15 *
Dexterity	—
Constitution	—
Charisma	—

* The number after the slash indicates that if the cleric has a Wisdom of 15 or higher, he gains a 10% bonus to all experience points earned.

Proficiencies:

Proficiencies	Weapon/Nonweapon
Initial	3/4
Added	1/2 per 3 levels

Even though all clerics are governed by the above rules, each god has his own spheres of power so each religion is unique. All of the gods and their religions follow one of the three basic alignments in the DRAGONLANCE game world: Good, Neutral, or Evil. Clerics who follow a god of good alignment are in the Order of Good; neutrals are in the Order of Neutral, etc. The differences between these three orders are as follows:

Clerics of Good
Game data

Level	Experience Points	Hit Dice (d8s)	Title
1	2,000	2	Acolyte
2	4,000	3	Deacon
3	7,500	4	Adept
4	15,250	5	Priest
5	25,000	6	Curate
6	40,000	7	Prefect
7	90,000	8	Canon
8	160,000	9	Elder
9	250,000	9+1	Patriarch
10	500,000	9+2	High Priest
11	750,000	9+3	
12	1,000,000	9+4	Apostle
13	1,250,000	9+5	
14	1,500,000	9+6	
15	1,750,000	9+7	Prophet *
16	2,000,000	9+8	
17	2,250,000	9+9	
18	2,500,000	9+10	Chosen Prophet **

* There is only one Prophet for each god of good. Should more than one cleric of a god reach this level, the DM should choose one of them for the title, the other remains an apostle.

** There is only one Chosen Prophet for all the gods of good at any given time. This character must be the Prophet of Paladine. No other character can reach this level.

Clerics of Good—Base Spells Table

Cleric Level	Spell Level 1	2	3	4	5	6	7
1	1	-	-	-	-	-	-
2	2	-	-	-	-	-	-
3	2	1	-	-	-	-	-
4	2	2	-	-	-	-	-
5	3	3	1	-	-	-	-
6	3	3	2	-	-	-	-
7	3	3	2	1	-	-	-
8	3	3	3	2	-	-	-
9	4	4	3	2	1	-	-
10	4	4	3	3	2	-	-
11	5	4	4	3	2	1*	-
12	6	5	5	3	2	2	-
13	6	6	6	4	2	2	-
14	6	6	6	5	3	2	-
15	7	7	7	5	4	2	-
16	7	7	7	6	5	3	1**
17	8	8	8	6	5	3	1
18	8	8	8	7	6	4	2

* Usable only by clerics with Wisdoms of 17 or greater.

** Usable only by clerics with Wisdoms of 18 or greater.

Clerics of Neutrality
Game data

Level	Experience Points	Hit Dice (d8s)	Title
1	1,500	1	Aspirant
2	3,000	2	Ovate
3	6,000	3	Initiate
4	13,000	4	Disciple
5	27,500	5	Master of Earth
6	55,000	6	Master of Fire
7	110,000	7	Master of Water
8	225,000	8	Master of Winds
9	450,000	9	Master of Mystery
10	675,000	9 + 1	Master of Light
11	900,000	9 + 2	Master of Time
12	1,125,000	9 + 3	Master of Elements
13	1,350,000	9 + 4	Master of the Book
14	1,575,000	9 + 5	Archmaster *
15	1,800,000	9 + 6	
16	2,025,000	9 + 7	Starmaster **
17	2,250,000	9 + 8	
18	2,475,000	9 + 9	

* There is only one Archmaster for each god of neutrality. Should more than one cleric of a god reach this level, the DM should choose one of them for the title; the other remains a Master of the Book.

** There is only one Starmaster for all the gods of neutrality at any given time. This character must be the Archmaster of Gilean. No other character can reach this level or above.

Clerics of Neutrality—Base Spells Table

Cleric Level	Spell Level						
	1	2	3	4	5	6	7
1	2	-	-	-	-	-	-
2	2	1	-	-	-	-	-
3	3	2	1	-	-	-	-
4	4	2	2	-	-	-	-
5	4	3	2	-	-	-	-
6	4	3	2	1	-	-	-
7	4	4	3	1	-	-	-
8	4	4	3	2	-	-	-
9	5	4	3	2	1	-	-
10	5	4	3	3	2	-	-
11	5	5	3	3	2	1*	-
12	5	5	4	4	3	2	1**
13	6	5	5	4	3	2	1
14	6	6	6	6	4	2	1
15	6	6	6	6	4	3	1
16	6	6	6	6	5	4	1
17	7	6	6	6	5	4	2
18	7	6	6	6	5	4	3

* Usable only by clerics with Wisdoms of 17 or greater.

** Usable only by clerics with Wisdoms of 18 or greater.

Clerics of Evil
Game data

Level	Experience Points	Hit Dice (d8s)	Title
1	1,500	1	Acolyte
2	3,000	2	Deacon
3	6,000	3	Adept
4	12,500	4	Priest
5	20,000	5	Curate
6	35,000	6	Prefect
7	60,000	7	Canon
8	90,000	8	Spiritor
9	200,000	9	
10	400,000	9 + 1	
11	650,000	9 + 2	High Priest
12	1,000,000	9 + 3	Nightmaster *
13	1,350,000	9 + 4	
14	1,700,000	9 + 5	Nightlord **
15	2,050,000	9 + 6	
16	2,400,000	9 + 7	
17	2,750,000	9 + 8	
18	3,100,000	9 + 9	

* There is only one Nightmaster for each evil god. Should more than one cleric of a god reach this level, the DM should choose one of them for the title; the other remains a high priest.

** There is only one Nightlord for all the evil gods. This character must be a Nightmaster of Takhisis. No other cleric can be level 14 or above.

Clerics of Evil—Base Spells Table

Cleric Level	Spell Level						
	1	2	3	4	5	6	7
1	1	-	-	-	-	-	-
2	2	-	-	-	-	-	-
3	2	1	-	-	-	-	-
4	2	2	-	-	-	-	-
5	3	3	1	-	-	-	-
6	3	3	2	-	-	-	-
7	3	3	2	1	-	-	-
8	3	3	3	2	-	-	-
9	4	4	3	2	1	-	-
10	4	4	3	3	2	-	-
11	5	4	4	3	2	1*	-
12	6	5	5	3	2	1	-
13	6	6	6	4	2	2	-
14	6	6	6	4	3	2	1**
15	6	6	6	5	3	2	1
16	6	6	6	5	4	2	1
17	6	6	6	6	4	3	2
18	6	6	6	6	5	4	3

* Usable only by clerics with Wisdoms of 17 or greater.

** Usable only by clerics with Wisdoms of 18 or greater.

the Gods of Good
Paladine

As the Father of Good and Master of the Law, Paladine is the spokesman for the gods of good. A supreme leader, he does not interfere with the affairs of his fellow beings as long as their doings do not counter the law of good. It was Paladine, during the Age of Twilight, who led the gods of good from Beyond at the direction of the Highgod, to create this place and time. He led the gods of good in the All-Saints War and represented his order to the other orders of the gods.

He knew better than his brothers the need for balance and the interdependence of the three major orders of gods. His vision saw the need for balance and conflict as the catalyst for learning and progress.

Many believe that Paladine assumed mortal form as the ancient hero Huma to drive the dragons from the land during the Age of Dreams. This was not so, but Paladine's hand is evident in the history of that time. There are many tales of Paladine's presence in that time

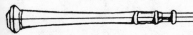

and this may account for the belief that he was Huma.

Paladine's constellation traditionally guards the Gate of Souls, keeping the dragons from returning to Krynn. It is of no small historical interest that his constellation disappeared at the time of the Cataclysm and that dragons reentered the world soon afterward. Now that his constellation is once again in the night sky, dragons still remain in the world of Krynn, but no visitations from Paladine have occurred since then.

The Gate of Souls no longer holds what Paladine himself described as the Balance of the World. During the time of the Cataclysm, he and his fellows withdrew their direct influence from the world and caused the Cataclysm. Astinus records that for 60 days after the Cataclysm, Paladine's tears filled the night sky with their brilliance.

When the time came to reclaim Krynn in the name of good, Paladine took the form of a rather befuddled old wizard named Fizban the Fabulous, who wandered the world to prod those who could change the destiny of the world. It is most important to note that while Paladine often intervened in seemingly minor matters, he never directly used his vast powers in affairs of great consequence. Paladine worked through men and their free agency to accomplish his desires. He would offer what guidance he could, but it was up to men to save their world.

Paladine rules the Dome of Creation that surrounds all that is. It is an ethereal land of perfect beauty. These lands are vast indeed and those who have walked them yearn to return.

paladine

Cleric/Magic User (40th level in each)
Alignment: Lawful Good
Movement: 12"/29"
Armor Class: −10
Hit Points: 999
Hit Dice: 40
# of Attacks: 5
Damage/Attack: 1-1000 *

* The damage done by this attack is 1d10 times a number between 1 and 100, inclusive (Paladine gets to pick this number!). For example, Paladine may choose a multiplier of 20. In this case, the damage per attack is 1d10 x 20. If Paladine rolls a 6 for damage, the result is 6 x 20 or 120 points of damage.

Followers' Abilities:

Spheres:
Astral, Charm, Guardianship, Protection, Stellar HEAL
Specials:
Detect Balance, Reflecting Pool
Additionals:
I: Bless, Cure Light Wounds
V: Flame Strike

majere

Majere is the favored god of monks. He is said to give his followers symbols that, when cast upon the ground, become insects that fight for their owner. One of the gods who came from Beyond, he followed his friend Paladine into this great adventure of creation.

majere

Monk (53d level)
Alignment: Neutral Good
Movement: 18"/24"
Armor Class: −5
Hit Points: 530
Hit Dice: 53
# of Attacks: 5
Damage/Attack: 1d8/1d8/2d10/2d10/2d20

Followers' Abilities:

Spheres:
Astral, Charm, Divination, Summoning
Specials:
Charm Animals, Summon Insects, Silence 15' rad
Additionals:
IV: Repel Insects
V: Insect Plague
VII: Creeping Doom

kiri-jolith

Kiri-Jolith is the war god of good. He is the favorite god of paladins and good-aligned fighters. His constellation seems to threaten that of the Queen of Darkness in the night sky.

Kiri-Jolith is the son of Paladine and Mishakal, but he is their peer in ability. His twin brother is Habbakuk. These twins, with Paladine, form an alliance that supports the Knights of Solamnia in all their works. Each of the three Orders of the Knights was established around one of these three gods.

Clerics of Kiri-Jolith are powerful in battle but must use these formidable powers carefully, for they can lose their powers if Kiri-Jolith feels they have violated the principles of good.

kiri-jolith

Fighter/Cleric (29th level in each)
Alignment: Lawful Good
Movement: 12"/29"
Armor Class: −8
Hit Points: 500
Hit Dice: 29
#of Attacks: 6
Damage/Attack: 3d20/3d20/2d20/2d20/1d10/1d10

Followers' Abilities:

Special Bonuses:
+1 on all attacks if in good standing
Spheres:
Astral, Combat, Guardianship, Healing (Reverse)
Specials:
I: Detect Magic
III: Create Food & Water
Additionals:
I: Detect Snares & Pits, Penetrate Disguise, Predict Weather
II: Find Traps, Heat/Chill metal
III: Death's Door, Magical Vestment
IV: Cloak of Fear/Bravery
V: Quest, Slay Living
VI: Heroes' Feast
VII: Finger of Death, Wither, Energy Drain, Destruction

mishakal

The fabled goddess of healing is known in nearly every culture and country on the face of Krynn. In ancient times, she was the most revered of the ministering gods and in her name many temples were built for the teaching of the healing arts.

In more recent times, Mishakal is known as the Bearer or Light Bringer as it was through her that the knowledge of the true gods was restored to the world. Mishakal's gift of the Disks of Mishakal again brought knowledge to men of healing power and true clerics.

Mishakal is Paladine's companion and advisor. They have twin sons and a third son in Solinari, the god of good magic.

In post-Cataclysmic Ansalon after the War of the Lance, clerics of Mishakal's order were the

most numerous of all clerics. Nearly every community on the face of Ansalon had a cleric of this order to minister to the needs of the people. These clerics were especially sought after by adventuring parties for their curative abilities.

mishakal

Cleric (25th Level)
Alignment: Lawful Good
Movement: 24"/48"
Armor Class: −3
Hit Points: 350
Hit Dice: 25
# of Attacks: 2
Damage/Attack: 3d8/3d8

Followers' Abilities:

Special Bonuses:
  +1 die on all healing spells
Spheres:
  Astral, Charm, Creation, Divination, Healing, Necromancy, Stellar
Specials:
  III: *Prayer, Remove/Bestow Curse*
Additionals:
  I: *Animal Friendship, Bless/Curse, Endure Cold/Heat, Resist Cold*
  II: *Chant, Silence 15' rad*
  III: *Stone Shape, Water Walk*
  VII: *Holy Word*

habbakuk

The god of animal life and the sea, Habbakuk holds a special place in the hearts of sailors and rangers. His skills of the wild and belief in the harmony with nature constitute a peaceful teaching. He is seen as a symbol of eternal life beyond the world and a strong enforcer of natural justice. He is the twin brother of Kiri-Jolith. With his brother and father, he helped form the Knights of Solamnia.

habbakuk

Druid (27th Level)
Alignment: Neutral Good
Movement: 18"/38"
Armor Class: −3
Hit Points: 490
Hit Dice: 27
# of Attacks: 2
Damage/Attack: 3d8/3d8

Followers' Abilities:

Spheres:
  Animal, Elemental
Specials:
  I: *Locate Animals*
  II: *Spiritual Hammer, Detect Life*

Additionals:
  III: *Create Food & Water*
  V: *Commune with Nature*
  VI: *Heroes' Feast, Speak with Monsters, Forbiddance, Conjure Animal*

branchala

Before the world was created, Branchala was a companion to Habbakuk. Branchala followed his friend so that he too could help forge worlds.

His music is that of the souls of all who live. No one who has heard his melodies can ever remember the depths of feeling they brought into mind. It is said that his music resides in us all and that all hearts beat to its unknown melody.

branchala

Fighter/Bard (35th level in each)
Alignment: Neutral Good
Movement: 15"/33"
Armor Class: −7
Hit Points: 590
Hit Dice: 35
# of Attacks: 2
Damage/Attack: 2d20/2d20

Followers' Abilities:

Special Bonuses:
  +2 on any artistic proficiency
Spheres:
  Plants, Stellar, Weather
Specials:
  II: *Detect Life, Locate Plants*
Additionals:
  I: *Detect Snares & Pits*
  II: *Slow Poison*
  III: *Create Food & Water, Neutralize Poison*
  V: *Quest*
  VI: *Aerial Servant, Heroes' Feast*

Solinari

This son of Paladine is the master of good magic. He spins through the sky over the world and keeps his watchful eye on all magic. The tale of Solinari is given in more detail in the section on the Wizards of High Sorcery.

Solinari

Wizard of the White Robes (40th level)
Alignment: Lawful Good
Movement: 12"/48"
Armor Class: −5
Hit Points: 930
Hit Dice: 40
# of Attacks: 4
Damage/Attack: 2d20/2d20/2d10/2d10

Followers' Abilities:

Spheres:
  All spheres of White Robe sorcery (see *Wizards of High Sorcery*)

the Gods of neutrality

Gilean

Gilean is the patriarch of the neutral family of gods. He holds a book, the *Tobril*, that contains all the knowledge possessed by all the gods. All truth is contained in that single tome, but portions of it are sealed. Gilean resides in the night sky between the constellations of Paladine and the Queen of Darkness, as if to hold them in their places and keep them from destroying each other. His real abode is believed to be the Hidden Vale, a perfect valley of nature that exists everywhere and yet nowhere. The ways to the vale are sometimes opened to those who follow the wisdom of Gilean.

Gilean

Cleric/Red Robed Wizard (40th level in each)
Alignment: Neutral
Movement: 12"/29"
Armor Class: −10
Hit Points: 980
Hit Dice: 40
# of Attacks: 2
Damage/Attack: 1-1000 */1-1000 *

the gods of neutrality

* The damage done by this attack is 1d10 times a number between 1 and 100, inclusive (Gilean gets to pick the number!). See the prior entry for Paladine for more information.

Followers' Abilities:

Special Bonuses:
  +1 on any nonweapon proficiency roll
Spheres:
  Astral, Creation, Divination, Protection
Specials:
  None
Additionals:
  I: *Speak with Animals*
  II: *Messenger*

SIRRION

The god of flame and natural power, Sirrion is the guard of the neutral way and the bringer into being of nature. His companion is Shinare, the goddess of industry and creation from nature. They are traditionally seen as a quarrelsome couple and their disputes are of cosmic proportions.

Sirrion

Fighter/Cleric (35th level in each)
Alignment: Neutral
Movement: 18"/38"
Armor Class: −8
Hit Points: 530
Hit Dice: 35
# of Attacks: 4
Damage/Attack: 2d10/2d10/2d20/2d20

Followers' Abilities:

Special Bonuses:
  +1 die damage on fire-based spells
Spheres:
  Combat, Guardianship, Healing, Summoning
Specials:
  None
Additionals:
  None

REORX, the FORGE

Reorx was the hand by which all of chaos was brought under the direction of the gods in this place and time. He commands creation and technology.

Humans tend to portray this god as a paunchy squire to Kiri-Jolith, but dwarves and gnomes hold him as the highest of the gods. Reorx also forged the Greystone of Gargath and is thus the father of gnomes, dwarves, and kender. For greater background on this god, see the section on the races of Krynn.

REORX

Fighter/Cleric (37th level in each)
Alignment: Neutral
Movement: 9"/18"
Armor Class: −6
Hit Points: 840
Hit Dice: 37
# of Attacks: 2
Damage/Attack: 1d100/1d100

Followers' Abilities:

Special Bonuses:
  +2 on any craft proficiency
Spheres:
  Combat, Creation, Elementals, Stellar
Specials:
  None
Additionals:
  None

Chislev

Companion to Zivilyn, Chislev is nature incarnate. She is served by large numbers of animated wooden creatures who carry out her wishes.

Both she and her companion are said to dwell in Zhan, the grandest of forests. It is said that worthy elves come here when they leave Krynn for the next world.

Chislev

Druid (34th level)
Alignment: Neutral
Movement: 16"/24"
Armor Class: −6
Hit Points: 780
Hit Dice: 34
# of Attacks: 3
Damage/Attack: 3d20/3d20/2d100

Followers' Abilities:

Spheres:
  Animal, Healing, Plants, Weather
Specials:
  None
Additionals:
  None

Zivilyn

Zivilyn is said to exist in all times and in all lands and to possess all the wisdom of all the planes of existence. He is the advisor to Gilean, the god of knowledge. Zivilyn's companion is Chislev; their relationship is seen as the ideal blend of harmony and understanding.

Zivilyn

Cleric/Monk (35th level in each)
Alignment: Neutral
Movement: 16"/48"
Armor Class: −6
Hit Points: 890
Hit Dice: 35
# of Attacks: 3
Damage/Attack: 2d10/2d10/1d20

Followers' Abilities:

Spheres:
  Astral, Divination, Necromancy
Specials:
  None
Additionals:
  None

Shinare

Shinare is the goddess of wealth, money, and industry. She is the favorite god of the dwarves (although she is male in their tales) and is the patron god of merchants and commerce. Her companion is Sirrion whose fondness for nature often runs against Shinare's desire for progress.

Shinare

Cleric/Fighter (25th level in each)
Alignment: Neutral
Movement: 18"/38"
Armor Class: −5
Hit Points: 370
Hit Dice: 25
# of Attacks: 3
Damage/Attack: 2d10/2d10/1d20

Followers' Abilities:

Spheres:
  Charm, Creation, Guardianship, Protection
Specials:
  III: *Locate/Obscure Object*
Additionals:
  None

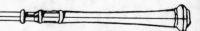

lunitari

Lunitari is the god of neutral magic. She is the sole daughter of Gilean, but her mother is not known. See the history of the Wizards of High Sorcery for more background on this goddess.

lunitari

Red Robe Wizard (40th level)
Alignment: Neutral
Movement: 12"/18"
Armor Class: −5
Hit Points: 970
Hit Dice: 40
# of Attacks: 3
Damage/Attack: 1d10/1d10/1d10

Followers' Abilities:

Spheres:
    All spheres of Red Robe sorcery

the Gods of Evil

takhisis

Takhisis, the Queen of Darkness, Dragon-queen, She of Many Faces—in all lands and cultures, her countenance has been the visage of evil. Her name is the call of darkness. Takhisis led the shadows from Beyond and brought them to aid in the creation of this cosmos. Her deeds have ever since been a constant struggle to assert her rule over all creation. It is, in her view, only right and just that this be so.

Sargonnas is her consort and has been since before the beginning of all things known to Krynn. They have but one offspring, that being Nuitari, their dark son of black magic. There is a respectful peace between Takhisis and Sargonnas, yet they do not hesitate to use their power to better their relative positions.

The Dark Queen instigated the All-Saints War before the beginning of Krynn and was primarily responsible for the separation of the gods at that time. She saw the prized spirits of mortals that fell to Krynn as her key to final triumph over all the other gods. To this end, has she moved throughout the centuries to take control of the world through the force of her will and the power of her minions.

All three of the Dragon Wars were instigated at her behest and for her betterment. This continued until Huma, using a powerfully endowed *dragonlance*, drove the Dark Queen from the face of Krynn and banished her to the Abyss. Dragons of all kinds were banished deep into the ground from whence they came and soon passed into legend.

Then the pride of the Kingpriest provided Takhisis with new opportunities for her ambitions. She had been brooding for nearly a millennium over her plans of conquest and now they were about to come to fruition. As the Kingpriest and his nation fell into pride and boasting, the way was open for her cunning suggestions. The Cataclysm was the result.

The Cataclysm caused great destruction in the world of Krynn, but it did not destroy the Temple of the Kingpriest as many had thought. Instead, the temple was sent to the Abyss and was soon discovered by the Queen of Darkness. Using its presence and the great magics that she commanded, she was able to force a portal through Huma's banishment and again make her way into the world. That story and the tale of the Dragonlance Wars is told in more detail in the historical sections of this text.

Takhisis can appear in any form she wishes and often takes on a disguise. She is most often seen as either a five-headed chromatic dragon or as a beautiful temptress. She is equally deadly in either form.

takhisis

Cleric/Black Robe Wizard (40th level each)
Alignment: Lawful Evil
Movement: 18"/48"
Armor Class: −10
Hit Points: 999
Hit Dice: 40
# of Attacks: 4
Damage/Attack: 1-1000 */1-1000 */1-1000 */1-1000 *

* The damage done by this attack is 1d10 times a number from 1 to 100, inclusive (Takhisis gets to pick this number!). See the prior entry for Paladine for more information on this attack.

Followers' Abilities:

Spheres:
    Astral, Guardianship, Protection, Summoning
Specials:
    VI: *Animate Object*
Additionals:
    II: *Spiritual Hammer*
    III: *Create Food & Water*
    V: *Flame Strike*
    VII: *Unholy Word*

Sargonnas

Little is known of the consort to the Queen of Darkness. He is the god of vengeance and often participates in plots for and against his Queen.

Sargonnas

Cleric (30th level)
Alignment: Lawful Evil
Movement: 14"/24"
Armor Class: −7
Hit Points: 666
Hit Dice: 30
# of Attacks: 4
Damage/Attack: 2d20/2d20/2d20/2d10

Followers' Abilities:

Spheres:
    Astral, Charm, Combat, Healing, Summoning
Specials:
    II: *Resist Fire*
    III: *Know/Obscure Alignment*
Additionals:
    III: *Protection from Fire*
    VI: *Animate Object*

Morgion

Morgion is the god of disease, decay, and plague. Always the lone warrior, he does not act with the other gods nor does he often discuss plans with them. Instead he broods in his Bronze Tower that stands on the far borders of the Abyss and keeps his thoughts secret from all save his minions. Worshipers of Morgion meet in secret and dark places to do their foul deeds. Their priestcrafts are secret as well and none outside of their orders know their works fully.

Morgion

Druid (37th level)
Alignment: Neutral Evil
Movement: 24"/48"
Armor Class: −5
Hit Points: 730
Hit Dice: 37
# of Attacks: 1
Damage/Attack: Special *

* Morgion always attacks through pestilence and disease rather than by direct means.

His power is such that these attacks occur at a much-accelerated rate. Generally, his attacks inflict 5d20 points of damage on the round of the attack and 1d20 points of damage on each subsequent day until the malady either kills the victim or he is treated with a *heal* spell. Even then the *heal* spell does not recover the previously lost points—it only stops the loss of points. Subsequent spells and the passage of time will recover the lost hit points.

Followers' Abilities:

Spheres:
  Astral, Healing, Plants
Specials:
  None
Additionals:
  III: *Create Food & Water*

Chemosh

As the Lord of the Undead, Chemosh was called here to serve after being cast out from the Beyond by the High God. Takhisis saw his usefulness in her scheme and rescued him from the Void of Chaos.

Chemosh is the lord of false redemption; he offers immortality at the price of exaltation. Those who follow his ways hope to live forever but will do so in bodies that are eternally corrupted. Nearly all of the evil undead have at one time or another made a pact with Chemosh or one of his servants.

Worshipers of Chemosh generally wear white skull masks and black robes.

Chemosh

Cleric/Black Robe Wizard (29th level in each)
Alignment: Lawful Evil
Movement: 9"/48"
Armor Class: −9
Hit Points: 580
Hit Dice: 29
# of Attacks: 2
Damage/Attack: 1d100/1d100 +2 levels drained

Followers' Abilities:

Spheres:
  Astral, Combat, Necromancy
Specials:
  None
Additionals:
  VI: *Animate Object*

Zeboim

Also known as the Sea Queen, Zeboim is the daughter of Takhisis. Impetuous, manic-depressive, and constantly swinging to the edges of the emotional spectrum, she is the most temperamental of the gods and by far the most dangerous to deal with. She is the queen of tempests and weather. Those seamen who attempt to placate her may occasionally avoid her rage, but as often as not they manage to displease her in some way. Many have been the tales of those seamen who have somehow mistakenly offended Zeboim and were brought to their tragic ends by her.

Zeboim

Druid/Cleric (30th level in each)
Alignment: Chaotic Evil
Movement: 16"/48"
Armor Class: −4
Hit Points: 680
Hit Dice: 30
# of Attacks: 4
Damage/Attack: 1d20 each

Followers' Abilities:

Spheres:
  Animal, Elemental, Weather
Specials:
  None
Additionals:
  III: *Create Food & Water*
  VI: *Animate Object*

Hiddukel

Hiddukel is a deal maker who trades in souls. It is said that he is the only being who can barter with the Queen of Darkness and come out ahead. He controls all ill-gotten wealth in the world, which he uses to corrupt greedy men. He is the patron of evil businessmen.

Hiddukel is seen as grossly fat with cold eyes and a oily smile. He is also something of a mischief maker as his role in the making of the Greystone so well shows (see page 49).

Hiddukel

Cleric/Black Robe Wizard (25th level in each)
Alignment: Chaotic Evil
Movement: 12"/18"
Armor Class: −4
Hit Points: 450
Hit Dice: 25
# of Attacks: 3
Damage/Attack: 1d10/1d10/2d10

Followers' Abilities:

Spheres:
  Divination, Guardianship, Summoning
Specials:
  None
Additionals:
  None

Nuitari

Twin brother to Zeboim and son of Takhisis and Sargonnas, Nuitari left the ranks of evil to join with the other two gods of magic. Nuitari is the god of Black or Evil Magic.

Lunitari

Black Robed Wizard (40th Level)
Alignment: Lawful Evil
Movement: 12"/18"
Armor Class: −10
Hit Points: 780
Hit Dice: 40
# of Attacks: 4
Damage/Attack: 2d20 each

Followers' Abilities:

Spheres:
  All spheres of Black Robe sorcery

The heathens

Clerics who come from worlds far removed from the DRAGONLANCE® saga world are *heathens*. They immediately lose all of their spell-casting abilities until they find a god of Krynn to worship. (The gods of Krynn are the only ones who have powers in this world.)

All of the creatures on the face of Krynn sprang from one of five sources: dragons, ogres, animals, humans, or elves. Dragons were born from the world itself and are part and spirit with it, while the remaining four races were brought in as spirits from the realms of the gods.

Originally Krynn had but a few distinct types of creatures (though there was great variety within these broad classes). It was only after a period of time (and some rather extraordinary assistance) that the current diversity of creatures was achieved.

The following races are common in the DRAGONLANCE® saga and are described in either this book (DL Adv.) or in the *Player's Handbook* (PH).

Human	PH
Kender	DL Adv.
Gnomes	
Mad	PH
Tinker Gnomes	DL Adv.
Elves	
Dark	PH
Qualinesti	DL Adv.
Silvanesti	DL Adv.
Kagonesti	DL Adv.
Dimernesti	DL Adv.
Half elves	PH
Dwarves	
Fatherless?	PH
Hill Dwarves	DL Adv.
Mountain Dwarves	DL Adv.
Gully Dwarves	DL Adv.
Irda	DL Adv.
Minotaurs	DL Adv.

Those entries in italics are common to worlds other than Krynn, but have special clarifications in this book when they are encountered in Krynn.

There are no halflings or half-orcs in Krynn. Halflings who enter this world are considered kender and gain the special abilities (and obnoxious personalities) of kender in this world. Half-orcs would be considered magical freaks or aberrations as there are no orcs in Krynn.

age of twilight

The ogres, the most beautiful of races, fostered four subclasses of creatures: true ogres, goblins (smaller creatures) giants (larger creatures) and minotaurs (exploration- and conquest-oriented). In time, free-willed ogres calling themselves the Irda broke away from ogre-kind and the world in general. This sparked the Ogre Wars during the Age of Dreams; during these wars the Irda were lost to the knowledge of men.

The elves then awoke in the world. Elven tradition holds that the elves were the first beings to awaken in the world. This somewhat narrow view was generally accepted as the elves were the only chroniclers of the Age of Dreams and it was their version of history that was handed down from that time. In truth, the ogres were the first to awaken. The fact that the ogres and elves awoke in areas quite far apart and that it was many years before the two groups ran into each other has added fuel to the historical debate.

The elves of those days were highly individualistic and most peaceful. Though not truly immortal as were the ogres, they were quite long lived. Spread over a great area and without any centralized authority, however, the elves had no true civilization until the time of Silvanos.

The animals awoke next. They were of many types and vast numbers. Thoroughly neutral, they represent the balance of all nature.

Last of all came man. Quevalin Soth said that man "fell with blind vision to cause red dusk and dawn." His free will brought choice to the world and set all history in motion. It was during this time that, as legend has it, the gnomes were created as told in the Tale of the Greystone of Gargath.

When Reorx created the world, he needed the assistance of men to help him with the work. To this end, one-eighth of all men and their families followed Reorx across the sea in hopes of learning his crafts.

For many years, men worked happily under the guidance of Reorx. Inevitably (humans being human), the men became proud of their skills and used them for their own ends.

Reorx was angered. In his wrath, he remade these men into a new race. As they had become tinkerers, so they would remain for all time. He took from them the crafts he had taught, leaving only their burning desire to tinker and build, invent and construct. He made them into a small people—they became the gnomes.

Apart from the spirits the gods brought to the world, the dragons sprang from Krynn itself. Their natures reflected a refinement of the good and the evil that made up the world. The metallic dragons followed the path of good, while the chromatic dragons trod the course of evil.

It was also during this time that the single greatest event in the history of Krynn took place. While the tale is most fanciful, it is a fact that some fabulous event took place at about this time that brought about tremendous diversity in the creatures of Krynn.

The legends of that time are clear. Hiddukel saw the creation of the gnomes and smiled. Reorx had worked long and hard to forge order out of chaos. Yet now, Reorx saw that the balance of neutrality was not maintained. Hiddukel knew that Chislev also felt this swing in the balance. Herein was the foundation for mischief.

Hiddukel went to Chislev. With cunning words, he convinced Chislev that the forces of evil were losing ground. Their only hope, he said, was for neutrality to take ultimate control. Chislev agreed and, at Hiddukel's insistence, asked Reorx to forge the Greystone.

The Greystone was a marvelous artifact. A large clear grey stone of many facets, it was designed to hold and radiate the essence of Lunitari, the red moon of neutral magic. Hiddukel convinced Chislev that this stone would anchor neutrality to the world of Krynn and solidify the neutral position on the planet. Chislev convinced Reorx of the same thing and thus the stone was created. It was placed in Lunitari and magic swelled within it.

Reorx, although still angered at the gnomes, had never forsaken them. He loved them and now could see how they might yet serve him. He appeared to their priest and presented a plan for a Great Invention he wished the gnomes to construct. It would be powered by a magical stone that Reorx would provide. The gnomes, as was their wont, built the machine 30 times the required size and with mechanisms that never served any purpose. Their general consensus was that it would work once the stone was in place.

Reorx now finalized his plan. Among his servants he found a lowly gnome who truly worshiped his arts. In a vision, the little gnome saw the Greystone and wanted it more than anything. He approached the problem of getting it like a good gnome...he invented something.

His invention was truly worthy of the gnomes—a mechanical ladder that lifted itself into the sky. The strange device had pulleys and counterweights and wheels and cogs. It made a terrific racket when it worked. Reorx smiled upon that gnome and gave him a secret device. The gnome's ladder worked. One could set it upright on the ground, winch up the top section and then climb up to the top. From there, the bottom part could be winched up off the ground so that the ladder

hung steadily in mid-air. Then the operator would climb up the new section and repeat the process. Slowly, the ladder pulled itself up into the sky, and eventually reached the red moon.

With a magical net given to him by Reorx, the little gnome captured the Greystone. He lowered the ladder back to the ground and went to place the Greystone into the Great Invention. But the moment he opened the net, the stone leaped into the air and floated quickly off to the west. All the gnomes rushed to pack up their belongings and follow it. They followed it to the western shores of their land and quickly built ships. The Greystone floated westward across the waters with the gnomes in pursuit until the gem finally reached the shores of Ansalon.

Reorx was deeply disturbed, for the gem created magical havoc wherever it passed. Beasts and plants were reshaped in magical ways. New races of animals sprang up overnight and spell castings went wild. Instead of anchoring neutrality, the gem only made the pendulum of good and evil swing more rapidly than ever before. He then understood how he had been tricked by Hiddukel and Chislev.

At that time, there was a great ruler among men named Gargath. He was a barbarian prince who well loved the gods of neutrality and served their purposes.

One spring day, Gargath was in prayerful communion with Zivilyn. When he looked up, he saw a grey gemstone floating above the altar. It pulsed with a steely grey light. Gargath took this as a gift of the gods and placed it high in a tower. Here, by various traps and magic, he secured the stone so that all could see its light and yet none could take it away.

The grey light shone as a beacon for two armies of gnomes who had been pursuing the Greystone for many years. One army was filled with desire for the wealth the gem represented. The other army was made up of those most curious about the gem and its workings. The two joined forces to recover the gem and proceeded to march on the castle.

The gnomes first demanded the stone. Gargath refused to give it up. They threatened war. He welcomed the fight as the gnomes were outnumbered. There was only one thing left to do: they invented something.

Two weeks later, a giant siege engine came thundering toward the gates of the fortress. It broke down just short of its goal. The gnomes retreated with heavy losses.

Three weeks after that display of gnomish

technology, a humongous siege engine approached, sounding like a hundred ghosts wailing. This one rammed the first siege engine and caught fire. It burned to the ground and the gnomes retreated with heavy losses.

Nearly a month and a half later, a towering colossus of a siege engine roared toward Gargath's battlements. Charging through the ashes of the first two siege engines, the drive mechanism broke. The siege engine fell forward and shattered the outer wall of the castle. Although this wasn't exactly what the gnomes had planned, the result was good enough. The gnomes charged in through the broken wall.

As the gnomes rushed into the courtyard, both sides were amazed to see the grey light from the tower suddenly fill the area with unbearable light. When men could see again, the two factions of gnomes were suddenly fighting each other. One side was filled with lust for the gem and the other side was filled with curiosity.

The power of the gem had changed the gnomes. Those who lusted after wealth became dwarves. Those who were curious became the first kender. True gnomes yet remained in the far-off islands, but dwarves and kender quickly spread throughout the

continent of Ansalon.

Of the Greystone of Gargath, none knew where it had gone. That some gnomes followed it to the western shores of Ansalon is known, since to this day a great colony of them still survives on Sancrist. The rest of the gnomes, they say, followed the stone in ships to the west. The gnomes believe to this day that the stone will return some day with their kin still in pursuit. (This event is not pleasurably anticipated by any in Krynn.)

Thus were the races changed during the Age of Twilight. They have changed little since that time.

Some of the information given here is from articles appearing in *The Leaves from the Inn of the Last Home*, a book compiled by Tika and Caramon Majere and edited by Margaret Weis and Tracy Hickman. There are many articles in that work about various races of Krynn, not all of which can be repeated here for space considerations.

kender

appearance

Kender are small enough to resemble human children, though they are more heavily muscled. Males are typically 3'7" tall and weigh 75 lbs; females are slightly smaller. Adult kender are rarely more than four feet tall and seldom weigh more than 100 lbs.

Kender typically have sandy blond, light or dark brown, copper-red or even red-orange hair colors. Hair styles are usually long, with many varieties of braids and ponytails being popular. Often bits of colorful material such as bird feathers, ribbons, or flowers are carefully woven into their hair as well. Kender are fair-skinned but tan quickly, becoming nutbrown by midsummer. Their eyes are variously pale blue, sea green, olive, light brown, and hazel.

Kender are distinctive for their pointed ears that give them a faintly elven look. They are bright-eyed, and their facial expressions are quite intense. No one seems to look as happy as a joyful kender or as miserable as a crying one. Angry kender using taunts and insults can be shockingly vulgar, and can look quite devilish for a few moments. This intensity of emotion can be infectious.

Kender have been called wizened because of the fine network of lines that appears on their faces about age 40. These minute wrin-

kles give the kender a curious appearance when seen close up, though such lines are considered attractive by kender of all clans.

Kender have a wide vocal range, from deep and husky to high-pitched and squeaky. Older kender tend to have deeper voices, but they still maintain wide pitch ranges and can often perform remarkable sound imitations. When excited, kender tend to speak very quickly and ramble at the same time, making it hard to follow what they're trying to say.

history

Kender spread throughout Ansalon during the Age of Dreams, though little is said of them in official histories. The earliest known kender hero was Balif, a close friend of the elven lord Silvanos. Balif established the kingdom of kender that came to be called Balifor. (Balif died in the year 250 during the Age of Dreams).

A second kender kingdom was established in northwestern Ansalon in the year 400 of the Age of Dreams. Known as Hilo (because of the towering mountains and low plains), this second kingdom was brought into the empire of Ergoth in the year 800. Following the Rose Rebellion of Vinas Solamnus (also known as the War of Ice Tears, see *Knights of Solamnia*), Hilo again gained its independence and has kept it to this date.

Tragically, Balifor was destroyed during the Cataclysm. The few kender survivors wandered north and eventually established a city at Kendermore, renaming the area around it Goodlund. Kendermore is only a short distance from the remains of an old human citystate called The Ruins by the kender who explore it in droves. It is said that finding artifacts in The Ruins is easy, but leaving with them is practically impossible because of the local kender.

Many of the kender in Goodlund never returned to civilization, however, and remained in a state of semi-barbarism for centuries. One of these tribal kender, an unusually powerful and charismatic leader named Kronin, organized all the local kender to combat the draconians and Dragonarmies sweeping the area. Kronin is unusually antagonistic for a kender.

philosophies

Four things make a kender's personality drastically different from that of a typical human. Kender are utterly fearless, insatiably curious, unstoppably mobile and indepen-

dent, and will pick up anything that is not nailed down (though kender with claw hammers will get those things as well).

The fearlessness that all kender possess gives them a strong sense of confidence. They are quite carefree or matter-of-fact about a situation, even if things look hopeless and grim ("No sense in running away now. There's 500 goblins surrounding us!"). Kender react effectively to dangerous situations, fighting hard and fearlessly. They sometimes come up with some bizarre tactics that may carry the day in battle. But even kender don't let their fearlessness get in the way of self-preservation—most of the time.

Kender appreciate the need for caution, but their uncontrollable curiosity gets them into trouble on adventures. They forever have to check out unexplored places and peek into dark corners. They have no desire to be the second or third person to enter the Caverns of Unspeakable Doom; they want to be first. Pointing out that no one ever returns from the Caverns of Unspeakable Doom has no effect. In fact, describing what makes the caverns so unspeakable might even excite the kender further and make him or her determined to go to the caverns at once. ("An evil archmage and an army of ogres? Wow! Let's go see 'em!") Some kender might allow their curiosity to overcome their common sense when facing unusual opponents, such as dragons, though they eventually learn to run when running is best.

A kender's fellow adventurers often have to teach him that certain things have big, nasty teeth and that avoiding these things is often in the kender's best interests, regardless of what the kender's opinions are in the matter. Whenever a kender displays an inordinately sensible attitude about danger, it is probably because the kender realizes that continued curiosity will ruin any further chances of doing exciting things ever again.

Kender are intensely curious about everything unusual. Magic awes and fascinates them, as do large, unusual, or dramatic creatures like chimeras, centaurs, unicorns and, of course, dragons. Kender are drawn to beautiful things, but things that others find disgusting are often seen by kender as intriguing or humorous in some way (even gully dwarves).

Though strong-willed, kender are not prone to consider all the possible results of their behavior. A kender may quickly and impulsively paint himself into a corner, then wait for someone else to come along and get him out of the jam. Sometimes this means that the kender's fellow adventurers are painted into the same corner ("I guess I shouldn't

have opened that locked door with the warning signs on it, huh?"). Experienced adventurers quickly come to dread that most awful of kender sayings: "Oops!"

Another important point is that kender need action—and they need it now! They thrive on excitement and yearn for new adventures. "I'm just along for the fun" is a common saying among wandering kender. It has been suggested that the worst torture that could be inflicted on a kender would be to lock him up and give him nothing new to do or look at. (Conversely, it has been said that the worst torture one can visit on any nonkender would be to lock him up in a bare cell with a bored kender.) Some kender believe that evil creatures are condemned to an afterlife where they will be eternally bored.

Most kender are encountered during *wanderlust*, a particular phase in a kender's life that occurs for most kender during their early 20s. Apparently the kender's natural curiosity and desire for action suddenly go into overdrive at this time, and kender are driven to wander the land as far as they can go. Wanderlust may last for many years, and some kender have a habit of making maps of their travels during this time. Sadly, most kender are poor map makers, lacking the patience and skills to chart their travels accurately. Kender may collect other maps during this time to satisfy their curiosity about other places. This wanderlust is responsible for spreading kender communities across the continent of Ansalon.

Risky deeds draw kender like gold draws dragons, but risk must be combined with action or else they lose interest. Gambling with cards won't hold a kender's attention for long, but seeing if one can outrun a mad owlbear is another thing. Bravery is easily confused with recklessness where kender are concerned.

Kender are natural extroverts and enjoy making new friends and seeing new places. Most kender are very personable and friendly—too friendly for some people, who dislike their nosiness, their extreme talkativeness (which grows worse when they get excited), and their habit of pocketing everything that interests them.

Kender also resent being given orders; they want to do what they want to do when they want to do it. Telling them to do otherwise is worse than useless, as they will complain loudly and disrespectfully, taunting if they're mad enough. The best way to handle kender, say old adventurers, is not to give them orders, but to get them to volunteer.

Kender are sensitive and can be easily hurt by indifference or intentional cutting remarks

(triggering their taunting talents almost immediately).

Kender treasure their friends; if a kender's friends are injured or slain, the kender may become very depressed and upset. Death only seems to affect a kender when it comes to one that the kender knows and loves, or when it is meted out by disaster or warfare to innocent beings (including any kender). In such cases, the distress that the usually cheerful kender feels is terrible to behold. A story is told of a human ranger during in the Age of Dreams who wounded a deer that was the pet of a kender community. The sight of the entire village of small kender crying their hearts out was so upsetting to the ranger that he quested until he found a druid who could heal the animal, then retired and took up fishing.

Kender are masters of taunting, sarcasm, and outright rudeness when they are riled. Their intense curiosity gives them shocking insights into the characters and natures of other people, though such an awareness is generally shallow. It is acute enough, however, for a kender to forge an idea of another person's character flaws, giving the kender the ability to create the most stinging insults that can be imagined. Full-scale riots have been started by irritated kender who opened up on someone with their verbal guns.

Taunting is one of the few defenses that kender have. Being smaller than most other beings, kender resent anyone who takes advantage of them. A kender could not imagine taunting a fellow kender; after all, they're in this together. Taunting is especially effective if a kender has others to back him up or some trap that a maddened attacker can be lured into with little cost to the kender. Though not very effective against the largest creatures (who will not have their combat effectiveness reduced greatly), taunting can still give a hard-pressed kender an edge in a fight. It is best used against those who are either attacking or are about to attack; there's no sense in angering a potential friend.

theft vs. handling

The kender concept of personal property and theft deserves special attention. Because many kender develop thieving talents, most people assume they are merely innocent-looking but sneaky burglars. This is just not so. The intense curiosity that kender feel feeds their desire to know how locks can be opened, how to approach people unseen and listen in on their conversations, and how to reach into pockets or pouches to find interesting things

to look at. Thieving comes naturally to them—so naturally that they do not see it as thieving.

Kender do not steal for the sake of profit. First of all, they have little concept of value. Faced with a choice between a 2,000 steel piece diamond and a huge, glittering chunk of purple glass, 90 kender out of 100 will take the glass. (The rest will take both but will get rid of the diamond first.) They pick things up out of curiosity and wander off with them. Sometimes the owner of an item leaves before the kender can give the item back, or else the kender becomes enchanted with the item and forgets to return it. While adventuring, a kender regards anything found in an enemy stronghold as fair game for picking up, as such items are marvelous curios and might prove useful later on.

Even if caught red-handed while taking an item, the range of excuses a kender will offer is amazing:

"Guess I found it somewhere."

"I forgot that I had it."

"You walked off before I could give it back."

"I was afraid someone else would take it."

"You must have dropped it."

"You put it down and I didn't think you wanted it anymore."

"Maybe it fell into my pocket."

All of these lines are delivered with an innocent sincerity that is all the more maddening because the kender really is sincere! A kender might not necessarily remember where he found something, even if he picked it up half a minute before, and such responses are often delivered as part of a subconscious defense mechanism. Intense curiosity is a trait ingrained in their souls and minds from their racial creation by the Greystone of Gargath. They cannot be other than what they are—natural thieves.

On the other hand, kender, like everyone else, do not like the idea of someone deliberately taking an item from someone else without the latter's permission. To be called a thief is still considered a base insult. This assertion sounds remarkable in view of the fact that kender constantly borrow things from each other and from visitors (without asking) in their communities. Kender don't regard their idea of borrowing as stealing, however. If they need something, they'll take it. If they see something interesting, they'll pick it up and pocket it. A popular proverb defines a kender heirloom as anything that remains for more than three weeks inside a kender's home.

Society

The basic unit of kender society is the immediate family (parents and children). Because kender wander so much, extended families do not truly exist. A detailed discussion of kender politics, government, and society is impossible in the short space here available.

Suffice it to say that kender have the most horribly democratic system ever found on the face of Krynn—everyone is pretty much allowed to do as they please. Kender do not see any great need to impress their views on anyone else and are genuinely interested in the perspectives of others. Thus there seems to be little need for law or government.

Kender are naturally helpful and decent and thus have no need for a powerful central government. Interestingly, when an emergency does occur that requires the kender to cooperate, they do so naturally; with little preparation they can become a formidable unified group.

This is not to say that the idea of government has not impressed the kender. Having seen the importance of civilization to all other societies in Krynn, kender have done their best to keep up. They have tried every conceivable type of government (and several types never imagined by nonkender) and are more than happy to give a new type of government a chance. They will also follow any leader for as long as it seems like fun...usually at least five minutes.

Kender society can also be hard to take. Nonkender visitors rarely stay longer than a week in any major kender town, unless they have a great sense of humor. It is not uncommon to be relieved of one's possessions at every turn (occasionally by the constables themselves). Visitors are pelted by a constant barrage of questions and told a million lies and tall tales without rest or letup. Couple this with the constant flux of kender government (the rules change from moment to moment on a whim) and most civilized men quickly flee in terror.

There has never been a standing kender army; those few invaders who have taken kender territory have never found the heart to stay very long. Indeed, most kender communities find an occupation by invading forces to be a tremendous boost to their local economy since invaders always bring such interesting things for the kender to handle.

kender
Game Statistics

Generating Abilities: The initial ability rolls are modified by a −1 penalty to Strength and a +2 bonus to Dexterity. The minimum and maximum ability scores for kender are as follows:

Kender Ability Ranges

Ability	Minimum	Maximum
Strength	6	16 *
Intelligence	6	18
Wisdom	3	16
Dexterity	8	19
Constitution	10	18
Charisma	6	18

Kender Classes: Kender can be of any class in the following list.

Kender Class Limits

Class	Maximum Level
Fighter	5 *
Barbarian	10 **
Ranger	5 *
Thief	Unlimited
Thief/Acrobat	Unlimited
Cleric (Heathen)	6
Druid (Heathen)	5 *
Holy Order of the Stars	12

* Kender who somehow gain 17 Strength can reach 6th level; those who manage to get Strength of 18 can become 7th-level fighters.
** Kender who somehow gain 17 Strength can reach 11th level; those who manage to get a Strength of 18 can become 12th-level barbarians.

Kender cannot learn to cast magic-user or illusionist spells because of their innate magic resistance, a legacy of their creation. They cannot become assassins because of their natural empathy with living things, and they cannot become monks because, regardless of alignment, they lack self-discipline. No evil kender are known to exist.

Kender who are not thieves are allowed a base 5% chance to perform any thieving skill except reading languages (no chance) and climbing (base 40% chance); these chances never improve except for Dexterity and racial modifiers (treat kender as halflings with regards to climbing). This also applies to NPC kender who have no levels (treated as 0th-level characters with 1d6 hp).

Special Abilities: Kenders have infravision that works out to 30 feet. They also have several unique abilities, as well as all standard halfling abilities.

kender pockets

If there are kender in a party of adventurers, the DM needs to keep track of the items in the kender's pockets. It is not necessary to keep a separate chart for each kender in a group, since two or more kender in a party tend to borrow from each other continuously.

This chart must have at least 100 spaces for entries. The first 92 entries are always filled. The first 82 positions on the chart consist of relatively harmless items that a kender might pull out of his pockets (although you never know what use they might have). This is followed by 10 objects that start out as harmless items, but they can be exchanged for more useful objects as the kender collects things on his adventures.

Slots from 93 up are filled one at a time each time the kender goes up a level. These slots should be filled according to the following table:

Kender Pockets Filling Table

D100	Filled With
1-20	Harmless Item
21-60	Basic Equipment (*PH* 123)
61-100	Magical Item (*DMG* pg. 121)

Harmless Items: These are the types of things parents find in kids' pockets all the time—string, nails, feathers, stones, etc. Take any item that suits your fancy and place it here. (No items bigger than bread boxes, please.) Let common sense be your guide.

Basic Equipment: Select an item of basic equipment from the basic equipment lists in the *Player's Handbook*. Be as random as possible in this determination with the following limitations: The object cannot be larger than the kender could reasonably conceal (this could be quite large if the kender has a *bag of holding*) and it cannot be magical in nature.

Magical Item: Using Treasure Table III on page 121 of the *DMG* and all subsequent tables, randomly determine a magical treasure. Reroll any artifact results.

When in a pinch, kender often try to grab something from their pockets. This action takes 1d6 segments to perform. When a kender declares that he is reaching into his pocket, roll percentile dice against the following table. For every level of experience the kender has attained, add 2 to the roll.

Kender Pocket Grab Table

D100	Description
1-3	Bird Feather
4-10	Purple Stones (2d6)
11-20	Multicolored Marbles (d100)
21-24	String
25-27	Animal Teeth
28-32	Whistle
33-35	Paper
36-43	Chalk
44-50	Charcoal
51-57	Handkerchiefs
58-63	Mice (1d4)
64-70	Deck of Cards
71-82	Useless Maps
83-92	Useful Map
93-100	Special Items

This table must be maintained by the DM during the course of the game. Each time a kender handles an object, that object must displace one of the special items. Displaced objects are placed carefully out of sight somewhere.

The kender's regular equipment is not subject to displacement. His hoopak or other weapon, his food and other essential objects would not be dropped. Similarly, he would not take essential items from another creature.

kender taunt and fearlessness

Kender have two unique special abilities: taunt and fearlessness.

When a kender taunts an intelligent creature who can understand the kender's speech, the creature must make a successful saving throw vs. spell (Wisdom bonuses apply). If the creature fails, it attacks the kender wildly for 1d10 rounds, with a −2 penalty to hit and a +2 penalty to his Armor Class because of the affected being's irrationality.

If a particular victim is assumed to be more or less vulnerable to such abuse, the DM can apply penalties or bonuses to saving throws as desired. (Long-time friends of a kender develop a high resistance to this power as they have grown used to the abuse.)

The kender's fearlessness grants him immunity to natural fear emanating from monsters such as dragons, androsphinxes, and demons, and to magical fear generated by wands or created by spells such as *cause fear, scare, emotion, symbol of fear,* and *fear.*

tinker Gnomes
appearance

Gnomes average three feet in height and weigh about 45-50 lbs. Females are as large as males. All gnomes have rich brown skin, either straight or curly white hair, china-blue or violet eyes, and surprisingly even, cavity-free teeth. Males have soft, curly white beards and mustaches; females are beardless. Both sexes develop facial wrinkles after age 50. Gnomes are very short and stocky, though their movements are quick and their hands are deft and sure. They have rounded ears and large noses.

Gnomes sound much like humans in vocal range and pitch, except for having a more nasal voice. They speak very intensely and rapidly, running their words together in unending sentences. Gnomes are capable of speaking and listening carefully at the same time. When two gnomes meet, each babbles away at the other until they've both finished their say, often answering questions later in their dialogue as part of the same continuous sentence. Gnomes have learned to speak slowly and distinctly when around other races. If frightened, startled, or depressed, a gnome may speak in much shorter sentences than is usual.

Gnomes involved in major industrial operations may develop industrial diseases from smog and other working hazards. Mild respiratory and eye infections are fairly common, but clear up quickly once the afflicted gnome is put in fresh air for a few days. Industrial accidents, noise and visual pollution, and other problems can temporarily or permanently disable a gnome, sometimes leading to early retirement from active pursuits.

history

Gnomish history is the most detailed of any of the races of Krynn—it is also the most inexplicable and boring stuff you could ever be forced to read. Every gnome, no matter how lowly his station, keeps a detailed diary of his work and inventions. These diaries form the official history of the gnomish race. Thus the historian must wade through tremendous amounts of tedious notes just to find a reference to a significant event in gnomish history. Even the most intrepid of scholars balks at the monumental task.

Nevertheless, there are enough references to the Greystone of Gargath to establish it as a major event in gnomish history and the major

motivation for their coming to Ansalon from across the sea. The history of the gnomes before they lived in Ansalon is unavailable since the older diaries are much more detailed and filled with minutae than those of present-day gnomes. The ancient history of the gnomes no doubt exists somewhere in the vast storage system of the gnomish libraries, but it has been impossible to ferret out. This task is also complicated by the fact that an early gnomish inventor tried to build a cam and shaft data storage facility (primitive computer) which burned to the ground and took many ancient works with it.

What little has been pieced together gives a dim picture of the history of gnomes since the Greystone. On Sancrist Isle, many of the gnomes who pursued the Greystone gave up the chase. They settled down rather than risk another dangerous ocean voyage. The rest of the gnomes built ships and sailed out of sight, with the best wishes of their fellows. Eventually, many gnomes who had scattered across Ansalon during the chase migrated west to Sancrist; only a few gnomes now remain on the main continent.

Throughout their history, gnomes have concentrated on developing scientific and technological devices, a vocation hampered by the predominantly magical essence of this world. They have working steam engines and steam-powered ships, clockwork mechanisms to keep time, ore-refining plants that make high-grade steel, and such mundane devices as screws, pulleys, drive shafts, toothed gears, coiled springs, music boxes, and mechanical toys.

Two notable events occurred following the escape of the Greystone. The first was the arrival of the Knights of Solamnia on Sancrist. The first Knight-gnome contact was rather unpleasant. Always suspicious of outsiders, the gnomes were alarmed to see ships arriving upon their shores, bearing hordes of tall, warlike humans. Determined to keep their mountain paradise secret from the humans, the gnomes lurched into action. Their first thought was to hide within their mountain caverns but then, being gnomes, they had a better idea.

After several months of unending toil by their greatest mechanical geniuses, the gnomes were prepared. They were going to make their mountain disappear. The engineers set off the device with great pride and much fanfare.

This day went down in the annals of Sancrist (even when almost everything else was lost during the Cataclysm) as the Day of Rotten Eggs. The island was covered in a dense

cloud of thick yellow smoke, redolent of eggs that had been sitting in the sun for a week.

Within hours everyone in the human colony was deathly sick from the smell. Packing up blankets and clothes, they headed for the beaches. Gratefully breathing the fresh salt breezes, they wondered if they would ever be able to return to their homes. While waiting anxiously for the vile yellow cloud to dissipate, the colonists were considerably startled to see an army of short, brown creatures stagger out of the smoke and fall almost lifeless at the humans' feet.

The kindly people of Solamnia immediately went to the aid of the poor gnomes. Thus did the two races of Sancrist meet.

As a result of this experiment, the gnomes now possess a formula for a poison gas that incapacitates its victims. More importantly, the gnomes have allied themselves with Solamnia's government and are now important trading partners of this kingdom. The Knights, ever suspicious of magical forces, are relieved to be dealing with a race that carries the banner of technology; Solamnia has profited greatly from this contact.

The second major post-Greystone event was the Cataclysm. This world-rending catastrophe produced tremendous upheavals that enlarged the size of Sancrist's mountainous northern half, where the gnomes lived. A number of gnomes were killed by landslides and tunnel collapses, but overall, the seismic activity was welcome. With vastly increased living space, the gnomes were little inclined to travel elsewhere. Many small groups of gnomes now make their homes in the northern Sancrist mountains, spending their days mining and gem-hunting.

Social Practices

Every gnome has three different names. One is the gnome's true name, which is actually an extensive history of the gnome's entire family tree, extending back to the race's creation by Reorx. This history is compacted into a single, enormous word that can easily fill a large book. In fact, the complete names of every gnome born on Sancrist are kept by the Genealogy Guild in the main library at Mount Nevermind. Interestingly, this record forms the only continuous history of the world since the Age of Dreams, though it says little about any race other than the gnomes.

Though each gnome can easily remember his complete name, or at least the first few thousand letters of it, gnomes have developed a shortened name for use when among

gnomes. This name takes merely half a minute to recite and is simply a listing of the highlights of the gnome's ancestry. Humans and other races who deal with gnomes have developed even shorter names for them. These consist of the first one or two syllables of gnomish names. Gnomes find these abbreviated names to be very undignified, but they have learned to live with them.

Society

The largest settlement of gnomes exists in the immense tunnel complexes beneath Mount Nevermind, an extinct volcano (and tallest mountain) on Sancrist Isle. A recent census of the community indicates that 59,000 gnomes live there, give or take the few hundred who are coming or going at any one time. The Mount Nevermind community is thousands of years old and is the most highly developed of all gnome cities on Krynn.

The city of Mount Nevermind is built into the rock surrounding the central shaft of the volcano. The volcano's caldera holds a small central lake that freezes over in the winter. Gnome engineers long ago excavated the ash and rock from the volcano's throat and smoothed out the floor of the crater for rough-

ly 400 yards. This smooth area came to be called the Inner Hall. A horizontal shaft (the Outer Hall) runs from the Inner Hall through the mountain to the outside world.

The central shaft is over 1,050 yards high and 800 yards across at its top. Illumination from thousands of lanterns, fires, candles, mirrors, and old glass globes with *continual light* spells brightens the Inner Hall.

Mount Nevermind is a scene of frantic, nonstop activity and noise. Everywhere one looks are gnomes hurrying from place to place, whistles blowing, gears turning, steam blasting, horns sounding, lights flashing, mechanical carts rolling, etc. The gnomes have developed catapults (gnomeflingers) for rapid transportation from the Inner Hall to the various levels of the city (35 levels in all). Hundreds of staircases, ramps, pulley elevators, ladders, and the like also cross from level to level. Steam-powered carts mounted on rails encircle the city on many levels, providing fast (but rather undependable) travel around a single level. In an emergency, gnomes can move through the huge ventilation shafts cut into the mountain, though the steam-driven fans would make the going difficult.

Beneath the main city is an enormous network of tunnels and mines that spreads out in

all directions. Called the Undercity, this tunnel system is as ancient as the city above and far more dangerous. Monster lairs and unfriendly subterranean races have been encountered, though gnomish technology has managed to isolate most of these hazards. Several engineering committees are investigating ways to harness geothermal energy from deep in the earth. These committees have set up research stations here and there in the Undercity. A number of tunnels also serve as dumping sites for hazardous wastes; unpleasant things may be encountered there as well.

Each level of the city and Undercity is well separated from all others by a thick expanse of rock. The tunneling is superbly engineered and reinforced, as insurance against earthquakes and other disturbances. Some areas of the city are built with shock-absorbing ceilings reinforced by enormous steel springs. Steel rods are often drilled through the rock to lend additional reinforcement. The possibility of a second Cataclysm has not been ignored by the gnomish engineers.

The slopes of Mount Nevermind have been extensively terraced. The terraces are carefully farmed and tended by the Agricultural Guild, which also maintains fungi-growth farms and herds of cave-dwelling goats and sheep in the Undercity. Additional food is provided by raising domestic animals in the surrounding countryside and from game caught by the Hunters Guild. Research is being conducted into creating artificial food, but previous experiments in this area have always resulted in poisonous morsels. A committee is still looking into the matter.

Mount Nevermind is governed by an elected Grand Council of clan leaders and guild masters. These gnome leaders serve in their positions for life. Methods of election vary from guild to guild and from clan to clan; some use closed ballots, debates, seniority, and contests, while some positions are actually hereditary.

Several hundred clans dwell within the mountain. There are perhaps 50 major guilds and a host of minor ones. The government is so heavily laden with bureaucracy that few major decisions are actually rendered in the Grand Council. Most of the decisions are made by guilds and clans who go off on their own tangents, regardless of the wishes of the rest of the community. Everyone insists upon regulation and doing things by the book, but this process is so tedious and time-consuming that even gnomes don't have the patience.

Each major guild is organized around a particular area of interest. There is a Mathematics Guild, a Philosophers Guild, a Mechanical Engineering Guild, a Weapons Guild, an Education Guild, etc. Coverage of the physical and technological sciences is very heavy, but only two guilds (the Agricultural and Medical Guilds) have anything to do with the life sciences. Scientific guilds without immediate application, such as Astronomy, are usually small and lack a say in the affairs of the community. The Acquisitions, Military, and Foreign Relations guilds regularly train and employ gnome thieves and assassins (and even gully dwarf assassins on occasion). Clerical gnomes (when some existed) belonged to the Priests Guild, which was the first and only guild to become completely extinct. Their functions were largely absorbed by the Medical and Philosophers Guilds.

Beyond the Mountain

The largest gnomish community away from Mount Nevermind has only a thousand inhabitants. Most others average 200-400 citizens and are found in mountainous or rough, hilly regions. Each of these small towns is organized similarly to Mount Nevermind, but with fewer guilds and some of the guilds perform multiple functions (e.g., the Medical Guild might also take care of agricultural needs).

Sages are very common in any gnomish community. Sages compile volumes and volumes of information, guesses, facts, figures, speculations, and philosophical doodles on their guild committee's selected topics. This pure research is sometimes (though rarely) helpful to future generations, but all of it is carefully labeled, archived, and cared for by the gnomish librarians in their huge book rooms. Sage gnomes almost never travel, preferring to devote themselves to lifelong study of a given subject.

It is worth saying a few words about gnomes' relations with other races. In areas where gnomes are known to exist, they are generally not well liked. Their technological bent makes them very alien to people accustomed to magic, and their poor grasp of social relations puts off most potential friends. War was narrowly averted in one area after a gnomish digging machine plowed through a sacred elven grove, and similar episodes have occurred across Ansalon at regular intervals. The humans on Sancrist have managed to adjust to the gnomes by avoiding contact with them whenever possible.

Tinker Gnomes
Game Statistics

Generating Abilities: The initial ability rolls are modified by a −1 penalty to Strength and a +2 bonus to Dexterity. The minimum and maximum scores for gnomes are as follows:

Tinker Gnomes Ability Scores

Ability	Minimum	Maximum
Strength	6	18
Intelligence	8	18
Wisdom	3	12
Dexterity	8	18
Constitution	8	18
Charisma	3	18

Gnome Classes: Gnomes in Krynn can only be of the tinker class, but their advancement in that class is unlimited.

Abilities: For details of gnomish technology, look under the tinker character class on page 21 of this book. Tinker gnomes of Krynn also have the special abilities of regular gnomes (such as infravision, magic resistance, detect grades, etc.) as listed in the *Player's Handbook*.

Mad Gnomes

Occasionally travelers come across *mad gnomes*. These creatures look like gnomes and have many of the same abilities as gnomes, but they have no talent for technology. They are almost always from distant lands far from Ansalon. Gnomes do their best to help them (the Medical Guild has treated several of them with a variety of devices of varying effect) but mostly it is for naught. The few mad gnomes who have learned technological skills just never do their work properly as far as the gnomes are concerned. (Their equipment usually works too well.)

Only off-world gnomes start out as mad gnomes. Non-mad gnomes get a yearly dice roll to see if they become mad gnomes. Roll 1d100, if the roll is a 100, roll again. If the second roll is also a 100, then that gnome has now become a mad gnome.

Mad gnomes from off world have a 1% chance of learning the technological skills of the tinker gnomes during any six-month period spent with them. This roll is not cumula-

tive and can only be checked once every six game months. If the gnome succeeds then he becomes a mad gnome with technological skills. Mad gnomes from Krynn start out with the gnomish technological skills.

Mad gnomes who can use technology get a +5 bonus to any success roll involved in creating a device. Also, the device is automatically 1d6 sizes smaller than a regular gnomish device of this type (with no increase in Complexity Level).

the Elves of Ansalon

Of the races that first sprang into being from the forging of the universe, the elves were the embodiment of good.

All of elvish tradition holds that they were the first to be born into the world. When they first awakened during the Age of Dreams, they were scattered across the land like the stars are spread across the sky. The passage of the Greystone left none on the face of Krynn untouched, but it seemed to effect the elves less than most. The only known change caused by that wondrous magical passage was that of those land elves who became Sea Elves,

later called Dimernesti and Dargonesti. Both developed their own cultures independent of the main elven histories. They lived in distant obscurity and peace, though trade was established between elves of the land and those of the sea.

Yet peace was not always possible in Ansalon. The dragons awakened with the world, some to evil and some to good. With the advent of the first Dragon War in the Age of Dreams, conflict entered the world of Krynn.

The Ogre Wars were but a precursor to the great struggle of the first Dragon War. Among the elves of that time was one named Silvanos. He was a powerful warrior and a great traveler. He visited many of the elves in the deep woods throughout Ansalon. Traveling with his companion, a kender by the name of Balif, he also encountered great suffering and death during the Dragon War. When at last he could take it no more, Silvanos traveled the lands again, but now with a purpose. He rallied the elves of the woods and convinced them to abandon their isolated villages. His vision of a united elven nation fired the minds of elves across all of Ansalon and brought them under his banner.

Thus Silvanos gave direction and a united front to the previously dispersed elves. He forged a nation whose ideals and order lasted

for more than two millennia and are still honored today in the courts of the Silvanesti elves.

During the first Dragon War, Silvanos called the Sinthal-Elish (Council of the High Ones) on a hill named Sol-Fallen. There many households and clans swore their allegiance to Silvanos and the fledgling nation of Silvanesti. Balif stayed to help Silvanos run the elven armies.

Silvanos wed Quinari and raised a family. Their first son was Sithel. When Silvanos died in approximately 2515 PC (Pre-Cataclysm), Sithel assumed the leadership of the elves of Silvanesti. His father was buried in a crystal tomb. Sithel also erected a tower in honor of his mother in the heart of Silvanost.

It was about 2308 PC that twin sons were born to Sithel. They were named Sithas and Kith-Kanan. Sithas was born but minutes before Kith-Kanan.

During this same time, the human Ergothian Empire was spreading across Ansalon and, inevitably, encroached on the expanding borders of Silvanesti. The Wildrunner elves of the House Protector were, naturally, at the front of the elven expansion and were the first to make contact with the rising human civilization. Kith-Kanan was the leader of the Wildrunner Elves and Sithas was the heir to the Silvanesti throne.

The sympathies of Kith-Kanan were with these Wildrunner elves who were more free of the constraints of their Houses and more open and friendly than the elves of the other Houses. Trade was soon established between the Wildrunner elves and the human settlements on their borders and, in the course of time, several marriages between Wildrunner elves and humans occurred. While this made sense to the elves of House Protector, Sithel looked on this with great suspicion. On Kith-Kanan's advice, he journeyed to the western reaches of the kingdom to judge for himself the results of Kith-Kanan's diplomacy.

The journey proved to be a terrible disaster. Sithel was killed while hunting for sport in the borderlands. Some say that the arrow that slew him was a stray that found its mark by accident. Others say that the humans assassinated him in order to remove any barriers to their expansion. There was also a tale that the killing was done at the order of Sithas in order to discredit his brother and place himself on the throne all at the same time.

The final result was the Kinslayer War that lasted until 2100 PC, in which the Silvanesti elves tried to drive the humans from the land. The elves of that region who had married humans sided with the Ergothians in what they perceived as an unjust war brought on by their own country. Kith-Kanan led the army of the western forces in Silvanesti in a terrible war against his own kin. Ultimately the war ended with a truce between the Ergoth Empire and Kith-Kanan.

By now, however, the western elves were tired of being subject to the rigid caste system of the Silvanesti. They sued for social change. The first civil war of the elves threatened. In secret negotiations with Ergoth, Sithas solved several of his problems.

The Swordsheath Scroll was signed and the nation of Qualinesti was formed—a place where the Wildrunner elves of western Silvanesti could establish their own nation. Kith-Kanan saw this for what it was—exile. Yet it seemed to be the only hope for his people. Thus the kingdom of Qualinesti born out of sorrow and hope. Kith-Kanan established his kingdom of elves in Qualinesti and never returned to Silvanesti.

> **Special Abilities of all Elves on Krynn:** All of the elves on Krynn have the special abilities of elves listed in the *Player's Handbook*. Unless otherwise noted in the race descriptions for a particular elven race, use the special abilities as specified in the *Player's Handbook*.

Silvanesti (high Elves)

appearance

The Silvanesti are a fair-skinned race with eyes of blue or brown and hair ranging from light brown to blonde-white. Hazel eyes are a symbol of the line of Silvanos. The Silvanesti prefer loose garments, flowing robes, and capes.

history

The history of the Silvanesti is largely the history of elves on Ansalon. Quevalin Soth, the great bard of the Silvanesti elves, was the first popular elvish historian. His writings form the basis of most commonly known history to this day. Thus the history of elves at the beginning of this section really details the history of Silvanesti in its early stages.

After the formation of Qualinesti, the Silvanesti elves remained isolated from the world until the time of King Lorac Caladon. Under his direction, Silvanesti established a flourishing trade with Istar, the great empire to the north. Then the Cataclysm closed the borders of Silvanesti and the elves withdrew from the rest of the world. Their borders were feared for few who crossed them ever returned.

The Dragonarmies did not fear the borders of Silvanesti. During the War of the Lance, the Dragon Highlords decided to deal with Silvanesti before venturing into the fertile Solamnic lands to the west.

So it was that dragons came at last to Silvanesti to spread terror. For some time the armies of the Wildrunner elves made the advancing Dragonarmies pay dearly for every step they took into the elves' land. This gave the Silvanesti nation time to board the ships prepared by King Lorac and flee to the west.

Lorac remained behind, saying he had the power to defeat the Dragonarmy. It was not known until much later that King Lorac had secretly used a *dragon orb* in a vain attempt to destroy the oncoming dragons. His hope turned against him and his own worst nightmares were given substance and created a horrible alternate reality over the entire kingdom. Through his tortured mind, the once-beautiful forest of Silvanesti was reshaped into a nightmare.

During the rest of the War of the Lance, the Silvanesti kingdom-in-exile was based on the island of Ergoth. Since the end of the war, the Silvanesti government has been located in Qualinost under the direction of Alhana Starbreeze, daughter of King Lorac. Her marriage to Porthios, Speaker of Suns of Qualinesti, is a symbolic union of their two peoples.

The Silvanesti elves are trying to reclaim their homeland from their base in Qualinesti. While the *orb* is no longer causing the nightmares to continue in Silvanesti, the effects of that magic still remain and make once-great Silvanesti a place of horror and twisted agony. The elves have a long and hard task ahead to reclaim their homeland.

philosophies

The Silvanesti elves are a prejudiced people, intolerant of other races and customs, which are seen by the Silvanesti as being highly inferior to their own. Their views are obviously the only correct ones. Racial purity is also a large part of the Silvanesti mindset.

Society

Silvanesti attitudes differ greatly from those of their Qualinesti brethren. Long years within a safe, settled empire have stratified the various crafts and tasks into a rigid system of castes, or Houses. At the top of the system is House Royal, the descendants of Silvanos who rule the land. Next is House Cleric, once a religious order, but now mainly concerned with keeping records and lore.

Beneath these two houses are those of the craftsmen and guilds: House Mystic, House Gardener, and House Mason, to name a few. The House Protector (the Wildrunners) serves as the army of the Silvanesti. Years of continual peace have stratified the guilds into rigid social institutions. No one marries outside his guild without permission, and permission is rarely granted.

The lowest guild is House Servitor, which includes apprentices, foreign traders, indentured servants, and slaves (the Silvanesti enslave races that lose wars with them).

The Silvanesti survived the Cataclysm and bolted their doors against the outside world. During the War of the Lance, the Silvanesti fled west through the Plains of Dust, crossed the straits to Southern Ergoth and settled on the western shores of Harkun Bay. There they founded Silvamori, the Hidden Realm.

Silvanesti Elves
Game Statistics

Generating Abilities: The initial ability rolls are modified by a −1 penalty to Constitution and a +1 bonus to Dexterity. The minimum and maximum scores for Silvanesti elves are as follows:

Silvanesti Elves Ability Scores

Ability	Minimum	Maximum
Strength	3	18
Intelligence	10	18
Wisdom	6	18
Dexterity	7	19
Constitution	6	18
Charisma	12	18

Silvanesti Class Limits

Class	Maximum Level
Cavalier	N/E
Paladin	12
Knight of the Crown	N/E *
Knight of the Sword	N/E *
Knight of the Rose	N/E *
Fighter	10
Barbarian	N/E *
Ranger	Unlim
Magic-User (Renegade)	N/E *
Illusionist (Renegade)	N/E *
Wizard of High Sorcery	Unlim
Thief	N/E *
Thief/Acrobat	N/E *
Cleric (Heathen)	N/E *
Druid (Heathen)	N/E *
Holy Orders of the Stars	Unlim

* N/E means not eligible for that class.

Qualinesti
Appearance

The Qualinesti are slightly smaller and darker than the Silvanesti. Their hair ranges from honey-brown to blond, and their eyes are blue or brown. They prefer woven slacks and jerkins for men, long dresses for women.

Philosophies

The Qualinesti are more friendly than the Silvanesti. They have traded more openly with other races and built Pax Tharkas as a joint venture with the dwarves of Thorbardin. During the Age of Might, Qualinesti-human relations were generally good. However the elves' dislike of interracial marriages was a continual barrier to improved relations with the other races in the area.

The situation deteriorated drastically with the Cataclysm. The elves were able to retain their civilization and society despite the terrible destruction of their land. The neighboring humans and dwarves were not so fortunate. Their societies were destroyed; the starving survivors heard rumors that the Qualinesti had treasures and food worthy of plunder. The subsequent raids destroyed the small outlying elven communities and earned the hatred of those elves that survived. Qualinesti closed its borders to the other races until the nation was forced to abandon its homeland and flee west before the Dragonarmies in the War of the Lance.

After the War of the Lance, the Qualinesti elves returned from exile in Ergoth to reclaim their homeland. Despite the fact that they had fought with the Knights of Solamnia against the Dark Queen, they still harbored deep resentments against the other races of the world. But they are the most willing of the elven nations to treat with other races. They are capable of the same snobbery shown by their Silvanesti cousins, but any snobbery they display is far more subtle than that of the High Elves.

History

The tragedy of the Kinslayer Wars marked the beginning of the Qualinesti race of elves. With Kith-Kanan leading them, the Qualinesti vowed to forge a more tolerant society. In the days prior to the Cataclysm, the Qualinesti elves founded many smaller communities in the hope that they would grow in trade and culture as had Qualinost.

This hope was dashed by the Cataclysm, which not only greatly damaged all the cities of Qualinesti, but caused the terrible period of terror and barbarism that followed. The elves were seen as easy prey by the other peoples who were struggling to survive in the shattered lands. Many terrible raids devastated the Qualinesti communities. (Many of Krynn's half-elves came from this time when humans raided the elven cities.)

In their flight from the advancing Dragonarmies during the War of the Lance, the Qualinesti fled across the Straits of Algoni to southern Ergoth and founded the city of Qualimori on the eastern shores of Harkun Bay. Here they almost immediately ran afoul of the already established Silvanesti kingdom-
in-exile and the Kagonesti nation to whom the land originally belonged. All three nations began bickering with one another and could only agree that the Dragonarmies had to be stopped.

After the War of the Lance, the Qualinesti mounted an expedition to reclaim their homeland. This they did with little difficulty and set about repairing their capital city. Porthios became the Speaker of Suns after the death of his father Solostaran. Porthios married Alhana Starbreeze in a political marriage intended to reforge the bonds between the elves of Qualinesti and those of Silvanesti. While the two nations remain sundered in many ways, this has taken the hostile edge off their relations.

The Qualinesti are now helping the Silvanesti elves to reclaim ancient Silvanost. This is not to say that all past injustices have been forgiven. The Qualinesti aid seems more in the way of "the sooner your house is ready, the sooner you'll be out of mine."

Society

The Qualinesti society is far less structured than that of their Silvanesti cousins.

The Qualinesti are ruled by a Speaker of Suns who must be a blood descendant of Kith-Kanan and thus of Silvanos. The Speaker serves primarily as a guiding and directing force in a government made up of a senate called the Thalas-Enthia. This group is appointed to represent the various guilds and communities of the elves. The recommendations of this group are then brought to the Speaker who makes the final determination on the matter.

Only one large city exists in all of Qualinesti—Qualinost, the capital. This city is a magnificent blending of elven architecture and natural features. The marvels of this city are many and are described more appropriately in the *Atlas of Krynn*. The Tower of Suns overlooks Qualinost, the city built in harmony with nature.

The Qualinesti dreams of fostering many sister elven cities died with the Cataclysm. There are many communities that still exist in the forests west of the Kharolis Mountains, but these are small, isolated farming communities with no desires for becoming anything more.

Qualinesti Elves
Game Statistics

Generating Abilities: The initial ability rolls are modified by a −1 penalty to Constitution and a +1 bonus to Dexterity. The minimum and maximum ability scores for Qualinesti elves are as follows:

Qualinesti Elves Ability Scores

Ability	Minimum	Maximum
Strength	7	18
Intelligence	8	18
Wisdom	6	18
Dexterity	7	19
Constitution	7	18
Charisma	8	18

Qualinesti Class Limits

Class	Maximum Level
Cavalier	10
Paladin	N/E *
Knight of the Crown	N/E *
Knight of the Sword	N/E *
Knight of the Rose	N/E *
Fighter	14
Barbarian	N/E *
Ranger	Unlim
Magic-User (Renegade)	11
Illusionist (Renegade)	N/E *
Wizard of High Sorcery	Unlim
Thief	Unlim
Thief/Acrobat	Unlim
Cleric (Heathen)	N/E
Druid (Heathen)	N/E
Holy Orders of the Stars	Unlim

* N/E means not eligible for that class.

Kagonesti (Wild Elves)
Appearance

The Kagonesti elves are about the same size as Silvanesti and Qualinesti, but they are much more muscular. They are very tan and draw designs on their faces and exposed flesh with clay and paints. Their hair is dark, ranging from black to light brown, with a rare throwback to the silvery white of their ancestors. Their eyes are hazel.

History

The Kagonesti elves, also called Wild Elves, are distantly related to all other elves, although their history as a separate people starts at the very beginning of the world. Their tales of the creation are much more fanciful than those of their cousins. This is primarily due to the fact that their history is handed down verbally from generation to generation.

According to the Kagonesti version of the early days of Krynn, the elves were the first to walk the lands and taste the waters. They found the land good and the waters pure and knew that this would not always be so. Some elves went east and gathered together under great chiefs to wage war upon other nations. Yet the Kagonesti did not follow this path. They wished only that which the gods had granted them. So the Kagonesti lived in harmony with the land, the gods, and the other peoples of Krynn. Though they did not war against other nations, their warriors were strong and protected the lands that were given to the Kagonesti by the gods.

Some Kagonesti are the descendants of Silvanesti and Qualinesti elves who left those nations centuries ago to live in harmony with the wild.

60

The troubles and wars of the world hardly affected these simple elves. They remained in the forests of western Ergoth and eventually became part of the Empire of Ergoth (or so Ergoth said). It mattered little to the Kagonesti. They were left alone and continued to live as they had for millennia. Ergoth waxed and waned and was soon forgotten under the glaring brilliance of Istar, but the elves of the wilds remained unchanged.

Eventually time caught up with the Kagonesti. They saw the Cataclysm as a sign from the gods, but they could not agree on what the sign meant. The War of the Lance shattered their peace as their land was invaded by the refugee Silvanesti elves fleeing west from the horrors of their own land. The Silvanesti subjugated the Kagonesti as slaves to their nation in exile. They claimed that their purpose was to educate their lost brothers in the ways of civilization, but the Kagonesti knew slavery for what it was. The coming of the Qualinesti helped the situation somewhat (at least the Silvanesti had someone else to bother), but the Kagonesti mourned the further destruction of their once-pristine land.

Yet the wheels of time still turned and soon the War of the Lance was over. The Qualinesti left and took the Silvanesti with them. This was not without its price, however, for many of the Kagonesti were taken as servants to the great houses of the Silvanesti. Many families were sundered in that leave-taking; there are still many Kagonesti who roam the lands looking for their loved ones.

Philosophies

The Kagonesti believe that harmony with nature is the key to a full and happy life. While they respect nature in all its forms, they also feel it can be used to further the purposes and well-being of the tribe.

While the Kagonesti do not start wars of aggression, this does not mean that they are pacifists. The Kagonesti are fierce and determined warriors when the need arises. They hunt game and enemies with equal deadliness. They are fiercely proud of their heritage and generally rather hot-tempered, in contrast to the reserved and stoic Silvanesti.

Society

The basic unit of the Kagonesti is the tribe, centered around a chief and his family. The Kagonesti tribe lives in structures that are easily portable. Permanent settlements are never

made.

The Kagonesti have a more animistic view of the cosmos than their elven brothers. They see the great spirits of the stars in everything. Inanimate objects are believed to be filled with the spirits of their Kagonesti ancestors.

The wild nature of the Kagonesti and their unorthodox customs (they send their dead down the river to the sea rather than build tombs of stone) have led other elven races to regard them as savages and lesser beings. The Silvanesti declared them House Servitor and enslaved them to build Silvamori. The Qualinesti have indentured them as well, thinking that the Kagonesti are some part-elven lesser race.

Kagonesti Elves
Game Statistics

Generating Abilities: The initial ability rolls are modified by a +1 bonus to Strength and Constitution and a +2 bonus to Dexterity. The Intelligence roll is subject to a −3 penalty. The minimum and maximum ability scores for Kagonesti elves are as follows:

Kagonesti Elves Ability Scores

Ability	Minimum	Maximum
Strength	8	18
Intelligence	3	12
Wisdom	8	18
Dexterity	8	19
Constitution	8	18
Charisma	8	18

Kagonesti Elves Class Limits

Class	Maximum Level
Cavalier	N/E *
Paladin	N/E *
Knight of the Crown	N/E *
Knight of the Sword	N/E *
Knight of the Rose	N/E *
Fighter	Unlim
Barbarian	Unlim
Ranger	Unlim
Magic-User (Renegade)	N/E *
Illusionist (Renegade)	N/E *
Wizard of High Sorcery	N/E *
Thief	Unlim
Thief/Acrobat	Unlim
Cleric (Heathen)	N/E *
Druid (Heathen)	N/E *
Holy Orders of the Stars	7

* N/E means not eligible for that class.

Dargonesti and Dimernesti
(Sea Elves)
Appearance

The Dimernesti and Dargonesti are races of Sea Elves, groups that separated radically from the elven land races during the Age of Dreams—partly as a result of the Greystone passage at that time. (The Dimernesti are also called Shoal Elves as they inhabit the shallows of many of Ansalon's coastlines.) They have been few in number ever since the devastation of the Cataclysm in which many of their citadels and homes were destroyed. They breathe both air and water and have light bluish skin and webbed fingers. They wear their silver hair long, braided with shells. The Dargonesti, or Deep-Elves, are the tallest elven race, a slender people with large eyes, extended fingers, and deep blue skin.

The most interesting aspect of the sea elves is their unique ability to *shapechange* into the form of a sea otter (Dimernesti) or dolphin (Dargonesti). This comes naturally to them and greatly aids them in moving about their underwater kingdoms. There are differences between actual dolphins and whales and their elven *shapechanged* counterparts but those differences are so minor as to be only distinguishable to another Dimernesti or Dargonesti.

History

The sea elves were created during the passage of the Greystone of Gargath. Originally elven mariners with a great love for the sea, their race became dwellers of the oceans and its main civilizing force.

Practically nothing of their history has been transmitted to the ears of surface dwellers. Those contacts that have been made indicate that the sea elves' history is as full and colorful as those of the land-dwelling elves. What is known is that great battles were waged during the War of the Lance by the Dimernesti and Dargonesti against the forces of the Queen of Darkness under the waters. The Shoal Elves seem to have the same stand-offish relationship with the Deep Elves as the Qualinesti do with the Silvanesti.

Long ago, the Dimernesti had a partnership with the Silvanesti, allowing elvish mariners to explore distant lands. Quarrels with the stiff-necked Silvanesti led to a break in all communication with the land elves; the

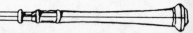

House Mariner is now a lost guild among the Silvanesti.

Throughout history, wondrous tales of these elves helping mariners in distress have been told in all seaports. However, these tales are almost always reported third or fourth hand and are undoubtedly greatly exaggerated.

philosophies

Shoal Elves take little interest in what happens above the watery surface of their domain. The few who have appeared on land did so only on a mission of importance or under the direction of the Speaker of the Sea, the leader of the Dimernesti. Dargonesti have rarely been seen by humans or any of their land-based kin.

Society

The Dimernesti follow the Speaker of the Sea, a hereditary position much like the Speaker of Stars. While there are many guilds that mirror those of Silvanesti, there is no caste system and the boundaries between guilds are not as rigid as for the Silvanesti.

The Dimernesti have recently taken to living in the sunken cities of the Cataclysm. They find them romantic and intriguing. The Dimernesti are not builders but they seem to enjoy living in buildings.

Most Dimernesti live in schools that are clan-oriented groups. There are no families as all of those in the group care for the young of the school. They are nomadic in nature and rarely stay in the same place for long.

dimernesti Elves
Game Statistics

Generating Abilities: The initial ability rolls are modified by a − 1 penalty to Strength and a + 2 bonus to Dexterity. The minimum and maximum ability scores for Dimernesti elves are as follows:

Dimernesti Elves Ability Scores

Ability	Minimum	Maximum
Strength	3	18
Intelligence	8	18
Wisdom	8	18
Dexterity	10	19
Constitution	3	18
Charisma	8	18

Dimernesti Class Limits

Class	Maximum Level
Cavalier	10/Unlim *
Paladin	10/Unlim *
Knight of the Crown	N/E **
Knight of the Sword	N/E **
Knight of the Rose	N/E **
Fighter	16/Unlim *
Barbarian	N/E **
Ranger	N/E **
Magic-User (Renegade)	N/E **
Illusionist (Renegade)	N/E **
Wizard of High Sorcery	10/Unlim *
Thief	N/E **
Thief/Acrobat	N/E **
Cleric (Heathen)	N/E **
Druid (Heathen)	N/E **
Holy Orders of the Stars	Unlim

* The level listed before the slash is the maximum allowable to the character while on land. The Dimernesti are unlimited while they are in the environs of the sea. Should a Dimernesti elf of a level higher than that listed leave the environment of the water, his hit dice, hit points, and all other related adjustments must be made to temporarily reduce the character to the maximum listed. This reduction goes away once the character returns to the water.

** N/E means not eligible for that class.

Special Abilities: The Dimernesti and Dargonesti elves have the ability to *shapechange* at will into the form of a sea otter or a dolphin respectively. This can take place up to three times per day and the transformation takes five segments. The elves take on all the movement rates and special abilities of these creatures, but they lose any spell-casting abilities they might normally have.

dark Elves

The outcasts of elven society, these are elves without a country and without a people. They are alone and beyond the society of all elves regardless of race. Only through the forgiveness of their own people can they again come back into the realms of the elvish people.

dark Elves
Game Statistics

The character class of Dark Elves cannot be chosen when a player creates a character. Characters enter this class when their actions cause them to be outlawed from elven society.

An elf who flagrantly violates his people's laws of conduct becomes a Dark Elf. The crime must be very serious and an offense against the ideals of the society. However, the most common way in which an elf becomes a Dark Elf is when his alignment shifts outside the range of those acceptable for his race.

Redemption can only occur after some demonstration of repentance by the Dark Elf. This should be treated in much the same way as with clerics who fall from grace with their deity. More specifically, the character's alignment must be brought back into line with those acceptable to his race and class.

half-Elves
appearance

Half-elves strongly resemble the racial stock of their elven parent, but they generally have facial hair (missing on all other elves) and a hair color that is not consistent with their elven heritage. They are generally more stocky than most elves and, while almost universally handsome or beautiful, lack the grace of their elven parentage.

history

The half-elves are considered "untrue elves" by all the other elven societies. They have no true history of their own but borrow it from their parentage.

The Kinslayer Wars were brought about, in part, due to the intermarriage of elves and humans in that region. During that time, half-elves in human society were considered a great blessing and brought honor to the human household. The elves, particularly the race-conscious Silvanesti, were revolted by these interracial marriages.

After the Cataclysm, there came a time of barbarism during which many elven towns were plundered and ransacked by human hordes. Many half-elves were engendered during this period of rapine and violence. The Silvanesti elves cast them from society as they would Dark Elves. Only the Qualinesti took them in and gave them a home, although even they were cold and sometimes cruel to these unfortunates.

It was, interestingly enough, one of these bastard half-elves who was partly responsible for the ultimate victory of the Whitestone Forces over the Dragonarmies. Tanis of Qualinost, who later married the Princess Laurana of Qualinesti, proved the worth of his unique race.

philosophies

As most half-elves are raised in an atmosphere of shame and scorn, it is little wonder that they generally display tendencies toward rebellion and anti-social activities. They are usually very insecure and seldom travel with others unless they feel accepted. They often overcompensate for this insecurity by performing acts of death-defying bravado.

Society

The half-elf is an outcast from the societies of both his parents. There is no society that consists solely of half-elves as they are primarily loners. If there is a home for a half-elf, it is in Qualinesti, where they are treated coldly but at least they have a place in the society.

half-Elves
Game Statistics

Generating Abilities: The initial ability rolls are modified by a +2 bonus to Dexterity. The minimum and maximum scores for half-elves are as follows:

Half-Elves Ability Scores

Ability	Minimum	Maximum
Strength	3	18
Intelligence	4	18
Wisdom	3	18
Dexterity	6	18
Constitution	6	18
Charisma	3	18

Half-Elf Class Limits

Class	Maximum Level
Cavalier	N/E *
Paladin	N/E *
Knight of the Crown	10
Knight of the Sword	10
Knight of the Rose	10
Fighter	9
Barbarian	N/E *
Ranger	11
Magic-User (Renegade)	7
Illusionist (Renegade)	N/E *
Wizard of High Sorcery	10
Thief	Unlim
Thief/Acrobat	Unlim
Cleric (Heathen)	5
Druid (Heathen)	Unlim
Holy Orders of the Stars	Unlim

* N/E means not eligible for that class.

DWARVES

According to the most reliable sources on the origins of Krynn's inhabitants, the dwarves of Krynn are descendants of the gnomes, created from that original stock by the magic of the Greystone of Gargath. This story is told in the beginning of this section (page 49).

The dwarves themselves, however, stubbornly cling to another view of their genesis. They believe that they were the last beings created by Reorx and that they were made in his image. Reorx, they say, learned from each of his creations until he knew the perfect form to make his own people—the dwarves, of course, represent this perfect form. While the rest of the continent accepts the Greystone theory over this tale, all know better than try to prove this point to a dwarf. The idea that dwarves are related to kender and gnomes is one that can cause a full-scale war with a dwarven nation.

There are other mysteries in the dwarven past as well. Long before the Empire of Istar blossomed, a great kingdom of dwarves known as the Kal-Thax existed that extended from Karthay into the very plains of Istar.

Quevalin Soth allegedly visited this realm in his travels and he supposedly wrote: "The kingdom left the ground above to its natural and pastoral state while below its surface was the greatest civilization my eyes have yet beheld. Unmeasured were its caverns, their depths untold and their beauty beyond description. And in all its splendor and wonder, never once was the nature of the gods tampered with. Millions upon millions of dwarves labored here in unity and peace; their works were beyond any to be found in all the realms of the sky!"

Similar tales from the Age of Might echo these remarks, although there still remains some question as to whether the kingdom actually existed or was simply a product of fanciful tales from that period.

Indeed, the reported remarks of Quevalin Soth may have been only a folk tale that was attributed to him. The tale continues to say that the kingdom vanished without a trace approximately 2800 PC and has passed beyond the knowledge of all Krynn. Their fate has long been the subject of speculation. Causes voiced range from the plague to being taken into the heavens by the gods. Astinus, the great historian of Krynn, remains oddly silent on this issue and refuses to confirm or deny the kingdom's existence.

Whatever the fate of this supposed kingdom, there were small colonies of dwarves that established underground residences in nearly every mountainous region on Ansalon.

Construction in Thorbardin began in about 2692 PC. This great dwarven kingdom was completed in 93 years. It soon began to spread its influence northward and ran into the Ergoth expansion in 2189 PC. The borders that were established between them held until the Ergoth expansion eastward ran into the Silvanesti borders. With nowhere else to establish new colonies, tensions between the dwarves and Ergoth began to heat up. The situation became uncontrollable in approximately 2142 PC when Ergoth began mining operations in the Kharolis mountains. Border clashes between the dwarves and the humans became more frequent.

In an effort to avoid another prolonged war (Ergoth had just fought the Kinslayer War), the Swordsheath Scroll was signed. This created a new state (Qualinesti) for the disaffected Silvanesti elves. Qualinesti was placed between the Thorbardin dwarves and the men of Ergoth to ease the friction between the two nations.

Much to everyone's surprise, the Qualinesti elves (who were more friendly to the dwarves than others had been) became fast allies of Thorbardin. As a symbol of the unity between the elves and dwarves, they jointly constructed Pax Tharkas in the pass between their nations.

Other dwarven kingdoms were also rising at this time. The kingdoms of Zhakar in the Khalkist Mountains and Kaolyn in the Darkenwal south of Solamnia both waxed in power as Thorbardin was completed. (Though Kaolyn suffered greatly from oppressive Ergothian rule and did not grow as quickly as the other kingdoms.) The dwarves of Zhaman saw the surface of Ansalon being claimed and fought over by many nations and did what dwarves do best—they took their kingdom underground where no nation would bother them.

These dwarven kingdoms were generally disinterested in the doings of the other races, as they were preoccupied with their own difficulties. This brought on great sufferings in dwarven nations at the time of the Cataclysm. While the full effects of this disaster on Kaolyn and Zhaman are not known, its effects at Thorbardin are well documented.

Thorbardin had become heavily dependent upon trade for her food supplies. These were received primarily from the Abanasinian Plains north of Pax Tharkas and from the elves of Qualinesti. Xak Tsaroth was a central city of trade for the southern plains and food was easy to purchase there. By this time, the dwarves not only had their great underground city but also many settlements above ground outside the gates of the mountain.

Having refused to become involved in the politics of the age, the dwarves were caught unaware by the Cataclysm. The extent of the dwarves' problem became quickly apparent to Duncan, king of the Thorbardin dwarves. His nation had only a small food reserve and he couldn't hope to feed both those inside the mountain and those in the fields beyond. He reasoned that the dwarves in the fields at least had a chance of surviving but that those inside had none if the food supply had to be divided among the entire nation. So he reluctantly ordered that the gates to the outside world be closed, leaving those dwarves who were outside the mountain to fend for themselves.

The hill dwarves, for that is what the dwarves who lived outside had come to be called, fled back toward the safety of their ancient capital only to find the gates shut to them and no answer to their pleas. The hill dwarves of that region call this deed the Great Betrayal, an act that sparked the still-smoldering hatred between the hill dwarves and the mountain dwarves of Thorbardin. The Dwarfgate Wars were an attempt by the hill dwarves and their human allies to retake Thorbardin.

To this day, most extant dwarf kingdoms remain shut against the outside world. Most dwarves that are commonly met are of hill dwarf descent. The hatred between these two groups still remains high.

> **Special Abilities of Krynn Dwarves:** The dwarves of Krynn have the special abilities granted dwarves as given in the *Player's Handbook*. This includes saving throw bonuses against magic and poisons, infravision, mining information skills, and combat bonuses against certain monsters.

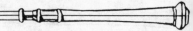

hill dwarves

appearance

Hill dwarves have deep tan to light brown skin and ruddy cheeks and bright eyes. Their hair is brown black or gray. They favor earth tones in their clothing although they will occasionally wear something bright. Hill dwarves have deep voices and actually sing quite well, but getting one to do so requires exceptional skill in diplomacy.

history

Hill dwarves were a part of the mainstream dwarven society until the Cataclysm. At that time, they were not permitted to return to their former homes and were forced to live permanently above ground. They have remained here more out of obstinacy than for lack of suitable mountains to delve.

Hill dwarves are considered Neidar dwarves by the mountain dwarves. This refers to their former clan status before being exiled from the mountain (see mountain dwarves below for further descriptions).

philosophies

Hill dwarves are as stubborn as their underground cousins (though each group claims to be more stubborn than the other). They tend to be rough and coarse and lack some of the refinement of their underground fellows. They complain often but usually do so to hide the fact that they have a rather pleasant and gentle nature.

society

Hill dwarves have small communities that live in above-ground villages. Unmarried hill dwarves often set out on their own, only occasionally returning to their original clan. The hill dwarves have maintained the clan system that dates from times long before the Cataclysm. They do not, however, come together in groups larger than their local clans as the clans tend to be suspicious, if not hostile to other clans.

hill dwarves
Game Statistics

Generating Abilities: The initial ability rolls are modified by a −1 penalty to Charisma and a +1 bonus to Constitution. The minimum and maximum ability scores for Hill Dwarves are as follows:

Hill Dwarf Ability Scores

Ability	Minimum	Maximum
Strength	9	18
Intelligence	3	18
Wisdom	3	18
Dexterity	3	17
Constitution	14	19
Charisma	3	12

Hill Dwarf Class Limits

Class	Maximum Level
Cavalier	N/E *
Paladin	N/E *
Knight of the Crown	N/E *
Knight of the Sword	N/E *
Knight of the Rose	N/E *
Fighter	Unlim
Barbarian	Unlim
Ranger	8
Magic-User (Renegade)	N/E *
Illusionist (Renegade)	N/E *
Wizard of High Sorcery	N/E *
Thief	10
Thief/Acrobat	15
Cleric (Heathen)	N/E *
Druid (Heathen)	N/E *
Holy Orders of the Stars	10

* N/E means not eligible for that class.

mountain dwarves

appearance

Mountain dwarves have light brown skin and smooth cheeks and bright eyes. Their hair is brown, black, gray, or occasionally white. They favor earth tones in their clothing.

Since mountain dwarves have a wide vocal range, communities often form choruses of dwarves that sing the traditional songs of the mountain dwarves. These songs can sometimes be heard echoing through the mountains where the dwarves live.

history

The history of the mountain dwarves is recounted at the beginning of this section. In recent years, some outsiders have gained entrance to the mountain kingdoms. At least one entire nation of refugees was allowed to move through the southern gate of Thorbardin after the group's extraordinary needs were presented to the ruling Council of Thanes.

philosophies

Communities of mountain dwarves have enough problems to keep them occupied without looking for more trouble in the outside world. With the number of classes and clans that exist within a community, there is continuous political friction between the various factions in the mountain. This keeps the dwarves too busy to pay much attention to the matters of the outside world. They are not interested in helping others or even in listening to their troubles unless they can be shown that the matter affects them somehow.

society

The dwarves of the mountains have traditionally been organized into clans. Each clan is led by a thane who acts as its representative to the Council of Thanes. The council consists of nine members. These nine chairs represent the following groups, each of which is thought of as a separate race.

Hylar: This is the oldest and most noble of the dwarven races. Most of the great dwarven kings have been Hylar. The Hylar traditionally live in the best accommodations that the nation can provide and are great craftsmen.

PC mountain dwarves are always of the Hylar clan.

Theiwar: These are a strange and degenerate race of dwarves. They hate light and indeed suffer from nausea in sunlight. Nevertheless, their dreams are of world conquest and domination. Of the dwarven races, they are the most concerned with spells and magic; most of their leaders have spell-casting abilities. The Theiwar consider themselves the highest of the dwarven races and seek to wrest leadership away from the controlling council. They want to take control by whatever means are necessary—including civil war.

Daewar: This clan is justly respected and

many important leaders have come from their midst. The Daewar are great fighters and were in the forefront of the Dwarfgate War at Thorbardin. Now they defer leadership to the Hylar but take an active interest in public safety and public works.

Daergar: These are dark dwarves who split off from the Theiwar many hundreds of years ago. Their culture flourished and is now widespread and powerful. They are, if possible, even more dangerous than their Theiwar cousins, favoring murder, torture, and thievery to get their way. Their leader is always the most powerful warrior of the Daergar kingdom, elected in a bloody combat to the death.

Neidar: The Neidar are hill dwarves who lived outside Thorbardin at the time of the Cataclysm. They are no longer represented in the Council of Thanes—a situation many hill dwarves would like to remedy.

Klar: The Klar are hill dwarves who lived inside Thorbardin at the time of the Dwarfgate War. Following the war, the Klar were deprived of property and persecuted terribly for their supposed sympathy for the Neidar (in fact, many Klar fought with bravery on the Hylar side). Now, they serve the wealthy dwarves of Thorbardin in menial roles. After centuries of suffering, they look for a leader to deliver them from their plight.

Aghar: These are gully dwarves. See that section for a description of this race. In the dwarven kingdoms they work in menial, dirty tasks, but that is all they are qualified to do. They have a seat on the council but the gully dwarf representative soon learns to just sit in his chair and not say or do anything. They generally sleep through such meetings, much to everyone's relief.

Kingdom of the Dead: The dwarves venerate their dead and consider the Kingdom of the Dead to be the 8th Kingdom. This has little practical effect on politics but has a profound effect on dwarven thinking about the afterlife. Dwarves use a variety of divination methods—some real, others only superstition—to contact their ancestors.

The High King: The High King is chosen by acclamation of the Council of Thanes and must be ordained by the people. The king can be from any clans, but he rules all of the clans.

Mountain Dwarves

Game Statistics

Generating Abilities: The initial ability rolls are modified by a −1 penalty to Charisma and a +1 bonus to Constitution. The minimum and maximum ability scores for mountain dwarves are as follows:

Mountain Dwarf Ability Scores

Ability	Minimum	Maximum
Strength	8	18
Intelligence	3	18
Wisdom	3	18
Dexterity	3	17
Constitution	12	19
Charisma	3	16

Mountain Dwarf Class Limits

Class	Maximum Level
Cavalier	8
Paladin	8
Knight of the Crown	N/E *
Knight of the Sword	N/E *
Knight of the Rose	N/E *
Fighter	Unlim
Barbarian	N/E *
Ranger	N/E *
Magic-User (Renegade)	N/E *
Illusionist (Renegade)	N/E *
Wizard of High Sorcery	N/E *
Thief	8
Thief/Acrobat	10
Cleric (Heathen)	N/E *
Druid (Heathen)	N/E *
Holy Orders of the Stars	10

* N/E means not eligible for that class.

Gully Dwarves (Aghar)

Appearance

Gully dwarves are short, squat demihumans, averaging four feet in height; they have an average weight of 100 lbs., give or take about 10 lbs. Females tend to be slightly smaller than males. Aghar are physically much like other dwarves, except that they are often covered with scars, boils, sores, and filth due to their living conditions.

Gully dwarves have skin tones ranging from olive brown to a light parchment color. Mot-

tled and splotched skin is not uncommon, and a few have a dirty gray-brown skin tone. Male gully dwarves wear long, scruffy beards; females have cheek hair but no beards. Hair color is usually dirty blond, brown, rust, gray, or dull black. Eye color can be watery blue, dull green, brown, or hazel.

Gully dwarves don't appear to be as heavy and stocky as other sorts of dwarves. They also have narrower fingers and limbs. Pot bellies are very common among both sexes, and gully dwarves develop wrinkles quickly after age 25.

History

Gully dwarves have an extensive oral tradition of their origins and history. Unfortunately, no two gully dwarf clans agree on any relevant details. The stories are very colorful and entertaining to others, though gully dwarves take them very seriously.

For our purposes, we turn to other sources. The tale of the Greystone of Gargath tells of how the dwarves and kender came into being. In the years that followed, a few intermarriages between gnomes and dwarves occurred in isolated communities across Ansalon. Surprisingly, the children of such marriages proved to be of an entirely new race, with their own particular characteristics. The members of this new race lacked all the better qualities of their parents.

Further intermarriages were banned by dwarven and gnomish societies. Members of this new race were driven out of their own clans, particularly by the dwarves, who regarded them as a blight. This new dwarven race became known as the Aghar ("the anguished"). Humans later christened them gully dwarves, noting the race's low status and poor living conditions.

The Cataclysm was at once the curse of the world and the salvation of the gully dwarves. The destruction of civilization in Ansalon opened up dozens of deserted, ruined cities to habitation by wandering gully dwarf tribes. Soon once-mighty towns like Xak Tsaroth became havens for the Aghar. Undisturbed by the rest of the world, the gully dwarves were free to establish their own cultures—such as they were.

Philosophies

The most important facets of a gully dwarf's personality are generally agreed to be survival instinct, pride, endurance, and stupidity. Though derided by other intelligent races of Ansalon, gully dwarves continue to thrive

under conditions that would have broken many others.

Gully dwarves are born to survive; they skillfully avoid exposing themselves to harm and regard cowardice as a virtue. Groveling has been raised to the level of an art form in their society.

The stupidity of gully dwarves is legendary. They can grasp the concept of a single item and of a group of items, but they cannot distinguish between large groups and small groups. Most Aghar don't recognize numbers greater than one, which may derive from the fact that they do not recognize the needs of anyone other than themselves. Any number greater than one is called "two," which simply means "more than one."

Although considered foolish by all other races, gully dwarves are a proud folk and act with great seriousness. They tend to have inflated ideas of their own places in the grand scheme of things; puncturing their egos is an almost impossible task.

Society

Gully dwarf communities are usually quite small. Aghar prefer to live in extended family units, called clans, which have 2-20 members. Some very large clans can have up to 60 members. Most live in villages abandoned by previous owners or in the wilderness in old mines and caves. Small clans may live in the slums and refuse dumps of large cities; several major cities in Ansalon have gully dwarves living in their sewer systems. The leader of a clan is responsible for keeping the family together and is the sole voice of authority (although his authority is frequently questioned).

Occasionally, several clans live together, usually in a ruined or abandoned city. Major Aghar communities hold between 40 and 400 adult dwarves and a similar amount of children. At least two clans are present and sometimes as many as five.

Each clan has a chieftain and the strongest, cleverest, and most charismatic of these chieftains becomes the local king. Kings are served by bodyguards and by a completely chaotic hierarchy of lesser functionaries with no clearly defined roles or duties.

Because of gully dwarves' egotism and inability to count, it is not unusual to find a succession of kings with the same name, each calling himself "the First."

Gully Dwarves

Game Statistics

Generating Abilities: The initial abilities for a gully dwarf are generated using special dice rolls, to reflect their unique nature. The following table shows maximum and minimum ability scores well as the dice to roll:

Gully Dwarf Ability Scores

Ability Roll	Minimum	Maximum
Strength 4d4 + 2	6	18
Intelligence 2d4 + 1	3	9
Wisdom 2d4 + 1	3	9
Dexterity 4d4 + 2	6	18
Constitution 3d4	3	12
Charisma 2d4 + 1	3	9

Gully Dwarf Class Limits

Class	Maximum Level
Cavalier	N/E *
Paladin	N/E *
Knight of the Crown	N/E *
Knight of the Sword	N/E *
Knight of the Rose	N/E *
Fighter	6
Barbarian	7
Ranger	N/E *
Magic-User (Renegade)	N/E *
Illusionist (Renegade)	N/E *
Wizard of High Sorcery	N/E *
Thief	8
Thief/Acrobat	8
Cleric (Heathen)	N/E *
Druid (Heathen)	N/E *
Holy Orders of the Stars	5

* N/E means not eligible for that class.

Irda

Appearance

The Irda are tall, slender creatures, averaging six feet in height. The females tend to be as tall as the males. Although slender, their strength is readily apparent in their strong musculature. Their skin tones range from midnight blue to a deep sea green. Their hair is often black but sometimes silver or white; it is always carefully combed and kept. Their drawn faces and drooping eyelids give the impression that they are bored or uncaring. Their eyes are almost always silver-colored.

The Irda move with a fluid motion so graceful that it is a joy to watch. Their voices are the most extraordinary in Krynn, rivaled only by those of the sirens.

The Irda have innate *shapechanging* abilities and can disguise their size and true nature in many ways. They can change their height by as much as two feet and can attain the features of any humanoid race (particularly elves, half-elves, and humans). This *shapechanging* ability requires several years of practice to perfect. Usually Irda learn to *shapechange* into one form perfectly and then use that form over and over.

History

During the Age of Dreams, the newly created beings of Krynn awoke to the first dawn of the world. Legends from that time (mostly passed down through elven bards) say the elves were the first to awaken. This was not so: the ogres were the first.

In the dawn of the world, the ogres were the fairest of the races and were truly immortal. Their dark grace and cold beauty was unsurpassed by any of the races that arose. Yet their hearts were cold and bent toward evil.

The *Irdanaiath*, a book unknown among men of Ansalon, tells a tale of the most ancient days. When ogres walked the world in beauty and power, men awoke and had dealings with this evil race. In this exchange, the humans unwittingly gifted Igrane, a great and powerful ogre clanleader, with free will. For this Igrane both cursed and blessed men, for he looked upon the world with new eyes.

The gift spread among his clansmen until they all saw the curse of evil and the future of

destruction and debasement that it held for them. They tried to convince other ogre clans of their folly but kindled anger. Civil war erupted among the ogres. The Ogre Wars of the Age of Dreams were fought in places hidden from the eyes of men.

So it came to be that the Irda, as the enlightened ogres called themselves, removed themselves from contact with the rest of the world. The Irda found a haven on a distant isle and confused the way behind them so that they might live undisturbed. The ogres who did not foresee their debasement eventually fulfilled the Irda's vision and became uglier and more misshapen until their appearance matched the evil in their hearts.

With the coming of the Cataclysm and the War of the Lance, the Irda were forced to recant their policy of total isolation. Now they have begun to send their people into the world to establish a tentative contact with other nations of the world.

philosophies

The Irda are a peaceful race who mean no harm to the world at large. They only wish to gather their lost children (those Irda captured by the Dragonarmies during the War of the Lance—see below) back to the hidden isle of the Irda.

The Irda's biggest difficulty is the superstitions that men have developed about them over the years. Tales are told of the terrible, ancient ogres who would return one day to bring death and destruction. Irda who have been discovered are almost always hunted by the populace. Evil beings who try to ally with the Irda soon find out that the Irda are good and try to destroy them as well.

Society

The Irda have been ruled by an unbroken chain of royal lineage since the beginning of the world. Except for the *Irdanaiath*, they keep no historical records. The balance of their writings contains reflections on their conditions and general observations on natural sciences and the arts. The Irda live on an island some distance north of Ansalon. It is here that they have sheltered from a barbaric and unsympathetic world.

Their life of pastoral bliss was, however, upset by the Cataclysm. With the reappearance of dragons in Krynn, the Irda's home was soon discovered by the servants of the Queen of Darkness. The Queen had been much aggrieved by the loss of the Irda in the begin-

ning of the world. She now sought to destroy them. The battle was fought by titanic magical forces and the Dark Queen's attack was eventually repelled, but not before many Irda were captured and taken to Ansalon.

When the War of the Lance ended, many of the surviving captives were freed. Those Irda now wander the land in disguise trying to find their way back to their homeland. They are usually alone, but occasionally small groups of two to 10 Irda are found traveling the lands of Ansalon. Families are sometimes encountered; the parents' fondest wish is to find a way to their island home, if not for themselves, then at least for their children.

The relative security of their island enabled the Irda to hone their magical skills to a fine art. Combat skills, however, are uncommon among them.

A variety of magics protect their island from being found, but the wandering Irda can hear the telepathic call of their homeland during High Sanction for Solinari. During these times they can find their way across the sea to their home (but only if they have the means to cross the sea). Unfortunately the journey lasts far longer than the duration of High Sanction and few lost Irda ever return to their homeland on their own.

Irda
Game Statistics

Generating Abilities: The initial ability rolls are modified by a -2 penalty to Constitution and a $+2$ bonus to Dexterity, Intelligence, and Charisma. The minimum and maximum scores for Irda are as follows:

Irda Ability Scores

Ability	Minimum	Maximum
Strength	12	18
Intelligence	5	20
Wisdom	10	18
Dexterity	8	20
Constitution	12	16
Charisma	15	20

Irda Class Limits

Class	Maximum Level
Cavalier	Unlim
Paladin	Unlim
Knight of the Crown	N/E *
Knight of the Sword	N/E *
Knight of the Rose	N/E *
Fighter	Unlim
Barbarian	N/E *
Ranger	Unlim
Magic-User (Renegade)	N/E *
Illusionist (Renegade)	N/E *
Wizard of High Sorcery	Unlim
Thief	Unlim
Thief/Acrobat	Unlim
Cleric (Heathen)	N/E *
Druid (Heathen)	N/E *
Holy Orders of the Stars	Unlim

* N/E means not eligible for that class.

Special Abilities: The Irda are the only race that can learn *shapechanging* as a proficiency. In addition, due to their special knowledge of magic and its workings, each cleric or wizard gains one additional spell of the highest level he can cast.

krynn minotaurs
appearance

Krynn minotaurs are gargantuan brutes over seven feet in height. They have short fur covering their massive muscles; the fur ranges from a red brown to almost black. Their faces are brutish and ugly by human standards, reminiscent of those of bulls. They have short horns that grow from their edges of their foreheads to a length of six to 12 inches for the females and one to two feet for the males.

Minotaurs wear clothing, usually a harness and leather skirt. The harness carries weapons in convenient locations as well as decorations from previous battles and victories. The minotaurs' favorite weapon is a double-edged axe, although many minotaurs have been known to use a broad sword in each hand.

Minotaurs were created during the Greystone's passage through Ansalon and are descended from the original ogres. Suggesting to a minotaur that he is descended from a cow (a common mistake for humans) is the deadliest insult one can offer a minotaur.

history

The minotaur race has been oppressed through most of its history. The legends of the minotaurs speak of the time during the Age of Twilight when their nation was enslaved by the Kal-Thax dwarves. The legends say that the minotaurs destroyed that dwarven nation, but most scholars tend to dismiss this claim.

The minotaurs dwelt in scattered groups without a nation or identity until late in the

Age of Twilight when they began to gather in the eastern regions of Istar. There they established the first minotaur kingdoms of Mithas and Kothas. Two kingdoms seemed a better idea to the competitive minotaurs. They soon developed shipbuilding to a fine art and their navigational skills remain some of the finest in the world.

This time of power was soon to end. With the advent of the Istar Empire, once again the minotaurs were brought into slavery, though at a great price to both armies. This continued until the Cataclysm, which the minotaurs saw as divine intervention on their behalf. The minotaurs soon afterward set sail for the newly created islands that were all that was left of Mithas and Kothas. With their nations now separated from the land by the Bloodsea, they could attain the true power they always knew they deserved.

philosophies

Minotaurs firmly believe in the superiority of their race and in their ultimate place as the rulers of the world. It is their destiny to bring the rest of Krynn under their rule.

They will go to any lengths to achieve domination over others. They are ruthless in battle and cold in their justice. They believe that the weak should perish and that might proves right. It is, to them, the natural process of life.

From their youth, minotaurs are trained for strength, cunning, and intelligence. The goal of this training is combat in the Circus, an annual contest that acts as a minotaur's rite of passage into adult society.

Society

Minotaur society is built upon the principle that might makes right and that no consideration of justice is necessary. The minotaurs are lead by an emperor who resides in the city of Nethosak on Mithas. Under the emperor is a Supreme Circle of eight minotaurs. The Supreme Circle deals with the day-to-day administration of the government. All posts are won by the strongest and cleverest minotaurs as proved by combat in the Circus. (All determinations of rank and justice take place in the Circus.)

Minotaurs claim to have the only truly classless society. Anyone can become the emperor—all he has to do is defeat the current emperor in single combat in the Circus. Minotaurs are trained from youth for specialized roles to which they seem most suited. This most often involves seamanship.

Families are the foundation of minotaur society; the honor of one's family is held supreme above all other considerations. Minotaur clerics invariably worship only one god: Sargas. This god is known as Sargonnas to the Solamnics.

kRynn mINotauRS

Game StatIStIcS

Generating Abilities: The initial ability rolls are modified by a −2 penalty to Wisdom and Charisma and a +2 bonus to Strength and Constitution. The minimum and maximum scores for minotaurs are as follows:

Krynn Minotaur Ability Scores

Ability	Minimum	Maximum
Strength	12	20
Intelligence	5	18
Wisdom	3	16
Dexterity	8	18
Constitution	12	20
Charisma	3	16

Krynn Minotaur Class Limits

Class	Maximum Level
Cavalier	N/E *
Paladin	N/E *
Knight of the Crown	N/E *
Knight of the Sword	N/E *
Knight of the Rose	N/E *
Fighter	Unlim
Barbarian	Unlim
Ranger	8
Magic-User (Renegade)	N/E *
Illusionist (Renegade)	N/E *
Wizard of High Sorcery	14
Thief	N/E *
Thief/Acrobat	N/E *
Cleric (Heathen)	N/E *
Druid (Heathen)	N/E *
Holy Orders of the Stars	10

* N/E means not eligible for that class.

character proficiencies

nonweapon proficiencies

Choosing Skills: The selection of nonweapon proficiencies for a character is basically up to the player. However, in the interest of faithful and accurate role playing, it is recommended that the player take into account the background of his character. This should eliminate initial nonweapon proficiencies that are illogical for that character.

The player should also be careful when selecting proficiencies as his character gains experience levels and becomes eligible for more proficiencies. Unless a character has spent a lot of time with dragons, for example, he should not acquire proficiency in dragon riding.

Ultimately, all proficiency selections are subject to the approval of the Dungeon Master. If he feels that a player character's proficiency selection is illogical, then he is obligated to refuse to allow that selection.

Success and Failure: Having a nonweapon proficiency does not mean that the character automatically succeeds in actions governed by that proficiency. Depending upon the particular proficiency or the circumstances surrounding the use of the proficiency, it is sometimes necessary for a character to make a successful Proficiency Check to use the skill.

A Proficiency Check is accomplished in the same way as an Ability Check. The player rolls 1d20, applies any modifiers, and compares the result to the character's ability score that relates to the proficiency being used. If the modified die roll result is less than or equal to the score of the appropriate ability, the Proficiency Check is successful. (In certain circumstances, the Dungeon Master rolls the Proficiency Check and he may or may not reveal the result to the player.)

Any die roll of 19 or 20 on a Proficiency Check indicates automatic failure, even if modifiers would bring the result down into the range needed for success. Also, for the purpose of a Proficiency Check, any ability score greater than 18 is treated as an 18. This means that a character with an ability score of 18 or greater always has at least a 10% chance (2 in 20) of failing a Proficiency Check.

Improving Proficiencies: When a character gains an additional nonweapon proficiency slot at 3d and higher levels, the player can improve the character's ability in an existing proficiency rather than acquire a new proficiency. If a proficiency slot is used to improve an existing proficiency, the character receives an automatic die-roll modifier of −2 on all subsequent Proficiency Checks for that proficiency. A roll of 19 or 20 still means failure, however.

If the player desires further improvement, additional die-roll modifiers of −2 are applied for every additional proficiency slot dedicated to this proficiency.

The proficiencies that can be used in Krynn are as follows:

DRAGONLANCE® Saga Proficiencies

Proficiency	Slots Req.	Approp. Ability	Found in Book
Alertness	1	Wis	WSG
Animal Handling	1	Wis	WSG
Animal Lore	1	Int	WSG
Animal Noise	1	Wis	DSG
Animal Trainer	1*	Wis	DSG
Armorer	2*	Int	DSG
Astrology	2	Int	DLA
Blacksmith	1	Str	DSG
Blind-fighting	1	—	DSG
Boating	1	Wis	DSG
Boatwright	1	Int	DSG
Bowyer/Fletcher	1*	Dex	DSG
Carpenter	1	Str	DSG
Charioteering	1	Dex	WSG
Direction Sense	1	Wis	DSG
Endurance	2	—	DSG
Fire-building	1	Wis	DSG
Fishing	1*	Wis	DSG
Foraging	1	Int	WSG
Fungus Identif.	1	Int	DSG
Gem Cutter	2	Dex	DSG
Healing	2*	Wis	DSG
Hunting	1	Wis	WSG
Leatherworker	1	Int	DSG
Miner	2*	Wis	DSG
Mountaineering	1	—	DSG
Plant Lore	1	Int	WSG
Potter	1	Dex	DSG
Riding, Airborne	2	Wis	WSG
Riding, Dragons	2	Dex	DLA
Riding, Land-based	1	Wis	DSG
Rope Use	1	Dex	DSG
Running	2	Con	WSG
Slow Respiration	1	—	DSG
Smelter	1	Int	DSG
Sound Analysis	1	Wis	DSG
Stonemason	1	Str	DSG
Survival, Cold	1	—	WSG
Survival, Desert	2	—	WSG
Survival, Heat	1	—	WSG
Swimming	1	Str	DSG
Tracking	1	—	WSG
Weaponsmith	3*	Int	DSG
Weather Sense	1	Wis	WSG

* These require a Proficiency Check each time they are used.

Books in Table:
DSG = *Dungeoneer's Survival Guide*
WSG = *Wilderness Survival Guide*
DLA = *DRAGONLANCE Adventures*

The airborne riding proficiency covers riding creatures such as griffins, pegasi, and the like, but not dragons. Dragon riding is treated as a separate proficiency.

new proficiencies

Astrology: This proficiency enables a character to read the stars for information concerning his future. The Proficiency Check is made by the DM. If successful, the character sees a general condition that he is likely to encounter within the next 30 days. This may be a great battle, an enemy who will become a friend, an important encounter, etc. If unsuccessful, then the attempt gives similar information but it is inaccurate.

Dragon Riding: This is identical to airborne riding except it deals exclusively with dragons. A character needs to check this skill when attempting combat on dragonback with a mounted lance or when he is attempting special maneuvers (such as a loop) with his dragon.

CREATURES OF KRYNN

Common Creatures of Ansalon

Much has already been said about the origins of the unusual races of Krynn. Many creatures that are common to other worlds are also found in Ansalon. These creatures are best described in other books. However, the statistics for most creatures of Krynn can be found on page 115 and 116.

Unique Creatures of Ansalon

While most creatures encountered on Krynn are commonly found in many universes, there are also many that are special to this universe alone. Such special creatures are presented here in greater detail.

Draconians

Draconians, or Dragonmen, are the special troops of the Dragon Highlords. They are more predictable than human forces and more apt to follow orders than the ogres and goblins that make up the bulk of the army. Draconians are not frightened by dragon awe, rather they seem to rally around the evil dragons. There are five types of Draconians: the stony Baaz, the magic-wielding Bozaks, the poison-tongued Kapaks, the shape-shifting Sivaks, and the mind-bending Auraks.

The first four types of draconians have wings, but of these only the Sivaks can truly fly. They move either by walking upright, gliding down from heights, or running on all fours while flapping their wings. This latter form of movement enables them to move very fast along the ground (see the bracketed movement rates under "Move" in the listings of draconians' statistics) and the dust cloud kicked up by their wings makes them a very intimidating sight in battle. The fifth type of draconian, Auraks, have no wings but possess a limited *dimension door* ability.

Draconians serve many roles for the Dragon Highlords. Kapaks, wielding poison blade and arrow, are used as assassins and archers. The magic-using Bozaks are used as special forces and as commanders of squads of Baaz. Sivaks form the elite forces, wearing heavy armor and easily swinging two-handed

swords. Baaz are the common soldiers, the bulk of the troops. They are often used as scouts since they can disguise themselves in robes. The Auraks are rare and special generals of the draconian armies. They are also used as special agents who can pass undetected among humans.

Draconians are created by corrupting good dragon eggs. Baaz are derived from brass eggs, Bozaks from bronze eggs, Kapaks from copper eggs, Sivaks from silver eggs, and Auraks from gold eggs. These are the eggs that the Queen of Darkness swore to protect in return for the good dragons' pledge not to interfere in her war against the peoples of Krynn.

The corruption of the eggs is the work of an evil triad, Wyrllish the cleric, Dracart the mage, and the ancient red dragon Harkiel, the Bender. Through arcane spells they cause the eggs to grow and their occupants to multiply. Then Wyrllish opens the gate to the Abyss and the abishai, the Dark Queen's minions, rush forth to inhabit the new bodies. Draconians are creatures of magical origin and when they are slain, the odd enchantments that formed them create spectacular death scenes (see the draconian descriptions).

While units of draconians are often found in evil human armies, they remain aloof from other races. They answer directly to the Queen of Darkness despite the command structure of the army they are in.

Auraks

Auraks are the special agents of the Dragon Highlords. They are the most powerful of all draconians and the most devious. In natural form, Auraks appear to be 7-foot-tall, sinewy draconians with short tails and no wings.

Auraks cannot fly, but they move as fast as other draconians on the ground. Auraks possess a limited ability to *dimension door* three times per day at will. Their most feared form of attack is their mind control (see page 74).

Auraks	
FREQUENCY:	Rare
# APPEARING:	1-2
ARMOR CLASS:	0
MOVE:	15″
HIT DICE:	8
% IN LAIR:	10%
TREASURE TYPE:	K, L, N, V
# ATTACKS:	2 or 1
DAMAGE:	1d8 + 2 (x2) or spell
SPECIAL ATTACKS:	Spells & Breath
SPECIAL DEFENSES:	Save at +4
MAGIC RESISTANCE:	30%
INTELLIGENCE:	Exceptional
ALIGNMENT:	Lawful Evil
SIZE:	M (7 ft.)
XP VALUE:	1,800 + 10/hp

Auraks can *dimension door* up to 6″ away, three times per day at will.

The senses of Auraks are heightened so that they have infravision good to 60 feet, and can *detect hidden* and *invisible* creatures within 4″. They can also see through all illusions. Auraks have several natural defenses that they can invoke at will. They can turn *invisible* once each turn until they attack. They can *polymorph self* into the shape of any animal their size, three times per day. But the most diabolical ability is to *change self* three times per day to resemble any human or humanoid and to perfectly imitate its voice. This effect only lasts for 2d6 + 6 rounds.

Auraks have three modes of attack. They can generate blasts of energy from each of their hands (1d8 + 2 points of damage with each), striking targets up to 6″ away. When using *change self*, they appear to be using an appropriate weapon, but are really attacking with energy blasts. They can also attack with claws and fangs (1d4/1d4/1d6). Three times per day they can breathe a noxious cloud (five-foot range). Victims caught in the cloud must roll a successful saving throw vs. breath weapon (for half damage) or suffer 20 points of

73

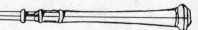

damage and be blinded for 1d4 rounds.

Auraks can also cast two 1st- to 4th-level magic-user spells. Their preferred spells include these: *enlarge, shocking grasp, ESP, stinking cloud, blink, lightning bolt, fire shield,* and *wall of fire.*

The Auraks' most insidious power is mind control. They can use *suggestion* once per turn at will, but they must concentrate. And once per day they can *mind control* one creature of equal or fewer hit dice for 2d6 rounds through unbroken concentration. *Mind control* lets the caster control the actions of the target as if it were his own body. The target must roll a successful saving throw vs. breath weapon to avoid the effect.

When an Aurak reaches 0 hit points, it does not die, but immolates itself with eerie green flames and enters a fighting frenzy (+2 to hit and damage). Anyone attacking it suffers 1d6 points of damage each round from the flames, unless a successful saving throw vs. petrification is rolled. Six rounds later, or when the creature reaches −20 hit points, it transforms into a whizzing ball of lightning, striking as a 13-HD monster and causing 2d6 points of damage to those struck. Three rounds later it explodes with a thunderous boom, stunning all within 10 feet for 1d4 rounds (2d4 if underwater) and causing 3d6 points of damage to all within 10 feet (no saving throw allowed). Any items within range must save vs. crushing blow or be destroyed.

when they can get away with it. Baaz are often encountered in disguise. They conceal their wings under robes and, wearing large hoods and masks, pass through civilized lands as spies.

Baaz

FREQUENCY: Uncommon
APPEARING: 2d10
ARMOR CLASS: 4
MOVE: 6″/[15″]/18″
HIT DICE: 2
% IN LAIR: 5%
TREASURE TYPE: J, K, L, U
ATTACKS: 2 or 1
DAMAGE: 1d4/1d4 or by weapon
SPECIAL ATTACKS: None
SPECIAL DEFENSES: None
MAGIC RESISTANCE: 20%
INTELLIGENCE: Average
ALIGNMENT: Lawful Evil (Chaotic)
SIZE: M (5½ ft.)
XP VALUE: 81 + 1/hp

When a Baaz reaches 0 hit points, it turns into a stone statue. The person who struck the death blow must make a successful Dexterity Check with a −3 penalty or his weapon is stuck in the statue. The statue crumbles to dust within 1d4 rounds, freeing the weapon. Its armor and weapons remain.

Bozaks

Bozaks are magic wielders and can cast spells as 4th-level magic users. They are cruel and very cunning warriors, sparing a life only if it benefits them. Their favored spells: *burning hands, enlarge, magic missile, shocking grasp, invisibility, levitate, stinking cloud,* and *web.*

Bozaks

FREQUENCY: Uncommon
APPEARING: 2d10
ARMOR CLASS: 2
MOVE: 6″/[15″]/18″
HIT DICE: 4
% IN LAIR: 15%
TREASURE TYPE: U
ATTACKS: 2 or 1
DAMAGE: 1d4/1d4 or by weapon
SPECIAL ATTACKS: Spells
SPECIAL DEFENSES: Saves at +2
MAGIC RESISTANCE: 20%
INTELLIGENCE: High
ALIGNMENT: Lawful Evil
SIZE: M (6 ft. +)
XP VALUE: 175 + 4/hp

When a Bozak reaches 0 hit points, its scaly flesh shrivels and crumbles from its bones in a cloud of dust. Then the bones explode, causing 1d6 points of damage to all within 10 feet (no saving throw).

Kapaks

Kapaks are distinguished by their venomous saliva. They often lick their weapons before attacking.

Kapaks are larger than Baaz and often bully and abuse their smaller cousins. Because of the Kapak's venomous nature, the Dragon Highlords employ these draconians as assassins as well as warriors. Kapaks are sly and conniving, seeking to lure prey into traps and tripping foes to gain an advantage.

Baaz

Baaz are the smallest and most plentiful of draconians. They are the Dragon Highlords' common ground troops. At the bottom of the draconian social order, these draconians often tend to be chaotic in nature and self-serving

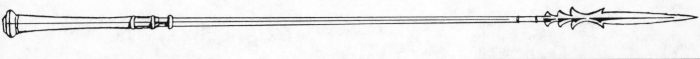

ALIGNMENT: Neutral Evil
SIZE: L (9 ft.)
XP VALUE: 350 + 6/hp

Sivaks who are killed by creatures larger than themselves will burst into flames, causing 2d4 points of damage to all within 10 feet (no saving throw), rather than change form.

Dreamshadows

Dreamshadows are the creations of a *mindspin* spell. Dreamshadows take the shape and appearance of any real person or creature known to the dreamer or to anyone experiencing the dream. These incarnations are quite believable and in all ways appear to be the real person. Dreamshadows are, however, only illusionary and cause only illusionary damage.

Dreamshadows can be of any alignment and can be either harmful or helpful to those who experience them.

Dreamshadows

% IN LAIR: 100%
TREASURE TYPE: As for person mimicked but illusionary.
DAMAGE: As for person mimicked but illusionary.
MAGIC RESISTANCE: By dream level of the *mindspin*: Normal/10%/20%
INTELLIGENCE: As the dreamer
XP VALUE: As creature mimicked + 10%

All other statistics for this creature are the same as those of the person or creature being mimicked.

Dreamwraiths

Dreamwraiths are the violent creations of the subconscious. These creatures can appear in many forms, almost always horrible and frightening. Freed through the evil influences of a *mindspin* spell, they attack the minds of their victims through illusion.

Dreamwraiths attack with terrible swiftness and with the fury of a berserk fanatic.

Dreamwraiths are not undead and therefore cannot be *turned* by clerics. They are illusionary, however, and if their illusion is discovered, their blows do no harm to the nonbeliever. Because the *mindspin* spell weaves real people into its illusion, maintaining disbelief in these creatures is nearly impossible (−5 penalty to the check).

Kapaks

FREQUENCY: Uncommon
APPEARING: 2d10
ARMOR CLASS: 4
MOVE: 6"/[15"]/18"
HIT DICE: 3
% IN LAIR: 15%
TREASURE TYPE: K, L, M
ATTACKS: 1
DAMAGE: 1d4
SPECIAL ATTACKS: Poison
SPECIAL DEFENSES: Acid Pool
MAGIC RESISTANCE: 20%
INTELLIGENCE: Average
ALIGNMENT: Lawful Evil
SIZE: M (6 ft.)
XP VALUE: 105 + 3/hp

The paralysis induced by a Kapak's poison lasts for 2d6 turns if the victim fails his saving throw vs. poison. Weapons licked with poison remain poisoned for only three rounds.

When a Kapak reaches 0 hit points, its body instantly dissolves into a 10-foot-wide pool of acid. All within the acid pool take 1d8 points of damage each round they remain there. The acid evaporates in 1d6 rounds. All items possessed by the Kapak are useless thereafter.

Sivaks

Sivaks are some of the most powerful draconians, second only to the Auraks. They are useful both on the battlefield and as advance infiltrators in areas such as Ergoth or western Solamnia where people are suspicious of the robed Baaz. Sivaks normally attack with two wicked-edged swords, but are just as dangerous with their claws. In addition, they attack with long, armored tails. They can only use this attack when in draconian form.

Sivaks are shapeshifters, capable of changing their form under two specific conditions. When a Sivak slays a humanoid of its size or smaller, it may take the form of its victim. The Sivak does not gain the memories, experiences, or spell use of the victim and, like all draconians, radiates magic, but its appearance and voice are exact matches to those of its victim. The Sivak can change back to its normal form, but after doing so cannot *polymorph* again until it kills another humanoid. A Sivak will also change shape when it is slain—it assumes the form of the creature that killed it. This death-shape lasts for three days, then the entire body decomposes into black soot.

Sivaks

FREQUENCY: Uncommon
APPEARING: 2d10
ARMOR CLASS: 1
MOVE: 6"/[15"]/18"
HIT DICE: 6
% IN LAIR: 10%
TREASURE TYPE: Q
ATTACKS: 3
DAMAGE: 1d6/1d6/2d6
SPECIAL ATTACKS: None
SPECIAL DEFENSES: +2 on Saves
MAGIC RESISTANCE: 20%
INTELLIGENCE: High

Dreamwraiths

FREQUENCY: Very Rare
APPEARING: 1-400
ARMOR CLASS: 3
MOVE: Variable
HIT DICE: 8
% IN LAIR: 100%
TREASURE TYPE: Nil
ATTACKS: 1
DAMAGE: 1d10 (illusionary)
SPECIAL ATTACKS: Illusionary Weapons
SPECIAL DEFENSES: Nil
MAGIC RESISTANCE: By dream level of mind spin: Normal/10%/20%
INTELLIGENCE: Of the person dreaming
ALIGNMENT: Chaotic Evil
SIZE: Variable
XP VALUE: Variable

Dreamwraiths gain a +1 bonus to every initiative check. Checks for disbelief must be made separately for each group of dreamwraiths encountered.

Fetch

Fetch are the harbingers of death. Existing on the fringes of the Abyss, these creatures can only reach into our world through reflective surfaces (mirrors, calm pools, etc.).

A fetch appears to be a haggard and deathly pale imitation of the person gazing into the surface. To the person gazing at their reflection, the fetch appears to be standing immediately behind them. A fetch attacks with stunning speed, using an exact replica of the weapon of its victim (this replica disappears if the fetch is killed).

Fetch are always invisible, even while attacking, to all but their victim. The victim can only see the fetch by looking in the reflective surface.

The chilling touch of a fetch drains the essence of life from the victim with horrific speed.

Fetch

FREQUENCY: Very Rare
APPEARING: 1
ARMOR CLASS: 4
MOVE: 6"
HIT DICE: 9
% IN LAIR: 100%
TREASURE TYPE: Nil
ATTACKS: 2
DAMAGE: Special
SPECIAL ATTACKS: Drains 2 levels per hit
SPECIAL DEFENSES: Invisible except to victim
MAGIC RESISTANCE: Normal
INTELLIGENCE: High
ALIGNMENT: Chaotic Evil
SIZE: M
XP VALUE: 650 + 10/hp

A fetch attacks twice per melee round. The victim can only see the fetch by looking into the reflective surface. Thus the victim suffers a penalty of −2 to hit and +2 to their AC. All others suffer a −4 penalty to hit the invisible fetch.

Ice Bears

These great white bears are carnivores whose diet consists mainly of fish. Any other prey that stumbles into an ice bear's path is likely to be consumed as well, however. While their color is that of a polar bear, ice bears more closely resemble cave bears in size and ferocity.

Ice bears have an uncanny ability to track prey over snow and ice, and the thanoi use them for this purpose, sharing the reward, if any, with the bears.

Ice Bears

FREQUENCY: Uncommon
APPEARING: 1d4
ARMOR CLASS: 6
MOVE: 12"
HIT DICE: 6+2
% IN LAIR: Nil
TREASURE TYPE: Nil
ATTACKS: 3 (claw/claw/bite)
DAMAGE: 1d8/1d8/2d8
SPECIAL ATTACKS: Hugs for 2d6 if both claws hit
SPECIAL DEFENSES: Immune to cold
MAGIC RESISTANCE: Standard
INTELLIGENCE: Semi-intelligent
ALIGNMENT: Neutral
SIZE: L (12 + feet)
XP VALUE: 475 + 8/hp

If no new snow has fallen since a track was made, an ice bear has a 100% chance to follow a trail one day old or less. For each day since the trail was made, subtract 10%. Subtract 10% for every inch of snow that has fallen. A 1d100 roll must be made once per day—if successful the ice bear can follow the trail for the entire day, otherwise the trail is lost forever.

Bloodsea Minotaurs

Minotaurs on Krynn are a highly organized warrior race that operates from bases on the islands of Mithas and Kothas on the eastern borders of the Bloodsea. The minotaurs believe themselves to be superior to the other races of Krynn—it is their destiny to conquer and enslave the world. Minotaurs of Krynn will ally with adventurers if they can be convinced that this serves their own purposes. See the section on minotaurs (page 69) under *Races of Krynn* for more details.

Bloodsea Minotaurs

FREQUENCY: Rare
APPEARING: 1d8
ARMOR CLASS: 4
MOVE: 12"
HIT DICE: 8+4
% IN LAIR: 10% (80% on home isles)
TREASURE TYPE: C
ATTACKS: 2
DAMAGE: 2d4 or by weapon type
SPECIAL ATTACKS: Nil
SPECIAL DEFENSES: Surprised only on a 1
MAGIC RESISTANCE: Standard
INTELLIGENCE: High
ALIGNMENT: Lawful Evil
SIZE: L
XP VALUE: 600 + 12/hp

Shadowpeople

The shadowpeople are a race of mammals that has dwelled in Sanction since the city was founded, centuries before the Cataclysm. Their existence has always been rumored, but never proven to the satisfaction of scholars.

Shadowpeople dwell almost exclusively underground and suffer greatly in the light of the sun. Under an overcast sky (the usual weather conditions in Sanction), they can operate but do so in great pain. This pain is even more extreme when in direct sunlight.

The shadowpeople's bodies are covered with dark, smooth fur. A long, stretchable membrane connects their arms to their flanks. The membrane enables the Shadowpeople to glide through the air, covering 10 feet of ground for every foot they drop. Under certain thermal air conditions, this allows them to soar and gain height as they fly.

Shadowpeople have a close, clannish culture. The young are cared for by whatever adults happen to be nearby. The adults are divided into two classes: warriors and councilors. The warriors patrol the race's underground tunnel network and defend the clan against intrusion. The councilors meet regularly to educate the young and make decisions about the survival of the race.

Shadowpeople can communicate via a set of squeaks and growls that forms a primitive language, but they are much more likely to use their advanced ESP abilities to send and receive messages. This ESP accounts for the Shadowpeople's low Armor Class: In combat they are able to anticipate the actions of their enemies and take measures to defend against it. They cannot be surprised by any sentient creature.

In combat each shadow warrior employs a wickedly curved hook to both attack and restrain opponents. Once an enemy has been impaled by the hook of a shadow warrior, the enemy's attacks are hampered and he continues to take damage from the hook.

Shadowpeople

FREQUENCY: Rare
APPEARING: 2d20
ARMOR CLASS: 2
MOVE: 12″/18″
HIT DICE: 3 + 1
% IN LAIR: 100%
TREASURE TYPE: Nil
ATTACKS: 1
DAMAGE: 1d8
SPECIAL ATTACKS: See Below
SPECIAL DEFENSES: See Below
MAGIC RESISTANCE: Standard
INTELLIGENCE: Very
ALIGNMENT: Neutral (good)
SIZE: M
XP VALUE: 85 + 4/hp

Shadowpeople suffer a −2 penalty to all to hit rolls under overcast skies. The penalty is increased to −4 in bright sunlight. They can glide 10 times the distance they launch themselves from. Any character who is successfully struck by the hook of a shadow warrior will suffer a −2 penalty on all to hit rolls and sustains an additional 1d8 of damage every round until one or the other combatants is dead or the fight ends.

Spectral Minions

Spectral minions are the spirits of humans or demihumans who died before they could fulfill powerful vows or quests. Even in death, spectral minions are bound to the vows or quests placed upon them when they were alive. Every day, they must relive the events leading to their deaths, trying to fulfill their vows or quests.

Outdoors, spectral minions must stay within 1,000 yards of where they died. Indoors, they must stay in the corridor or room where they met death. On very rare occasions where the quest was to perform an act over an area, they are free to roam within the area.

Spectral minions can only inflict damage if they died holding weapons. Such weapons becomes a part of them. The weapons and the spectral minions disappear forever if the minions' vows or quests are fulfilled or if a spell is cast to remove their curse.

Spectral minions appear as they were in life, but they are almost transparent. While spectral minions are hard to tell apart, they seem to fall into six general categories:

Berserkers: Some agents of evil are driven

into a berserking frenzy when they become minions. This happened in many cases during the Cataclysm. These beings have rebelled against their quests and have no hope of ever being freed from their charges.

Guardians: These minions were quested to guard some passage or object. Usually they require only a password or signal to allow a person to pass safely. Unfortunately, everyone who knew the password is usually long since dead. Guardians are always honest and good spirits endeavoring to complete their assigned task. Once the password is correctly given, they are freed of their responsibilities.

Philosophers: Philosophers love libraries and books and can spend decades studying the nuances of a single book. They usually attack an intruder only if their honesty is questioned. Philosophers can be of any alignment. Often they are found in groups of two or more engaged in heated debates.

Revelers: These minions revel through the halls and places to which they are tied. They are often found dancing madly or laughing in groups while drinking spectral ale. They dine gluttonously and play parlor games. Their frolicking has a dangerous, hypnotic effect on mortals who see them. Often adventurers are drawn into these revels. These unfortunate mortals dance uncontrollably, losing Strength and will power, and become spectral minions unless someone rescues them.

Searchers: These armed minions of evil stalk their haunts, forever searching to fulfill their quests. These minions are very dangerous, for they will destroy anything that stands between them and their unreachable goals.

Warriors: These groups of minions are the spirits of mortals who were locked in mortal combat at the time of death. In all such cases, the minion-versus-minion combat produces no lasting damage and the net effect is an eternal conflict between the groups. Only through the intervention of mortals can the tide of the battle be turned in the favor of one side or the other.

Spectral Minions

FREQUENCY: Very Rare
APPEARING: 1d40 or more
ARMOR CLASS: 2
MOVE: 30"
HIT DICE: Varies
% IN LAIR: 100%
TREASURE TYPE: Nil
ATTACKS: 0,1 or 2
DAMAGE: Varies
SPECIAL ATTACKS: See below

SPECIAL DEFENSES: +1 or better to hit
MAGIC RESISTANCE: 20%
INTELLIGENCE: Standard
ALIGNMENT: Varies
SIZE: M
XP VALUE:
  Philosopher: 525 + 8/hp
  Reveler: 525 + 8/hp
  Searcher: 525 + 8/hp
  Guardian: 900 + 14/hp
  Warrior: 900 + 14/hp
  Berserker: 900 + 14/hp

Thanoi (Walrus Men)

The thanoi are a bizarre blend of the human and walrus races. The creatures have huge, padded feet, stocky arms with fingers capable of holding a weapon or casting a spear, and faces much like walruses.

Two huge tusks grow from a thanoi's mouth, jutting wickedly downward. The beast can use these to attack or it can use a weapon, gaining the benefit of its tremendous strength.

A group of thanoi always has a leader. This leader is usually the meanest and most aggressive thanoi of the band. The walrus men are a vicious race, enjoying the torment of other creatures; often thanoi kill for the sheer joy of it. Their primary food source is the fish that are trapped in the ice-covered lakes on Icewall Glacier. They are not above eating carrion, bear meat, or any other protein that fate sends in their direction.

Thanoi are protected by a tough leathery skin and a thick layer of fat. They can swim in arctic waters without suffering from the cold. In fact, thanoi are immune to all forms of cold, both natural and magical. This immunity has its disadvantages: Thanoi suffer damage if exposed to a environment whose temperature is above freezing. They suffer extra damage from heat- and fire-based attacks.

Although large and clumsy-looking, a thanoi can maneuver its bulk surprisingly well. Their clawed feet enable them to maintain a good pace over ice or snow.

Thanoi (Walrus Men)

FREQUENCY: Uncommon
APPEARING: 1d20
ARMOR CLASS: 4
MOVE: 9"//15"
HIT DICE: 4

% IN LAIR: 25%
TREASURE TYPE: Individuals M; in lair C
ATTACKS: 1 or 2
DAMAGE: By weapon or tusk (1d8)
SPECIAL ATTACKS: None
SPECIAL DEFENSES: Immune to cold
MAGIC RESISTANCE: Standard
INTELLIGENCE: Below Average
ALIGNMENT: Lawful Evil
SIZE: L (8 ft.)
XP VALUE: 85 + 4/hp

Any weapon used by a thanoi does 2 more points of damage than usual.

The leader of a group of thanoi always has at least five hit dice.

Thanoi that are exposed to above-freezing climates lose one hit die per week of exposure. In addition, they suffer an extra point of damage per die from any fire-based attacks, whether magical or nonmagical.

Krynn Dragons
Background and History

Dragons are the true children of Krynn, embodying the elemental forces themselves. The dragons of Krynn are power incarnate and know it. They are—or at least they should be—the most fearsome of opponents, capable of inspiring awe and fear in all who behold them.

In the ancient days of Huma, the dragons were driven from the world that gave them birth. Since then, trapped on a far-off plane, the dragons of evil have conspired to return. The dragons of good, also exiled, resolved to leave the light of Krynn to the children of the gods.

The Evil Dragons
Black Dragons

Black dragons are typically found in swamps or marshes, although they also inhabit subterranean lairs. Some scholars conjecture that this preference for dark lairs indicates a sensitivity to light. Over 30 feet long, black dragons attack with sharp claws and teeth. They can also spew a stream of deadly acid upon their victims.

Black dragons are capable of speech, in both the secret language of dragons and in other languages they find useful, including

the language of magic. A favorite spell of black dragons is *darkness*, which they invariably use to cover their movements during attacks.

Since they are extremely independent and obey commands only if it serves their purposes, black dragons were rarely used by the Dragon Highlords in direct assault on cities during the War of the Lance. These dragons were more highly valued as guards for valued artifacts and spies.

This is why the Companions found the black dragon Onyx guarding the Disks of Mishakal in the ruins of Xak Tsaroth.

Blue Dragons

Although blue dragons live in caves, like others of their kind, they prefer to dwell in deserts and arid lands. They are large dragons—over 42 feet long. They fight with teeth and claws, but their most deadly attack is their lightning breath. Blue dragons were used to overcome fortified fortresses and towers during the War of the Lance.

Blue dragons are more gregarious than many of their cousins. They obey orders and can act and fight together as a cohesive unit. Thus they proved loyal allies of the Dragon Highlords. They have their own language and several others. Blue dragons are highly adept spell casters.

Kitiara's blue dragon, Skie, was renowned among his kind for his remarkable loyalty to his rider.

Green Dragons

Notorious even among evil dragons for their cruel natures and vicious tempers, green dragons are generally found living in wild, forested areas. They will obey orders, but only from leaders whom they respect. A master who falls low in the esteem of a green dragon had best beware. Over 36 feet long, green dragons attack with teeth and claws and can breathe a cloud of poisonous chlorine gas upon their victims.

Clever and subtle, green dragons prefer to use trickery and magic on an enemy rather than all-out assault. For this reason, they were rarely used in major offensive engagements, but often were called on for more sinister purposes.

Cyan Bloodbane, a green dragon, was responsible for breathing nightmares into the ears of the Silvanesti king, Lorac's. These nightmares caused the terrible transformation of the ancient elven homeland. It was also known that Cyan Bloodbane served the great archmage, Raistlin, for a time following the war.

Red Dragons

With their flaming breath and exceptional intelligences, the red dragons were the favored airborne assault force of the Dragon Highlords. The most ferocious and deadly of all dragonkind, save only for the Queen herself, red dragons are over 48 feet in length.

Not usually inclined to obeying orders, red dragons enjoy nothing more than setting cities ablaze, destroying, and looting. They quickly learned how to work together in flights to both attack and defend themselves against their enemies. The red dragons were loyal to their Dark Queen above all things, serving her first and the Dragon Highlords second. It was the primary responsibility of the red dragons to search for Berem Everman, the one person who could permanently block the Dark Queen's reentry into Krynn.

Ember, Lord Verminaard's red dragon, was responsible for the downfall of Pax Tharkas, the burning of Solace, and other acts of devastation in the lands of Abanasinia.

White Dragons

Unusual among dragonkind, these reptiles have not only adapted to cold climates, they actually prefer these over warm climes. Small in size—only 24 feet long—and not as intelligent as their cousins, white dragons were used mainly as scouts during the War of the Lance. They were also detailed to defend the Ice Wall, a relatively unimportant region in southern Ansalon.

White dragons attack with teeth and claws and can breathe a cone of frost upon their foes. Because of their low intelligence, few white dragons can cast magical spells.

Sleet was the white dragon who served the evil wizard Feal-Thas and helped guard Ice Wall Castle.

The Good Dragons
Brass Dragons

Brass dragons inhabit arid, sandy regions. Only about 30 feet long, brass dragons are boisterous and loud, with a tendency to selfishness. Brass dragons' one great weakness is their fondness for small talk. They will converse about nothing for hours on end and will trail along after parties of adventurers just for the pleasure of hearing themselves talk.

Brass dragons prefer to attack with claws and teeth, but they have two formidable breath weapons they can use if the need arises. Their *sleep* gas causes victims to slumber peacefully during the wildest battle; their *fear* gas sends enemies fleeing in panic. Brass dragons speak a wide variety of languages (mainly so they'll have someone to talk to).

Bronze Dragons

Fond of war and fighting, bronze dragons are large, nearly 42 feet in length. They prefer to live near large bodies of water, such as lakes or oceans. They are extremely interested in the affairs of mankind. In ancient times, it was believed that they often took the form of domestic animals simply to observe men.

Bronze dragons attack with teeth and claws or either of two breath weapons—a bolt of *lightning* or a *repulsion* gas cloud to keep victims at a distance. They speak a variety of languages.

The bronze dragon Khirsah, who later became known as "Tasslehoff's Dragon," is the only dragon ever known to allow a dwarf or a kender to ride upon his back. (Tas often claims that Khirsah has accompanied him on certain adventures following the war. If so, that would certainly be remarkable for the usually serious-minded dragons.)

Copper Dragons

Copper dragons make their homes in rocky, mountainous regions. Although basically good in nature, they are extremely fond of wealth and almost always ask "what's in it for me?" when invited to aid others. Thirty-six feet in length, copper dragons attack with teeth and claws or their two breath weapons: acid and a *slow* gas. They speak a variety of languages.

Gold Dragons

The most majestic (in their minds at least) of the dragons, gold dragons are over 50 feet long. They can dwell in any climate, but their lairs are

always made of solid stone—be it cave or castle. They have the ability to *polymorph* themselves and can appear in the guise of humans or animals. This they do only rarely, believing it demeaning to take on such puny bodies.

Gold dragons attack with teeth and claws or with their breath weapons. They can breath fire or chlorine gas upon their victims. Gold dragons are also extremely skilled in magic—even the very young ones. Highly intelligent, gold dragons rarely make use of spell books.

Pyrite, the most ancient gold dragon living upon Krynn, was the companion of the renowned wizard, Fizban the Fabulous.

Silver Dragons

Certainly the dragons most beloved by mankind are the silver dragons. These dragons mingled the most with the races of Krynn. Forty-eight feet long, silver dragons can *polymorph* into human or elven form. Unlike gold dragons, silver dragons sometimes seem to prefer this form to their own. They enjoy being around humans and elves and helping them if they can. Silver dragons attack with claws and teeth or use either of two breath weapons—a cone of frost or a cone of paralyzing gas. They speak many languages, but usually prefer human or elven tongues. Silver dragons are excellent magic-users.

The most famous of the silver dragons is Dargent, who met the Companions in the form of the Kagonesti elf maid Silvart. Sister to the silver dragon who fell in love with Huma, Dargent was also destined to fall in love with a mortal—Gilthanas, a lord of the Qualinesti elves. Their love affair was a tragic one, however, for Gilthanas could never bring himself to accept Dargent's true form.

The Gods as Dragons

Takhisis, Queen of Darkness

Although Takhisis can take any form from that of the most beautiful and alluring of women to the powerful and loathsome Dark Warrior, her favorite form is that of the five-headed chromatic dragon. In this form, she is over 60 feet long and has five heads. Each head has a different color (white, green, blue, red, and black), as well as a different power and personality.

She can attack with all five heads at once, as each head has its own breath weapon—frost, poison gas, lightning, flame, and acid, according to the color of the head. Each head is also capable of casting its own magical spells, regardless of what the other heads are doing.

Confined to the Abyss by the bravery and sacrifice of Huma, Takhisis never ceases her attempts to reenter Krynn. Her constellation in the night sky always appears directly opposite that of Paladine, symbolizing the two gods' continual opposition.

Paladine, the Platinum Dragon

Paladine, the God of Good, has many names among the different races of the world (one of his best-known incarnations is Fizban the Fabulous). In his dragon form, Paladine is truly impressive. (The same cannot be said, unfortunately, for Fizban.) Over 72 feet long, the Platinum Dragon can attack with teeth and claws or with one of his breath weapons. These include a blast of cold that can freeze any victims, a cloud of vapor that turns victims into *gaseous form*, or a sonic vibration that *disintegrates* solid rock.

Paladine is highly skilled in magic and can also cast clerical spells. Paladine's favorite form is that of the befuddled old wizard, Fizban (ofttimes seen with his senile gold dragon companion, Pyrite).

Dragon Rules

The dragons of Krynn are power incarnate and they know it. The DM has the responsibility of playing these magnificent beasts properly. There should be nothing so terrifying to PCs as dragons on the wing. When in flight at full speed, dragons rush across the world like a gale, but their ability to turn is greatly impaired (Maneuverability Class E).

When engaging earth-bound creatures in combat, dragons slow to half-speed, improving their maneuverability to Class D. At less than half speed, the creatures stall and lose altitude. They can climb at half speed or dive at double their listed speeds. Dragons can glide but they lose 1,000 feet of altitude per round. Dragons can perform a *wingover* if they stall while climbing. This enables them to turn 120 degrees as they dive to regain speed.

Very young and young adult dragons have maneuverability ratings one better than older dragons (Class D at full speed, Class C at half speed). Dragons cannot fly higher than 10,000 feet because the air becomes too rarefied to breathe at that altitude.

When attacking from the air, dragons employ their breath weapons and awe ability while swooping down low over their opponents and then climbing back into the sky.

Flying dragons can swoop down and either claw or bite, but not both. Diving dragons inflict double damage with their claws if they dive. Dragons cannot cast spells while flying, but can cast spells on the ground or while gliding.

Most dragons tend to use their breath weapons twice and then wait for a strategic moment to use their third breath attack.

Dragons are haughty creatures and may refuse to fight except as it suits their own purposes. When using spells, they often cast them before melee to avoid the conflict, weaken their opponents, or gain the upper hand. Once in melee, dragons cast spells only if losing.

Dragons do not knowingly place themselves in a position to be subdued, although they are clever enough to pretend to be subdued to lure unwary adventurers into a trap.

Dragons are very clever opponents. They have been known to feign death, unconsciousness, sleep, or subdual to trap opponents. They can see, hear, and smell much better than most creatures and automatically *detect hidden* and *invisible* beings at a range of 1" per age level. They are rarely surprised.

Dragons adapt their tactics to the situation, as is appropriate for very clever creatures. The following tactics are frequently used.

1. Dragons stay in the air as much as possible during melee to cause awe (see below) and stay out of hand-held weapon range.

2. If the combat area is dusty, they beat their wings, stirring up clouds to blind fighters and disturb spell casters.

3. They use clever conversation and promises to talk their way out of bad situations.

The power to cause *awe* and *fear* is one of dragons' most potent weapons. Flying or charging dragons cause *awe* under the following conditions:

1. Watchers with less than 1 hit die automatically panic and flee for 4d8 turns.

2. Watchers with 1 to 3 hit dice must roll a successful saving throw vs. spell or be paralyzed with fear (50% chance) or flee as above (50% chance).

3. All others must roll a successful saving throw vs. spell or suffer a −1 penalty to hit.

Even the draconians are subject to these effects from good dragons. If the draconians are within 12" of the evil dragon they serve, however, they have a +1 bonus to hit.

Dragons younger than adult cannot inspire awe.

the World that Was

"Their world was folly and ours the price,
but oh how brightly shines
the glory of their folly.

Astinus of Palanthus, the renowned historian, has worked for centuries to chronicle and order the history of Krynn. His set of scrolls, the *Iconochronos*, is certainly the definitive work on the topic—almost all other histories are drawn from the *Iconochronos*.

The scrolls now fill a huge library, and the Lorekeeper continually adds to their number. One scroll, longer than the rest and still unfinished, depicts the history of Krynn as a continually unfolding series of events along a timeline. Much of this line is recorded in pictures of exquisite beauty and detail. The origin of the artwork is shrouded in mystery, although the accompanying text is certainly the work of Astinus.

A reader of this scroll quickly notes that Astinus has divided the history of his world into five ages: the Age of Dreams, the Age of Light, the Age of Might, the Age of Darkness, and the Age of Dragons.

The latter two are of most concern to the modern reader, as they include the history of Krynn following the Cataclysm—the AC (Alt-Cataclius) period. The prior ages lead into the mists of antiquity, and are recorded as the PC (Pre-Cataclius) years. Exact dating in the PC period is difficult, whereas AC history is documented with great reliability.

the ages of krynn

The Age of Dreams is a span of uncertain years, mostly chronicled by the folk songs and ballads of the Age of Light that followed. These ballads were compiled on the Lifescroll of Song by the Silvanesti bard, Quevalin Soth. A copy of that scroll was presented to Astinus near the end of the Age of Light, and it is from this work that our knowledge of the Age of Dreams is derived.

The Age of Light was a period of peace and learning, during which the elven culture of Silvanesti shone as a beacon of civilization throughout the world. The history of the Age of Light was chronicled in the songs and artwork of the elves. Thus, the members of that long-lived race have provided beautiful and fanciful, if not entirely accurate, records of the age.

The Age of Might signaled the rise of humanity on Krynn. Humans spread across the world, bringing their frantic energy and aggressive confidence to all corners of Krynn. The initiation of the Age of Might is tied to the rulership of Karthay Pah in Istar. It was he who first ordered the keeping of a chronicle. Scribes carved his deeds upon plates of gold and silver, storing them on rings in his trea-sury. During this period, the young Astinus journeyed from the Library at Palanthus to Istar and spent three decades copying these plates onto scrolls for transport to the Library.

The Age of Might lasted for many centuries. Finally, the energy and arrogance of man resulted in the Cataclysm. In a single hour, the world of Krynn passed from the Age of Might into the Age of Darkness. As Palanthus was one of the few cities spared by the Cataclysm, the recording of history continued uninterrupted. The black years of the Age of Darkness are described thoroughly, and make for very grim reading.

Finally, the arrival of the Queen of Darkness through the gate she had partially opened from the Abyss allowed her minions, the evil dragons, to return to the world. Gradually, as the world fell under the reign of Darkness, the shadow of the Queen's monstrous evil began to spread across the lands. Thus began the newest age, which is still in its infancy—the Age of Dragons.

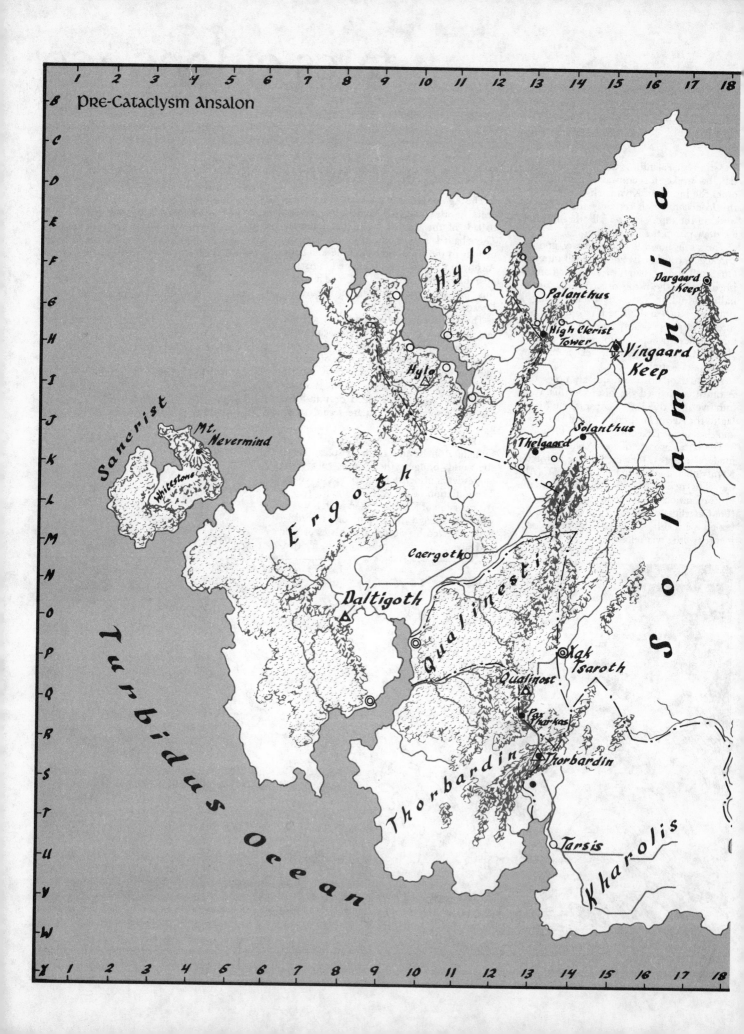

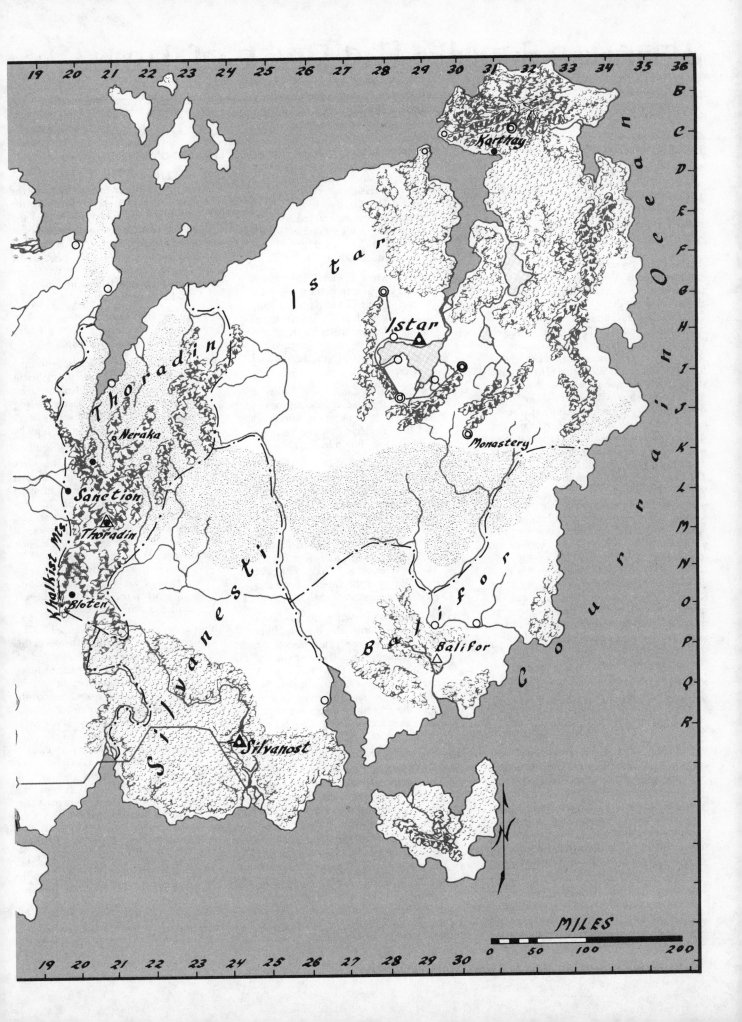

Astinus's Scroll: The River of Time

The Age of Dreams

The events of the Age of Dreams are not dated to a specific year, or even century. It is probable that the measuring of time during this period occurred at a scale incomprehensible to man.

—Astinus

The Gods Awaken: From swirling chaos emerge the gods. Taking realms of chaos unto themselves, they establish the Balance. Chaos slows and is subdued by the triumvirate of Good, Evil, and Neutrality.

The Stars are Born: The universe is forged from chaos. Sparks fly from the anvil, creating stars in the sky. Worlds are wrought by the hammer strokes and left to cool. The spirits of the races dance among the stars.

The All-Saints War Begins: The three realms of the gods vie for control of the sentient spirits. The gods of good press to give the spirits power in physical worlds, nurturing them toward the greater good. The evil gods desire to subjugate the spirits as servile beings. The gods of neutrality wish to free the spirits to their own desires.

End of the All-Saints War: The war ends with an alliance between the good and neutral gods, in which the spirits gain power in the physical world, yet retain the freedom to choose good or evil.

Krynn is Populated: Gnomes, elves, ogres, dragons, and humans are given the world of Krynn as their domain. The races quickly spread across the world, claiming regions as their own. The other races force the humans into small, desolate corners of the world, and then ignore them.

The Age of Light

circa 4000 PC Rise of the House of Silvanos: The first Synthal-Elish (Council of the High Ones) is formed by Silvanos, on the hill called Sol-Fallan. The many households of the elves swear allegiance to each other through Silvanos. Balif, the general, becomes Silvanos's lieutenant. Now united, the elves look to the menace of dragons encroaching into eastern Silvanesti.

Birth of the Gnomes: Reorx, who forged the world, becomes displeased with a group of his human worshipers. He turns them into gnomes.

circa 3500 Greystone Created: Magic is unknown upon Krynn. Reorx, the god of the forge, creates the Greystone of Gargath. In it is concentrated the magi-cal essences of the grey moon, Lunitari.

Elves Triumph: The dragons are driven from Silvanesti. Elven clans again swear allegiance to the house of Silvanos. The Kingdom of Silvanesti is decreed. Lands are granted immediately to the major families of the Synthal-Elish. A central government overlooks independent states.

circa 3100 Greystone Released: The gnomes pull the Greygem from the skies, and it floats across the face of Krynn, leaving disruption and chaos in its wake. Through the gem, magic is brought to the world. Some gnomes are changed by the gem, creating the kender and dwarven races.

circa 2800 Kal-Thax Closed: The region of Ansalon inhabited by the dwarves is sealed against all intrusion. Rumors of dark horror emerge from the land, but messengers are forbidden entry.

2692 Second Dragon War of Silvanesti Begins: Dragons again strike southward from central Ansalon, this time aided by potent magic. The elves rally and resist. Elves from the western provinces save the capital from destruction, forcing the dragons onto the defensive.

Construction of Thorbardin Begins: The dwarves of Kal-Thax commence the building of their mighty fortress as a defense against the world.

2645 Second Dragon War Ends: The elves of the west drive the dragons from Silvanesti, and are held as heroes of the land. Humans join in the war to banish dragons from the face of Krynn. A mighty hero, Huma of the Lance, discovers the Dragonlance and uses it to drive the dragons to a negative plane, where they are ordered to sleep for the rest of eternity.

2600 Thorbardin Completed: The dwarves withdraw into their fortress, turning their backs upon the rest of the world.

Rise of Ergoth: The humans of Ergoth exert their influence beyond the borders of their land. Ergoth expands rapidly to the east and south.

2515 Death of Silvanos: The venerable leader of the elven nation dies and is buried in the Crystal Tomb. His son, Sithel, assumes the leadership of Silvanesti. Sithel orders construction of a tower in honor of his father, to be called the Palace of Quinari.

The Age of Might

2500 to 2200 Ergoth Dominant: The expanding nation of Ergoth reaches the northern border of Thorbardin to the south. Skirmishes between dwarves and men eventually lead to an uneasy truce. The humans also expand eastward and establish outposts on the edge of the Silvanesti forest. The western elves begin to trade with humans; some elves and humans intermarry.

2308 Sithas and Kith-Kanan Born: Twin sons are born to Sithel. Sithas is born minutes before Kith-Kanan.

2192 Sithel Slain: Sithel leads a hunting expedition into the western reaches of Silvanesti. His party accidentally meets a human hunting party that is stalking prey. The elf is concealed by thick brush and a human hunter shoots him by mistake. The Kinslayer War begins.

2192 to 2140 Kinslayer War: The elves attempt to drive the human outposts from Silvanesti, while the humans defend fiercely. Many more humans arrive to aid their side in the war. The elves who married into human society are forced to fight against their human kin in a war of great savagery.

Kith-Kanan skillfully leads the western elves in war, while Sithas solidifies his hold upon the the throne. The war finally ends with a truce.

2140 to 2100 Sundering of Silvanesti: The western elves are again the heroes of the land. They, however, are ashamed of the bloodshed wrought by the Kinslayer War. The philosophies of the western elves have strayed from the rigidly structured order determined by the high elven caste system. With their army still intact, the western elves sue for freedom of self-determination.

Ergoth/Thorbardin Clash: A series of disputes over borders and mineral claims leads to renewed skirmishing between dwarves and humans. The threat of all-out war looms.

2073 Swordsheath Scroll Signed: A pact of peace is signed by the emperor of Ergoth, the elves of Silvanesti, and the dwarves of Thorbardin. The Swordsheath Scroll solves the most pressing problems of the age.

The elves of western Silvanesti are granted a huge tract of enchanted woodland north of Thorbardin, where they can live as they wish. This land, called Qualinesti, also serves as a buffer between the dwarves of Thorbardin and the humans of Ergoth. Ergoth agrees to stop mining the Kharolis Mountains, and the dwarves agree to relax trading restrictions between their peoples and the humans. All hostilities cease.

2050 to 2030 *The Great March:* The elves of western Silvanesti, under their leader Kith-Kanan, migrate to Qualinesti and begin to colonize their homeland.

2000 to 1400 *Peace:* Krynn prospers. Kith-Kanan strengthens the bonds of peace between the elves of Qualinesti and the dwarves of Thorbardin. Together, the races erect the fortress of Pax Tharkas as a monument to their lasting peace. Ergoth passes through a succession of emperors of the Quevalin line, the majority of whom rule with just and benign hands.

1400 to 1250 *Rebellions in the East:* Gradually the Ergothian rulers begin to abuse and exploit their subjects. After much repression and heavy taxation, the provinces in the eastern corners of the empire begin to revolt. These wars are usually brief, but very violent. The emperors are forced to use their troops regularly, and each rebellion is larger than the last one.

1262 *Vinas Solamnus Commands Imperial Guard:* This skilled commander, who has been instrumental in crushing several rebellions, is appointed to the highest military post in the empire.

1251 *Great Rising in Vingaard:* The largest rebellion yet shakes the plains of Vingaard and Solanthus. Solamnus marches east with a huge army to once again crush the rebellion.

1250 *Year of Waiting:* Solamnus studies the grievances of the eastern peoples, determined to end the rebellion without a massacre. Gradually he comes to realize that the empire has incited the rebellions through vile and repressive treatment of its citizens. Solamnus, and most of his army, join the rebel cause at the end of the year.

1249 to 1242 *Union of the Plains States:* The nations of eastern Ergoth rally to Solamnus, achieving quasi-independence.

Patiently, Solamnus trains a mighty army.

1241 *Fall of Ergoth:* Solamnus and his army march west. The general outmaneuvers the Ergothian army and lays siege to the capital. Solamnus accepts the emperor's surrender in the spring of 1240.

The surrender terms require the emperor to grant each of his subject states the right of self-determination. Although the nations of Ergoth remain loyal to the crown, outlying states become independent or join the new nation of Solamnia.

Solamnus assures the elves and dwarves that he will abide by the terms of the Swordsheath Scroll.

1225 *Knights of Solamnia Formed:* An order of knights, dedicated to the causes of goodness and freedom, is formed by Vinas Solamnus. Solamnia prospers, as the states of Palanthus, Lemish, and Caergoth join the new nation voluntarily.

1100 to 800 *Foundation of Istar:* The tribes of far eastern Ansalon, until now a bickering collection of barbarians, gradually unite. The Council of Istar establishes a unified government. Istar begins to trade with Solamnia.

Solamnia Prospers: The dynasty founded by Vinas Solamnus is extended by his descendants. Ergoth depends on Solamnia for protection and trade.

773 to 760 *Istar and Silvanesti Clash:* A series of border skirmishes between the expanding Istarian nation and Silvanesti again threaten the elven homeland. With the aid of Solamnia, the elves persuade Istar to add its signature to the Swordsheath Scroll.

700 to 600 *Ogre Wars:* Pillaging armies of ogres emerge from the Khalkhist Mountains of central Ansalon, raiding across the plains of Solamnia and the fertile fields of Istar. Solamnia and Istar unite, eventually driving the ogres back into the mountains.

600 to 280 *Union of Solamnia/Istar Solidified:* The two great human nations grow more and more interdependent. The Knights of Solamnia become the military strength of both nations, while the artistic and educational talents of Istar are spread throughout the continent. Istar gradually becomes the dominant partner.

280 *First Kingpriest Declared:* The capital city of Istar is proclaimed the center of the world. The anointment of the first

Kingpriest solidifies the bond between the military might of Solamnia and the spiritual guidance of Istar.

260 *Construction of the Temple of the Kingpriest Commences:* The finest artisans of Krynn are brought to Istar to build a temple that will proclaim to the world and the gods alike the glory of the nation of Istar.

212 *Temple Completed:* Widely proclaimed as the finest example of architecture ever, the temple is blessed by the Kingpriest, who immediately takes up residence.

250 to 100 *Elves Shun Other Races:* Increasingly disgusted by the frantic pace of human life and the arrogance of man about his own accomplishments, the Silvanesti elves withdraw into their forests. They bar commerce with the outside world, and visitors are prohibited from entering.

118 *Proclamation of Manifest Virtue:* The Kingpriest declares that evil upon Krynn is an affront to the existence of the gods and men. A rigidly defined set of evil acts are listed; those found guilty of committing any of these acts are to be put to death. Clerics of good, appointed by the Kingpriest, journey throughout Krynn, seeking to find and report any evil acts or individuals.

94 *Extermination of Evil Races Sanctioned:* The Kingpriest, not satisfied with the Proclamation of Manifest Virtue, adds a clause stating that certain races—goblins, ogres, etc.—are inherently evil and must be exterminated. High bounties are offered, and bounty hunters immediately set about to eliminate these creatures.

80-20 *Rise of Clerical Power:* With the full approval of the Kingpriest, Istarian life falls increasingly under the influence of the clergy. Clerical approval is required for marriage, business contracts, and military expeditions.

The rise of the clerics is accompanied by a corresponding loss of magic-user influence. Hounded as an unrepentant source of evil, mages are driven farther and farther underground.

6 *Edict of Thought Control:* The Kingpriest asserts that evil thoughts constitute evil acts, and declares that his clerics are to employ *ESP* spells in an increased effort to rid the world of evil.

npcs of long ago

The best part of role playing the DRAGONLANCE® saga is in meeting and interacting with the people and creatures of this fantasy realm. A good DM can make the NPC characters come alive for his players. To help the DM, the following are capsule summaries of various NPCs the player characters might meet, plus information to help role play them effectively.

huma, knight of Solamnia

Huma is a tall, well-built man of approximately thirty years, although he looks older. He has long, chestnut brown hair, streaked with gray. He wears the traditional long moustache of the knights, also streaked with gray. His eyes are deep brown and appear to be able to see a man's strengths and weaknesses. Huma's face is weary and sorrowful, for he has seen the evil in the world and grieves over it. His rare smiles are warm and caring.

Although only a Knight of the Crown (Huma did not have the requisite pure blood line to become a Knight of the Rose), he is a natural leader and even higher ranking Knights follow him willingly. His men love him and would gladly lay down their lives for him. Huma is a devout Knight and a faithful follower of Paladine. He is the soul of honor and chivalry.

If his spirit is met after his death, the downfall of the Knights will grieve Huma deeply, though he is wise enough to admit that the Knighthood has problems that must be remedied or it will be lost forever. His spirit will fight beside any true Knight, particularly if that Knight calls upon Paladine to aid him.

huma (npc)

(8th-Level Human Knight of the Crown)

STR	INT	WIS	DEX	CON	CHR
18/56	8	14	16	15	13

THAC0: 14
AL: Lawful Good
HP: 56
AC: 0

There are many ways in which a player character could meet Huma. His spirit could appear to a Knight fighting during the War of the Lance, for example. The DM can devise a campaign based on the early Dragon Wars, in which players can might fight beside Huma.

the Silver Dragon

Huma fell in love with the Silver Dragon when she was in the form of a woman. She loved the Knight and prayed to Paladine to allow her to become a mortal woman so that she could remain with Huma. Paladine showed them the future. If she remained a dragon, she and Huma would be given the *dragonlance* and the power of defeating the evil dragons. If she became mortal woman, she and Huma could find happiness for a time, but the evil dragons would remain in the world. She and Huma both chose to fight the evil, even though it meant sacrificing their love.

The spirit of the Silver Dragon might well appear with Huma to help a true Knight battle his enemies. Those campaigning with Huma would certainly know her. In woman form, she is extraordinarily beautiful, with silver hair and silvery grey eyes. In battle, she wears silver armor that appears to be made of dragonscales. The sight of her fills all who see her with awe and reverence. She and Huma are devoted to each other.

Besides appearing to any true Knight in much the same way as Huma, the spirit of the Silver Dragon might fight at the side of any woman battling the forces of evil.

the Silver Dragon (npc)

THAC0: 10
AL: Lawful Good
HP: 70
AC: −1

Other statistics are as a very old silver dragon in the *Monster Manual*.
Abilities: Change shape to human form.

Magius

A powerful wizard of the Red Robes, Magius was a childhood friend of Huma's. Their friendship was very unusual since most Knights disliked and distrusted magic-users. It was also unusual because the two men were so different: Huma was noble and self-sacrificing, while Magius seemed to be self-centered and cynical. In appearance, Magius is a very handsome 30-year-old man, well-built, with long blonde hair and a blonde beard and moustache. His eyes are blue and piercing. He is sarcastic and even irreverent, often making jokes about the Knights that they don't usu-

ally find amusing.

Most Knights do not like Magius, believing he should take himself and life more seriously, and they cannot understand Huma's affection for the mage. Magius does not hesitate to criticize Huma and often teases him, treating him disrespectfully as far as the other Knights are concerned. But the practical Magius is Huma's best counselor and advisor, bringing the overly romantic Knight back to harsh reality.

During Huma's time, wizards were not allowed to carry any weapons other than their magic. A wizard was expected to be protected by warriors and to get out of any battle if he felt himself becoming weak.

Because of this stricture, Magius always fought side-by-side with Huma. During one of the battles near the end of the war, however, the two were separated. Although he had a chance to escape, Magius stayed and fought until his magic gave out. Having no other weapon, the weakened mage was quickly overwhelmed and captured. Carried back to the Dark Queen as a prize, Magius was tortured and died after days of torment. The Dark Queen sent the mage's battered body back to Huma, hoping to demoralize the Knight.

Huma grieved deeply over his friend and prayed to Paladine that Magius's sacrifice be remembered. Paladine answered his prayers and, from that day, all wizards have been allowed to carry daggers in remembrance of Magius.

magius (npc)

(14th-Level Human Red Robe Wizard)

STR	INT	WIS	DEX	CON	CHR
9	18	15	17	10	9

THAC0: 16
AL: Neutral Good
HP: 38
AC: 2

fistandantilus

The appearance of this great, evil wizard depends on when the characters meet him. If the characters meet him prior to his battle with Raistlin, he is an extremely frail old man with wrinkled hands and face and long white hair and beard. A tremendous feeling of power and of evil radiates from this old man.

He takes an interest in any adventuring party, particularly if there is a young Black Robe or Red Robe male magic-user present. Fistandantilus will either attempt to lure the young mage away from his companions or will abduct the mage. Once he has the young mage, Fistandantilus will attempt to wrest his life from him by using the *bloodstone pendant*.

fistandantilus (npc)

(17th-Level Human Black Robe Wizard)

STR	INT	WIS	DEX	CON	CHR
12	17	12	18	13	Var *

THACO: 13
AL: Chaotic Evil
HP: Variable *
AC: Variable *

* Fistandantilus maintained his existence throughout the ages by the use of the *Bloodstone of Fistandantilus* (page 97), which allowed him to steal the life essences of others. When Fistandantilus takes the essence of another, he assumes that victim's hit points and Armor Class. See *Bloodstone* in the *Magical Items* section for more details.

astinus of palanthus

Rumors abound that Astinus of Palanthus is actually the god Gilean. Astinus is popularly known as the Ageless One, for legend has it that he has been on Krynn forever. Those fortunate enough to receive admittance to the Great Library and an audience with Astinus find themselves in the presence of a man whose face is handsome and ageless. The eyes of the man are intense—dark, aware, constantly moving, seeing everything. Astinus speaks politely yet is always somewhat distant. If disturbed at his studies, he may be annoyed at the interruption. He will probably continue to write even as the player characters are talking to him.

Astinus is neutral in all things. He generally refuses to give advice; when he is willing to offer council, he often restates the obvious, letting the players draw their own conclusions. Astinus cannot see into the future. He knows, however, everything that is happening in the present and everything that has happened in the past. Getting him to part with this information, however, is a major undertaking, since he refuses to do or say anything that might affect the future.

astinus of palanthus

THACO: 2
AL: Neutral
HP: 980
AC: −10

Players can also meet Astinus during war councils or other important meetings that take place in Palanthus.

Reorx (Dougan Redhammer)

When this neutral god comes to Krynn, it is in the form of a huge, black-bearded dwarf who has a taste for dwarven drink and a weakness for gambling. The dwarf can drink anyone—man or minotaur—under the table. His gambling skills are not as refined, however. Impetuous and quick-tempered, Reorx—or Dougan Redhammer, the name he uses in his dwarf form—will stop whatever he's doing (including fighting) to bet on anything, from which paw a cat will lick next to which house a dragon is most likely to burn down.

Unfortunately, Dougan's luck at cards or dice or betting is very bad. He always loses whatever money and equipment he has. Worse, he invariably drags his companions into trouble by offering their money or their equipment (often without their permission) as stakes in his games. ("I'm sorry I lost yer magic sword in that card game, lad, but it was a sure thing!")

Since Dougan is a god, there is usually an ulterior motive to all he does. He does not interfere in anyone's free will to make a decision, however. He has a special interest in dwarves. It is rumored that Dougan is on Krynn searching for the Greystone of Gargath.

See page 45 for the statistics of Reorx/Dougan.

the kingpriest of istar

Few who come into the presence of the Kingpriest ever see what he truly looks like. Most characters of good alignment feel that they are in the presence of someone very beautiful and truly good. They experience a tremendous sense of peace and well-being. The thought of leaving this man's presence fills them with sadness. They would not think of doing or saying anything that might upset or disturb this truly good and wonderful man. They want only to stay and bask in his light.

Those of evil alignment are hardly able to look into the blinding light surrounding the Kingpriest. Only those evil beings of extremely strong will can remain long in his presence.

Kender, who hold no one and nothing in awe, see the Kingpriest in his true aspect—a middle-aged, balding human with pale blue eyes that have a hunted look to them.

the kingpriest of istar

(15th-Level Human Cleric of Paladine)

STR	INT	WIS	DEX	CON	CHR
12	13	12	17	9	18

THACO: 12
AL: Lawful Good
HP: 75
AC: −3

Arack, Master of the Games

Arack's past is unknown. Once a gladiator in the Games when they were real, Arack now runs the fake Games for the vicarious delight of the wealthy of Istar. The dwarf is one of the strongest of his race and extremely ugly. A long scar that runs vertically across his face gives him a perpetual scowl that appears especially sinister when he is smiling.

Arack has two major interests: money and the Games. He is a born showman and knows exactly what will please an audience. He takes great pride in his Games and works extremely hard to make them a success. He hires the best trainers in all areas of fighting and takes excellent care of his athletes, despite the fact that they are slaves. No slave is ever tortured. They are well fed and their quarters are comfortable if not luxurious.

But Arack is a political realist. He knows that the Games have become a means of settling accounts among the wealthy and he sees no reason why he shouldn't make a profit out of it. Large sums of money are wagered on the athletes and the nobleman who owns a popular fighter generally makes a considerable fortune.

The only person Arack is truly loyal to (and will not betray) is his bodyguard, Raag the ogre.

Arack, Master of the Games

(13th-Level Dwarf Fighter)

STR	INT	WIS	DEX	CON	CHR
18/53	13	9	15	14	8

THACO: 8
AL: Chaotic Evil
HP: 73
AC: 2

Raag

A gigantic and not overly bright ogre, Raag is Arack's devoted bodyguard and the dwarf's only friend. Raag is extremely fond of Arack and would unhesitantly lay down his life for the dwarf. Arack is also fond of Raag—the two have been together a long, long time.

Raag

(Ogre)

STR	INT	WIS	DEX	CON	CHR
18/79	5	6	12	15	6

THACO: 15
AL: Chaotic Evil
HP: 33
AC: 2

Steeltoe, the Half-Ogre Bandit

The product of a loathsome alliance between an ogre and a wretched human woman, Steeltoe was abandoned by his mother at birth. A nobleman of Solamnia found the child, took pity on him, and gave him a home. The half-ogre proved unusually intelligent. The nobleman provided for his education and made Steeltoe master of his estates when the half-ogre reached maturity. Steeltoe repaid his master's kindness by murdering the nobleman and stealing his money.

Crimes of this sort were not unusual in the bitter days following the Cataclysm. The half-ogre escaped easily into the wilderness of Solamnia, gathering around him other men living outside the law. Because of his education, Steeltoe found it easy to attract many disillusioned young men, particularly reviled Knights of Solamnia, who otherwise would have had nothing to do with bandits. Steeltoe is a clever speech maker, continually reminding his men that the world owes them a living and it is their right to take what they want.

The half-ogre is about seven feet tall, powerfully built, with a steel peg leg in place of his missing lower left leg (lost in a battle with a griffon). Attached at the knee, the peg leg has a round toe and is a formidable weapon.

The half-ogre is skilled in wrestling techniques and swordsmanship. He is a brutish-looking man with a yellowish cast to his complexion and a large, flat nose. He appears human in all other aspects.

Steeltoe

(9/9-Level Half-Ogre Fighter/Thief)

STR	INT	WIS	DEX	CON	CHR
16	9	7	12	17	8

THACO: 12
AL: Chaotic Evil
HP: 50
AC: 3

magical items of krynn

In the early days of Krynn, magic was a powerful force and many fabulous items were crafted. But those days were short lived, for near the end of the Age of Might, magic came under the displeasure of the church of Istar and was persecuted relentlessly. Many of the centers for magical research were sealed or destroyed and wizards disappeared from the general knowledge of men. With them went their wondrous devices.

We list here many of those items for your consideration, as well as a few items that come from the Age of Dragons. This is but a sampling of the magical items that can be found on Krynn. Many magical items on Krynn also exist in other planes of existence, but the devices described here are unique to Krynn.

Potions

Istar's truth

This is a potion used in the courts of Istar to ascertain the truth in matters brought before the Kingpriest or his appointed ministers.

This potion forces its recipient to truthfully answer a number of questions. The person who administers this potion can ask the victim 2d4 questions requiring yes or no answers and 1d4 questions requiring longer responses. (An example of a question requiring a longer response: "What happened to you three days ago?") The

victim is allowed a saving throw with a −5 penalty to the die roll. If the save is made, then the potion simply makes the victim sleepy but does not cause him to lose control of his will. The victim can then give false answers.

The length of the answer to a question is up to the victim so long as it is absolutely truthful and answers all the stated parts of the question. The DM can use this opportunity to impart important information to the PCs. The formula for this potion is known to any good cleric in Istar of at least 5th level. The formula is lost in post-Cataclysm Ansalon.

Scrolls

Scroll of the Stellar Path

A powerful magic on the scroll of the Stellar Path confers the favor of the gods of magic upon the user. Since the magical powers of the wizards of Krynn wax and wane depending upon the position of the moons in the sky, only rearrangement of the cosmos can bring additional power to a wizard during a time of disadvantage. This is the purpose of this powerful scroll.

Reading the scroll makes the moon of the wizard's order appear at its most advantageous position in the sky, regardless of that moon's natural position. This does not actually change the position of the moon in the sky, but rather creates a magical condition in which the wizard's powers are as if the moon is at its most advantageous position.

How advantageous this position is will depend upon the natural locations of the moons of other orders. If reading this scroll causes a conjunction of one or more of the moons, that conjunction has its usual effect upon the wizard's powers (see *The Moons of Magic*, page 27).

Once the scroll is read, it disintegrates in the hands of the reader. The runes of the spell can be copied down into spell books for safe transport, but the spell can only be cast from the scroll itself, which is the physical component of the spell.

The enhancement of the wizard's powers lasts for 48 hours and then his powers are back to the level dictated by the true positions of the moons.

Rods, Staves, and Wands

Staff of Striking/Curing

Common among the clerics of the Age of Might, these devices were most often used as both protection for the cleric on journeys and as a means of furthering the wills of their deities.

This staff combines the functions of a *staff of striking* and a *staff of curing*, with the following limitations. It recharges itself at a rate of five charges per day when in sunlight, to a maximum of 50 charges.

As a *staff of striking*, it strikes as a +3 weapon. It inflicts 4-9 points of damage with each blow without draining a charge. It inflicts double this damage if two charges are used, but it cannot be used for curing until an hour has passed for each double-damage blow struck.

As a *staff of curing*, the staff drains two charges for each cure. It can only perform this function six times in a single 24-hour period and no more than once per day on a given individual.

Diviner of life

Often called a baton, the *diviner of life* was used during the Age of Might by commanders who wished to determine the general condition of their troops. After first finding his troop's top condition during a long rest, the general could get a good view of his troop's degree of readiness by referring to this baton.

This magical object is a four-foot-long rod. Each end is capped by a six-inch-wide band of gold and steel. The rod has a three-foot-long section of what appears to be clear crystal in the middle (it withstands 20 points of damage before breaking). If the glass breaks, the staff is useless.

There seems to be a swirling white fog within the glass section. When the keyword is spoken, this fog clears completely. If the staff then touches any living being, the life force (hit points) of that being registers as a bright green line, one inch long per 10 hit points.

Crystals and Gems

Brooch of Imog

This traditional reward is given to mages who serve the elven realms. It can grant the blessing of magical protection to the owner. None have been forged since the Cataclysm.

This beautiful piece of jewelry is made of gold leaf and shaped like a circlet of mistletoe. When worn by a magic-user who knows the brooch's command word, it can be used once per day to create a *minor globe of invulnerability*. The *globe* lasts for 10 rounds.

The Medallion of Faith

Since the return of the gods during the War of the Lance, all true clerics have received *medallions of faith* as outward signs of their inner commitment. These *medallions* can create other *medallions of faith* for clerics who profess faith in the true gods. (The new *medallion* bears the symbol of the new cleric's god, regardless of the symbol on the original *medallion*.)

The *medallions of faith* have no powers other than creating more *medallions*. All clerics of the true gods wear their *medallions* at all times.

Miscellaneous Magic

Flute of Wind Dancing

Constructed by sirens in the depths of the sea, these flutes were given long ago to favored mariners who had performed some great service for the siren kingdoms below the seas. Much prized, the flutes often found their way into the royal courts of the land.

This flute can only be used by a character who knows how to play a flute or other wind instrument. While playing this flute, the user can summon and control small breezes.

After two rounds of playing, the user can create a *zephyr*; after three rounds, a *gust of wind* can be summoned. If an entire turn is spent playing the flute, a *dust devil* can be created in a 30″ area, blowing up dust and leaves

and acting as an *obscure* spell. The *dust devil* will dissipate gas and mist in the area of effect. The winds created start at the player and move at the player's will up to 6″ away. The winds die down as soon as he stops playing the flute.

Glasses of Arcanist

These magical lenses are set in solid platinum frames. The frames are so narrow that the glasses will only fit on a kender or an elf.

The *Glasses of Arcanist* were designed by the mage Arcanist several centuries before the Cataclysm. The glasses enable their wearer to read all writings, rendering a perfect translation of any topic in any language. Magical scrolls and spell books can also be read using these glasses.

The glasses do not enable a non-spell caster to cast spells. However, they do enable a low-level caster to cast higher level spells from scrolls with no chance of failure.

Golden Circlet

The *golden circlets* were created in Istar toward the end of the Age of Might. They were designed to guide the people into aiding the church. Their use, however, tended more toward slavery than service. Even so, they could only be used by one of good desires and so their abuse was somewhat limited. Many of these survived the Cataclysm though they are guarded most carefully.

This thin gold band, when worn on the head of a cleric of good alignment, grants two magical abilities. Once per turn, the wearer can *command* up to 8 Hit Dice of creatures. Also once per turn, as long as the user concentrates, one creature of up to 4 Hit Dice can be controlled by the *circlet*'s wearer. The creature is not *charmed*, however, and cannot be forced to hurt itself.

Keys of Quinarost

Created for the royal family of Silvanost, these ancient keys provided the only known way to enter the tower at the center of the city. Each of the members of that household had a key. At the time of the Cataclysm, several members of the royal household disappeared. Their fates, and those of their keys, are unknown.

These are elven keys, magically linked to the life forces of their designated users.

Each key appears to be an ordinary key with extraordinarily delicate workmanship. It is made of fine crystal twined with strands of platinum. It is about 6 inches long and the handle is 1 inch wide extending down to a 1/4-inch-wide shaft.

These keys can be reset to another person if the current owner wills it reassigned. The original owner must still be alive, however, to do this. Keys whose owners have died cannot be reset and will not open the tower doors. However, these artifacts are highly prized by the royal family (mainly to prove the end of a lost relative) and those who return a *key of Quinarost* will earn a rich reward.

Singing Statue

Created during the most powerful days of Istar's priests, these relics of Mishakal were often used to protect temple complexes. Not only did they open doors that were magically locked against unbelievers, but they also had additional powers to aid the clerics of the Healer.

This item appears to be a hollow statue of beaten gold, formed in the shape of Mishakal the Healer. If water is poured into the hole at the top, the *statue* begins to hum a varied, peaceful tune. The *statue* has the following

properties when singing: it acts as a *chime of opening* against any locked or held door; it prevents undead from approaching within 20 feet of its wielder; it heals 1d6 points of damage to any person within 10 feet (this property only works once per day).

Webnet

The webnets are spun by wizards of the Dimernesti. As delicate and beautiful hair ornaments, they are most sought after by human women on land, but their true powers are known only to wizards.

This item is only useful to a magic-user, though any character can wear it as an attractive hair ornament.

When worn by a mage who knows the command word, the *webnet* can be cast to the ground before a foe, or directly at a foe. It instantly grows to a 10-foot-diameter *net of entrapment*.

Alternatively, the net can be spun in a glittering circle, affecting up to 12 Hit Dice of creatures as if a *hypnotize* spell had been cast upon them, although the targeted creatures get saving throws vs. spell.

Armor and Shields

Dragonarmor

This armor has been used by the forces of the Queen of Darkness throughout the many ages of Krynn.

It consists of a padded tunic and leggings with a plate mail breastplate and shoulder

plates. Additional plates for the thighs and shins are attached separately. The helm is a two-piece affair that protects the back of the neck as well as the face. The design allows freedom of movement, protection in combat, and warmth while riding dragons at high altitudes.

Dragonarmor is custom fitted and does not encumber the person for whom it was intended. Others may find that it fits too loosely or too tightly; they suffer a −1 penalty on all attacks while wearing the ill-fitting armor. *Dragonarmor* is equivalent to *scale +2*. Additionally, those who wear the padded tunic and leggings subtract 1d6 points from any cold-based attacks or damage.

The Plate of Solamnus

There were several Knights whose armor was designed specifically for them when the Knighthood was formed. These suits were the finest in all the land and the deeds of their wearers are legendary.

Huma had one such suit even though he was not accepted as a Knight of the Rose. Other suits, including the one worn by Vinas Solamnus, have disappeared into legend. Folk tales about the locations of these suits of armor abound throughout Solamnia and Ergoth.

The *plate of Solamnus* consists of plate breastplate, shoulder guards, arm fittings, leggings, and helm. All are beautifully tooled with the markings of all three Solamnic orders. The Order of the Rose is prominent on the breastplate.

These suits are rare, and the DM is advised to take great care with them in his campaign. One such suit could be the goal of a prolonged quest.

The armor is equivalent of *plate +5*. There is an important catch: the user must be of unbesmirched good alignment to get this full benefit. Consult the character's alignment chart (see page 114). Subtract one bonus point for every point the character's alignment is away from the left edge of the good alignment section. If the character is far enough away, the armor's bonus may become a penalty (maximum of −5), actually making the character's Armor Class worse!

Evil or neutral characters suffer 1d10 additional points of damage from any damage

received while wearing this armor. It is important to note that this is not the armor that is worn by Lord Soth.

Shield of Huma

Huma is most famed for his use of the original *dragonlances* to banish the Queen of Darkness back to her own domain. His shield, however, figures quite prominently in many of his lesser tales. It was said that it never failed him and that it often saved his life during battles against dragons before the *dragonlance* was employed.

The shield appears to be a medium shield carved with intricate symbols of the Knights of the Crown.

Huma's shield is considered a medium *shield +3/ +5 vs. dragons*. Its shielding magically protects its wielder against breath weapon attacks so that a successful saving throw vs. breath weapon causes no damage and a failed save results in only half damage.

Solamnic Armor

The traditional armor of the Knights of Solamnia is granted to a Knight when he first attains the title of Lord.

The armor consists of breastplate, shoulder

plating, helmet, and spurs. Each is engraved with the symbols of the Knight's order and, in the case of Sword and Rose Knights, any Knighthoods held previously by the Knight.

> *Solamnic armor* is equal to AC 0 (*plate +1* and *shield +1*). It is only granted to those Knights who have demonstrated the finest qualities of Knighthood.
>
> These suits are only available at a Circle of Knights whose 1d6 roll plus modifiers is greater than 15 (see page 128).

Weapons

Dragonlance

Dragonlances are artifacts first created at the end of the early Dragon Wars and used to defeat the evil dragons. There were 20 surviving *dragonlances* hidden inside the Stone Dragon of Ergoth, 10 each of the two types. In addition, more *dragonlances* were forged for the War of the Lance. There are two types of *dragonlances*: mounted and footman's. Each type is made of the same silvery metal that gives off a healthy silver glow. The head is sharpened to a fine edge, and small barbs protrude from the sides.

How well the lance was made and under what conditions determines how the lance performs in battle. The ideal conditions for forging a lance require that it be forged by a man with the *Silver Arm of Ergoth* and the *Hammer of Kharas*. Legend says that only lances forged by these two artifacts can work properly.

> A *dragonlance* forged with only one of the two artifacts mentioned above (either the *Silver Arm* or the *Hammer of Kharas*) receives only a +2 bonus to hit and damage. A lance forged by both artifacts has a +4 bonus to hit and damage. These bonuses are *in addition* to any other bonuses listed for the weapon.
> END SCREEN

footman's Dragonlance

The footman's lance is eight feet long. It can be cast as a spear with some difficulty—it is most effective as a hand-held weapon.

> A footman's lance causes 1d6 points of

damage to man-sized foes and 1d8 against larger-than-man-sized targets. Against any dragon it inflicts damage equal to the hit points of the wielder (e.g., a 14-hit point fighter causes 14 points of damage). The weapon is always +1 to hit unless thrown, in which case it suffers a −2 penalty to hit.

mounted Dragonlance

The mounted lance is 16 feet long and is most often wielded while mounted on a dragon. It is buttressed by a harness mount that enables swift turning of the lance around its balance point. The mounted *dragonlance* is ineffective on mounts smaller than dragons because of the heaviness of the lance. The mounted *dragonlance* acts as a normal lance if it is not mounted on a dragon.

> The mounted lance does 2d4+1 points of damage versus man-sized foes and 3d6 points of damage against larger-than-man-sized targets. Against a dragon it inflicts damage equal to the hit points of the wielder plus those of his mount. A 15-hit point fighter on a 40-hit point dragon inflicts 55 points of damage when the *dragonlance* strikes another dragon. If not mounted on a dragon, the lance causes normal lance damage. This weapon always has an additional +2 bonus to hit when mounted on a dragon.

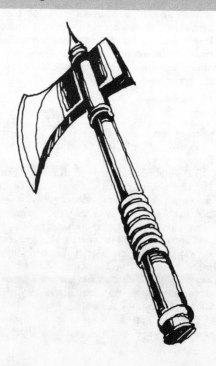

frostreaver

A *frostreaver* is a heavy battle axe made out of ice. This ice can only be gathered from a secret location on Icewall Glacier where tremendous pressure, exerted for centuries, has created ice of extraordinary density.

The knowledge needed to make a *frostreaver* is held only by the Revered Clerics of the Ice Folk—the barbarian tribes competing with the thanoi for control of Icewall Glacier. The blades are formed by using the oil of the thanoi and other ingredients to hone and flatten a sheet of the compressed ice. The cleric must work an entire month to create a *frostreaver*, and even then the chance for a working axe is only 33%.

The weakness of the blade is its nature, since temperatures above freezing cause the ice to melt and the axe to become worthless. One day of above-freezing temperatures will cause a *frostreaver* to become useless as a weapon. In a warm environment, the decay requires only 1d6 hours.

> A *frostreaver* is the equivalent of a *heavy battle axe +4*. Because of the weight and size of a *frostreaver*, the axe can only be wielded by a character with a Strength of 13 or greater.

Mantooth

This potent sword looks to be an ordinary long sword. It is also known by the names *Spellcleaver*, *Darkstar*, and *Magefool*. Its abilities are primarily directed at countering magic. Its history is unknown, although it has been among the Silvanesti elves for ages untold.

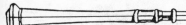

Mantooth is a *long sword +1/+2 vs. magic-users and enchanted creatures*. The sword might be able to sever a magical barrier—it has a 1% chance for every point of damage inflicted (cumulative). Finally, it can be used to turn a spell cast against the wielder. To activate the latter ability, which causes the spell to rebound against the caster, the wielder of the sword must successfully roll to hit AC 0, with no bonuses applied to the roll.

Nightbringer

Not just good wizards built weapons. The evil ones knew far better the need for a strong arm and exercised that might more quickly than their good brethren.

So it was that *Nightbringer* was created in the Tower of Ergoth. It was here that the power of the Black Robe wizards forged many evil weapons in the days when their kind were hunted by the church.

After the Cataclysm, *Nightbringer* fell into the possession of Verminaard, who received it from other evil clerics.

Nightbringer is a *footman's mace +3*. It is a powerful tool of evil. When the mace strikes a victim and the command word is uttered, the victim must make successful a saving throw vs. spell or become blind for 2d6 turns. The mace also inflicts its normal damage. If a character of good alignment tries to pick up *Nightbringer*, that character must roll a successful saving throw vs. spell with a −2 penalty to the roll. Failure means that the character is blinded permanently, or until a *cure blindness* spell is cast on him.

Wyrmsbane

An artifact from the third Dragon War, this sword was forged during the Age of Might and then lost later in that age. When dragons arose after the Cataclysm, the need for this potent weapon was great.

Wyrmsbane is a *two-handed sword +2* against most creatures. When used against dragons and draconians, however, it inflicts double damage. Against black dragons and sea dragons, it inflicts triple its usual damage. The sword does not become stuck in the statue created when a Baaz draconian dies and petri-

fies.

Wyrmsbane can also *locate objects* three times per day. If the user desires to find something that he knows well, and the object is within 18", the DM should steer him in the right direction.

Wyrmslayer

This mighty blade was the weapon of the ancient elven hero, Kith-Kanan. It was forged in Silvanesti during the second Dragon War and remained in the royal house until Kith-Kanan led his people to Qualinesti. He is said to have been buried with the sword.

This weapon looks very much like *Wyrmsbane*, except that it is a little larger. It normally functions as a *two-handed sword +3*. Like *Wyrmsbane*, *Wyrmslayer* is immune to the imprisoning effect of a dying Baaz draconian. The sword does double the usual damage against any dragon or draconian.

In addition, a character holding *Wyrmslayer* by the hilt gains a +3 bonus to all saves against dragon breath attacks and spells cast by dragons or draconians.

Wyrmslayer does have the disconcerting tendency to buzz aggressively whenever it is brought within 3" of a true dragon (not a draconian). This buzzing is loud enough to be heard clearly and always awakens a sleeping dragon.

Special Magical Items of Krynn

Icon of Truth

The *Icon* is a white marble rectangle carved into the shape of a book. It is jewel encrusted and has a magical aura. The *Icon* measures 6" x 4" x 1". It is the book held by the god Gilean that symbolizes all the knowledge of the gods.

Once per day, the *Icon of Truth* can be used to cast a *dispel illusion* at 21st-level in a 30-foot radius. Within this area, dream creatures (such as those created by the *mindweb* spell) and illusions cannot exist.

This *dispel illusion* must be cast on a fixed

location and cannot be moved about. Any magic-user or clerical PC who touches the *Icon* instantly knows how to activate this function. To cast the spell, the PC must present the *Icon* in a forceful manner and speak the word "Tobril" firmly. The person who carries this object suffers no negative adjustments for disbelieving illusions.

Orb of Dragonkind

Three of these powerful artifacts are known to exist upon Krynn. They contain the essences of evil dragons and are magical items of vast and dangerous power.

The *Orbs of Dragonkind* (also called *Dragon Orbs*) are fragile, etched crystal globes that are 20 inches in diameter when in use. When not in use, the *orbs* shrink to 10 inches in diameter. They expand if the command words, carved into the surfaces of the *orbs*, are spoken.

The *orbs* were employed long before the Cataclysm for the purpose of destroying evil dragons—according to the legends, at least. These legends are common throughout the civilized lands of Krynn. What is not known, unless characters have learned by experience, is that the *orbs'* actual purpose is to *summon* evil dragons. Powerful mages of old would *summon* the dragons with the *orbs*, and then destroy them with powerful magic.

A character attempting to use an *orb* must gaze into it and speak the command words. This character must then make a successful saving throw vs. spell or he is *charmed* by the dragon within the *orb*. The DM should secretly roll this saving throw, not informing the players of the roll or the result.

If the character saves against the *charm*, any evil dragons within 1d4 x 10 miles hasten to the *orb*. These dragons automatically attack any non-evil creatures they find near the *orb*. If the current gaming situation does not specify the location of nearby dragons, roll 1d6. On a 1 or 2, an evil dragon of randomly determined age, size, and color shows up.

If the character fails the saving throw, no dragons are *summoned*, but the character is *charmed* by the evil dragon within the *orb*. Inform the player, when you can speak to him alone without being obvious, that his character has been *charmed*. He must act normally unless told otherwise.

The controlling dragon will steer the *charmed* character so as to further the cause of evil. This is done as subtly as possible, so that the controlled character's companions should suspect nothing until a critical point is reached. For example, if the PCs are engaged in a desperate battle with an evenly matched group of evil characters, the *charmed* character might suddenly throw in with the evil characters to swing the balance in their favor.

Each *orb* has the secondary abilities of *cure serious wounds* three times per day, cast *continual light* at will, and *detect magic* at will. Any character who gazes into an *orb* and speaks the command word knows of these functions. Whenever it is used for any of these things, the using character must make the saving throw to avoid being *charmed*. If the save is successful, the check must be made to see if any evil dragons arrive.

Detect magic and *detect evil* spells will show a positive result if cast upon the *orb* or a character *charmed* by the *orb*. For purposes of *dispelling*, treat the *charm* effect as if it was cast by an 11th-level magic-user.

hammer of kharas

The *Hammer of Kharas* is a mighty artifact. According to legend, it is the only hammer that can forge a *dragonlance*.

The hammer is twice the size of a normal war hammer. Its name comes from the great dwarven hero Kharas who fought in the Dwarfgate Wars after the Cataclysm. Kharas is most remembered, however, for the heroic deeds he performed prior to that time. The hammer was given to him by the Kaolyn dwarves in recognition of his deeds on their behalf.

The *Hammer of Kharas* is needed to properly forge *dragonlances*.

The *Hammer of Kharas* is +2 to hit. It inflicts 2d4 + 2 points of damage on a normal hit. It cannot be lifted by a character with a Strength of less that 12, and anyone with a Strength of less than 18/50 suffers a −2 penalty to hit with it (cancels out the +2 bonus).

The hammer acts as a *mace of disruption* against undead and creatures from the Abyss. It turns undead as a 12th-level cleric.

This artifact is intelligent (Int 11, Ego 11) and can control anyone who touches it if the character's Intelligence and Wisdom scores do not total 22 or more. The hammer's motivations are to preserve the security of the dwarven race and to further the cause of good. The *Hammer of Kharas* has the following special abilities, at the 20th level of magic use:

* Detects evil as a paladin
* Gives wielder immunity to fear, both normal and magical
* Wielder cannot be affected by 1st — 4th levels of magic

* Casts *prayer* once per day
* Provides *protection from normal missiles* once per day
* Acts as a *potion of fire giant strength* once per day
* *Cures serious wounds* once per day
* Inspires *magical awe* in all dwarves and derro (see *Legends and Lore*, page 7, for a full explanation of this effect)

The hammer chooses when to activate any of its abilities.

Silver Arm of Ergoth

The *Silver Arm of Ergoth* was created by the good dragons, men, elves, and dwarves during the First Dragon War. It was used to create the original *dragonlances*, and was used again during the recent war against the Dragon Empire.

The arm must be attached to a human of at least 17 Strength who does not have a right arm. The human must be of good alignment. When a proper wearer places the silver arm to his right shoulder, the arm grafts itself to the character and becomes a normal arm for all common tasks.

When used with the *Hammer of Kharas*, however, the *silver arm* has the power to properly forge *dragonlances* from dragonmetal. Only with the *Hammer*, the *Arm*, and pure dragonmetal can perfect lances be crafted.

The *Silver Arm* acts as a *ring of regeneration* for the character wearing it.

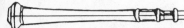

Staff of Magius

Magius was a wizard of legend who aided Huma in his quests. His staff was one of the most revered artifacts, not for its powers, but in honor of the mage who used it. Indeed, compared to other devices, it seems to be of little use. But many have suspected that there was more magic to the staff than met the eye.

In later years, the staff was given to Raistlin Majere at the completion of his tests. Whether it portended the power that he would attain or the tragedy that would befall him matters little now. The staff remains sealed the Tower of High Sorcery in Palanthus—entombed in Raistlin's laboratory as a monument to his folly. Certain reports of Raistlin's nephew, however, seem to indicate that the staff is free again in the world.

The *Staff of Magius* can only be used by magic-users. The abilities in the following paragraph are immediately known to the wielder, while those in the second paragraph can be discovered when casting certain spells.

The *Staff of Magius* functions as a *ring of protection +3*. It strikes as a +2 magical weapon and causes 1d8 points of damage. Once per day it can perform a *feather fall* and a *continual light* spell.

In the hands of a mage of 6th level or higher, the staff can enhance spell casting. It doubles the duration of spells that influence light, air, and minds. It maintains spells that require concentration for one round after wizard stops concentrating. It also adds 2 points of damage to every die of damage done by a spell cast by the holder of the staff.

The Dagger of Magius

Raistlin Majere purchased the dagger from the Tower of High Sorcery, giving in exchange a valuable magical item he found in his early days of mercenary service. He carried the dagger on his right forearm by means of a cunningly designed leather thong of his own making. This allowed the dagger to slip into his hand with a simple movement of his wrist.

Six inches long, this silver dagger is carved in the shape of a dragon with the tail as the blade. It is slender and lightweight and can easily be hidden upon the person of the mage.

The dagger has a +3 bonus to hit and damage. It also has the ability to remain undetect-

ed in a search of the mage's person.

Bupu's Emerald

This emerald was given to Raistlin by the gully dwarf, Bupu, in the ruins of Xak Tsaroth. Whether or not the emerald had any magical properties before Raistlin acquired it is unknown. Following the archmage's death, however, a legend sprang up that the emerald appeared in the pocket of a gully dwarf about to be killed by draconians. The gully dwarf gave the emerald to the draconians in an effort to purchase his life. The emerald killed the draconians and the gully dwarf escaped.

Bupu's emerald can be used only by a gully dwarf, gnome, or kender. When used as a defense in a life-threatening situation, it causes the attacker to be instantly overcome by its beauty to the exclusion of all else. The emerald kills the attacker on contact. It can be retrieved by its original owner.

In the hands of those of any other race, the emerald has only the standard value of that type of gem on Krynn.

When the victim touches the gem, he gets a saving throw vs. death. If successful, then he receives 2d20 points of damage. The victim dies if the saving throw is failed. Treat the obsession with the gem as a 15th-level *charm* spell.

The Bloodstone of Fistandantilus

This powerful gem came into Raistlin's possession after he defeated the evil wizard in mortal contest.

A powerful artifact from the early days of magic, the *bloodstone* is of evil alignment. About three inches in diameter, it is a green gem flecked with red. It is set in a plain silver setting and worn about the neck on a silver chain. It can be used to cure wounds inflicted upon the body by weapons (but it would have no effect on poison damage, for instance).

Its primary use, however, is to suck the life out of a victim and transfer that life force to the wielder of the gem, extending the life of the wizard. It also provides him with all the wisdom, memories, etc. of the person whose life he takes. While this can be beneficial (giving the wizard additional knowledge), it can also cause confusion and disorientation unless

the wizard is strong enough to retain his own identity.

The use of this device requires a 10-block shift in the direction of evil on the character's alignment tracking chart.

When this device is used, both victim and wielder must roll a saving throw vs. spell with the following results:

* *If Both Fail:* Each loses 1d10 + 5 hit points. The victim can make one attack. The wizard can elect to stop and deal with the victim in another way, or he can try again (both roll another saving throw).
* *If Both Save:* Both are locked in mental combat and must roll their saving throws again.
* *If Victim Saves and Wizard Fails:* The wizard takes 1d10 + 5 points of damage and loses initiative in the following round. The victim can take a free action this round.
* *If Wizard Saves and Victim Fails:* The victim's soul departs to the gods. His body is inhabited by the wizard's soul; the wizard's old body disintegrates. If the victim had a higher score for any of his abilities (Strength, Intelligence, Wisdom, etc.), this score replaces the wizard's score in that category. The wizard retains any of his scores that are higher than those of his victim. If the victim was of higher level than the wizard, the wizard attains that higher level, gaining the necessary experience points and powers of his new level.

Absorbing another character's life force is an extremely evil act. The wizard's alignment should shift at least 10 blocks toward evil (on the alignment tracking chart) each time he uses the *bloodstone* for this purpose.

Device of Time Journeying

Made during the Age of Dreams, this device was given to Caramon by Par-Salian. DMs should be aware that the device will have different properties depending upon when the player character encounters it. Originally, the device's use was restricted to the major races—humans, elves, and ogres—since all other races are prohibited from traveling in time. It was also originally designed to be used by one person only.

This jeweled scepter can fold down into a nondescript-looking pendant. Since the device was essential to the return of the person using it, it had several safeguards. Anyone

attempting to steal it (even a kender) immediately feels a strong revulsion to it and puts it back instantly. If lost, the device makes its way back to its owner through whatever means necessary.

An example of this occurred in the novels when Tasslehoff gave the device to Raistlin in the dwarven prison and was then discovered in possession of the device once more. It automatically returned to the kender. No force exists that can keep this artifact from finding its owner.

The properties of the device changed somewhat after Gnimsh—the only known gnome in the history of Krynn whose inventions worked—altered it. From that point on, the device transported more than one person and it also transported those of the minor races—kender, gnomes, and dwarves.

The correct version of the chant and instructions goes as follows: Holding the pendant in your hand, repeat the first verse, turning the face up toward you. At the second verse, move the face plate from the right to the left. At the recitation of the third verse, the back plate drops to form two spheres connected by rods. At the fourth verse, twist the top clockwise—a chain will drop down. The fifth verse warns to make certain the chain is clear of the mechanism. As the sixth verse instructs, hold the device by each sphere and, while reciting the seventh verse, rotate them forward . The chain will wind itself into the body. Hold the device over your head, repeating the final verse, and summon a clear vision of where you want to go and what time period you want to be there.

Thy time is thy own,
Though across it you travel.
Its expanses you see,
Whirling across forever.
Obstruct not its flow.
Grasp firmly the end and the beginning,
Turn them forward upon themselves.
All that is loose shall be secure.
Destiny be over your own head.

When the device is used, player characters within 10 feet of the device move to either the desired time (the place is up to the DM) or to the desired place (the time is up to the DM). Unfortunately for the players, they cannot have it both ways. Moving to the location of the treasure in a tower may seem like a good idea until you arrive there before the tower was built (and find a long drop to the ground). Moving to a certain time in history can be fun until you materialize in the middle of an arena. Use this little loophole to get your players where you want them when they want to be there or when you want them in a place they want to be.

Dalamar's Bracelet of Magic Resistance

An ancient artifact kept in the Tower of High Sorcery in Palanthas, the bracelet was given to Tanis by Dalamar to protect him from the magic of the death knight, Lord Soth.

The bracelet is of evil alignment and can only be worn by those of either evil or neutral alignment. Those of good alignment who touch it receive a jolt of electricity causing 3d10 points of damage.

The bracelet can be worn by characters of any class. It can protect against powerful magic, but its duration is limited. It offers 10% magic resistance against 3d- to 5th-level spells, 20% against 6th- to 7th-level spells, and 30% against 8th- to 9th-level spells. It imparts this magic resistance three times per day against each of these three groups of magic.

Dalamar's Ring of Healing

These rings were often used throughout the ages as wizards' last defenses against death.

This ring works only for magic-users and must be worn upon the right hand. It can cure a light wound (less than 6 points of damage) completely and can heal a mortal wound sufficiently to prevent death (it brings the character up to 1 hit point). It is activated by touch. Once used, the ring cannot be used again by that character.

Dalamar's Wand of Lightning

Though there have been many *wands of lightning*, this particular wand carries its own curse. Because the wand was used by Dalamar to kill Kitiara, the dead Dragon Highlord unceasingly hunts for the wand and its current owner.

This device works only for magic-users. The wand casts *lightning bolts* at 15th-level power. It normally carries seven charges and recharges itself at the rate of one charge for every week in which there is a local thunderstorm.

Each time the character uses the device, there is a 5% chance that his location is noted by Lord Soth, who comes to take the wand to his mistress, Kitiara. The death knight appears in 1d10 rounds to claim the prize.

Tasslehoff's Magic Mouse Ring

This ring is made of white ivory with two red jewels that resemble the eyes of a mouse. Magical rings of this type are generally designed by apprentice wizards learning how to create magical objects. Thus they are relatively common (at least among mages) and of little practical value.

Undoubtedly designed by some apprentice in order to help him escape observation (and possibly eavesdrop on conversations), the magic is activated by placing the ring on the finger. The wearer instantly becomes a white mouse. In order to return to his proper shape, the wearer merely wills it so.

The Nightjewel

Black as an evil dragon's blood, the jewel protects any who enter Shoikan Grove as long as they have the courage and will to use it. The *Nightjewel* helps to alleviate the fear generated by the Grove, though it does not cancel it completely. The *Nightjewel* can be used in defense against the undead who stalk the Grove, but the person using it must have the courage to touch the undead with the jewel if the undead attack. No other weapon can be used with the *Nightjewel*.

The *Nightjewel* is black, unlovely to look at, and cold to the touch. It can be worn about the neck on a silver chain, but must be held in the hand, high in the air, when entering the Grove. The character who uses the jewel must remove helm and hood so that the light of the jewel shines on his face and in his eyes. This light can be seen only by the undead. To all others, the jewel looks as black and ugly as a lump of coal.

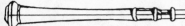

The *Nightjewel* can be used by anyone. When a party of adventurers enters the Grove, the *Nightjewel* must be held high by the leader of the party. It modifies the fear roll for everyone in the group so long as no weapon is drawn or spell is cast. Once a weapon is drawn or a spell is cast, the *Nightjewel* instantly loses all power, leaving the adventuring party at the mercy of the Shoikan Grove.

Those properly presenting the Nightjewel may ignore the −10 penalty to saving throws while in the grove but must still roll their saving throws. If a character fails, he loses the benefit of the *Nightjewel* until he succeeds in a subsequent saving throw.

Warbringer

This gigantic two-handed sword, forged during the Age of Might, was in the possession of the half-ogre bandit, Steeltoe. The fine quality and workmanship of this sword mean that it once must have belonged to a nobleman, possibly a Knight of Solamnia. Caramon won the sword when he slew the half-ogre. Caramon brought the sword forward into the future with him. It remains in his family, having been passed on to his eldest son.

> The sword has a +3 bonus to hit and does 1d8 + 3 points of damage.

The Axe of Brotherhood and The Sword of Friendship

During the Dwarfgate Wars, Caramon used a contest to bring the two quarreling factions of hill dwarves and plainsmen together. Caramon raised a tall wooden post in a sea of mud, placing an axe and a sword of rare and magical value at the top. Whoever climbed the post could claim these as prizes. There was a catch of course. Not only was the post greased, but Caramon had the contest rigged so that the dwarves and men had to work together to reach the prizes.

> The *Axe of Brotherhood* has a +2 bonus to hit and damage; the *Sword of Friendship* has a +3 bonus to hit and damage.

Raistlin's Cursed Money

During the Dwarfgate Wars, Raistlin (or Fistandantilus) made a deal with the dark dwarves to betray their king and leave the gates of the fortress of Pax Tharkas open when Raistlin's army attacked. Thus victory for the wizard was assured. Raistlin paid the dark dwarves with a coffer of 100,000 steel coins.

These coins were cursed, however, to prevent the dark dwarves from double-crossing the wizard. If the owner of one of these coins goes back on his spoken word, the flesh of hands begins to turn black and rot away. This dread curse spreads slowly and inexorably to the rest of the body until the victim dies.

> The legendary effect of this money occurs only when the money is actually part of a promise. (If a character promised to guard you in exchange for this money and then fled with it, then the curse would claim him.) A person under the curse suffers 1d4 points of damage from rotting each day until he either makes good on his promise, receives a *remove curse*, or dies.

Rabbitslayer, Tasslehoff's Knife

Whether this was really one knife Tas managed to keep with him or simply a series of knives the kender picked up is not known for certain. Tasslehoff always claimed it was the dagger he discovered in the ruins of Xak Tsaroth. He called it *Rabbitslayer* because Caramon once told him it would be of use only if they were attacked by ferocious rabbits. Actually the dagger, blessed by clerics of the ancient days, has far more power than Tasslehoff ever guessed.

> This dagger inflicts 1d4 + 4 points of damage and strikes with a +4 bonus to hit. It always returns to the kender within 1d20 hours after it is lost or stolen. The only way it can go from one person to another is if the owner gives it away of his own volition.

The Helm of Griffon Mane

Discovered in the ruins of Xak Tsaroth, the helm was given to Flint Fireforge by his friend Tasslehoff. The helm is of dwarven make and is decorated with a horse's mane. Having always claimed he was allergic to horses, Flint refused to admit that the long white tassel had ever belonged to a horse. He insisted—to his dying day—that it was from the mane of a griffon and thus the helm acquired its name. The helm fits only dwarves.

> This helm subtracts 1 from the AC of any dwarf who wears it.

the War of the Lance

*"Hear the sage as his song descends
like heaven's rain or tears,
and washes the years and dust of many stories
from the High Tale of the DRAGONLANCE."*

astinus's scroll: the river of time

history

The years following the Cataclysm were filled with horror and despair for several centuries. Battles for lost glories were a token of the age. Yet all races of Krynn managed to find the courage to fight the darkness.

Though the full tale of those days is known only to Astinus, the following events lend perspective to that time.

age of darkness

0 *Cataclysm:* The wrath of the gods descends upon Krynn. The Thirteen Warnings strike, one per day, preceding the end of the year. Trees weep blood, fires die or rage uncontrolled, and cyclones strike the Temple of the Kingpriest. On the thirteenth day, mountains of fire fall from the skies, ravaging the landscape.

Istar is immediately destroyed, its remnants sinking far below the surface of the newly formed Bloodsea. Ergoth is sundered from the mainland to form two great islands. Waters pour into central Ansalon, forming the New Sea and shrinking the formerly vast plains of Ansalon. To the south, the land rises and the water recedes. The port city of Tarsis is unscathed, but now lies far from the sea. The Temple of the Kingpriest is shattered with the destruction of Istar, its pieces scattered throughout the planes of the universe.

1 to 100 AC *Chaos and Pestilence:* The survivors of the Cataclysm struggle desperately to stay alive. Famine spreads across the world and plague follows. True clerics are unknown. The Knights of Solamnia are persecuted throughout the land, as people find them a handy target for blame. Many villages and towns, initially untouched by the Cataclysm, soon vanish because of disease or war. Sometime during this period, the Foundation Stone of the Temple comes to rest in the Abyss, and is discovered by Takhisis, the Queen of Darkness.

141 *Stone Planted in Neraka:* Takhisis places the Foundation Stone on the barren plain of Neraka, far from any center of population. The stone begins to grow into a twisted and perverted form of the Temple. The Dark Queen enters the world through the portal opened by the stone. Walking among the creatures of Krynn, she awakens her evil dragons and prepares them for the work she has in mind. She then returns through the portal to gather her forces on the Abyssal Plane.

157 *Berem Finds the Stone:* A young man and his sister discover the Foundation Stone. The man pries a gemstone loose, against the advice of his sister. They struggle, and the sister is accidentally killed. Her spirit, imbued with goodness, inhabits the Foundation Stone. The man, Berem Everman, is cursed with the stone he has stolen, as it becomes embedded in his chest. He cannot gain the peace of death until his sister's soul is released from imprisonment in the stone.

210 *Takhisis Returns:* The Queen of Darkness attempts again to enter Krynn through the portal opened by the stone. To her great frustration, she discovers that the portal is closed by the presence of the sister's spirit. Enraged, she casts about for a solution.

287 *Dragon Eggs Stolen:* The evil dragons, awakened by Takhisis, keep their presence in the world a secret. They raid the Isle of Dragons, where the good dragons lair, and steal the good dragons' eggs. Fleeing with the eggs to the Lords of Doom, the evil dragons hide their cache in the bowels of the volcanoes.

296 *The Oath:* Acting upon the orders of their Queen, the evil dragons exact the Oath of Neutrality from the good dragons. The oath binds the good dragons to noninvolvement in the coming war. In return, the evil dragons promise to return the eggs, unharmed, at the conclusion of the war.

300 to 320 *Agents of Evil:* Takhisis sends her agents through the world, seeking the man with the green gemstone embedded in his chest. She knows that this man is the key to opening her portal once again. She grows increasingly frustrated at Berem's apparent disappearance. Eventually, she decides to put her plans into operation.

age of dragons

332 *Dragons Appear:* The savage and warlike humans of Sanction, Neraka, and Estwilde are allowed to discover the evil dragons. From among the most evil of these men are recruited the Dragon Highlords and their officers. These men set about gathering armies under the watchful eyes of the evil dragons.

340 *Humanoids Recruited:* The ogres and hobgoblins are gathered into the evil fold and trained as troops in the Dragonarmies.

342 *Draconians Created:* Takhisis instructs the Highlords in the corrupting process whereby draconians are created from the eggs of the good dragons. The generation of draconians in the fiery underground regions around Sanction begins in earnest. The first draconians, Baaz, are created from brass dragon eggs. Soon, copper dragon eggs are used to create Kapak draconians.

343 to 347 *Evil Armies Marshall:* Draconian creation continues, with Bozak (bronze), Sivak (silver) and finally Aurak (gold) draconians. The draconians are formed into military units and trained for combat, while the training of human, hobgoblin, and ogre forces continues. Periodic outbreaks of violence occur among the Dragonarmies themselves; the Highlords encourage this aggressive behavior. Near the end of 347, Takhisis judges that her forces are ready. The opening campaign of the war is planned for the following spring.

348 *War of the Lance Begins:* With the melting of the snows in the high passes around Neraka, the Dragonarmies pour eastward upon the unsuspecting peoples of Krynn. The lands of Nordmaar and Goodlund are swiftly overrun, while the humans of Khur ally themselves with the evil forces to avoid conquest. Little resistance is met by the massed armies. What few battles are fought are decided swiftly by the awesome power of the dragons. By the end of the year, the hold of the evil forces over their occupied territories is uncontested.

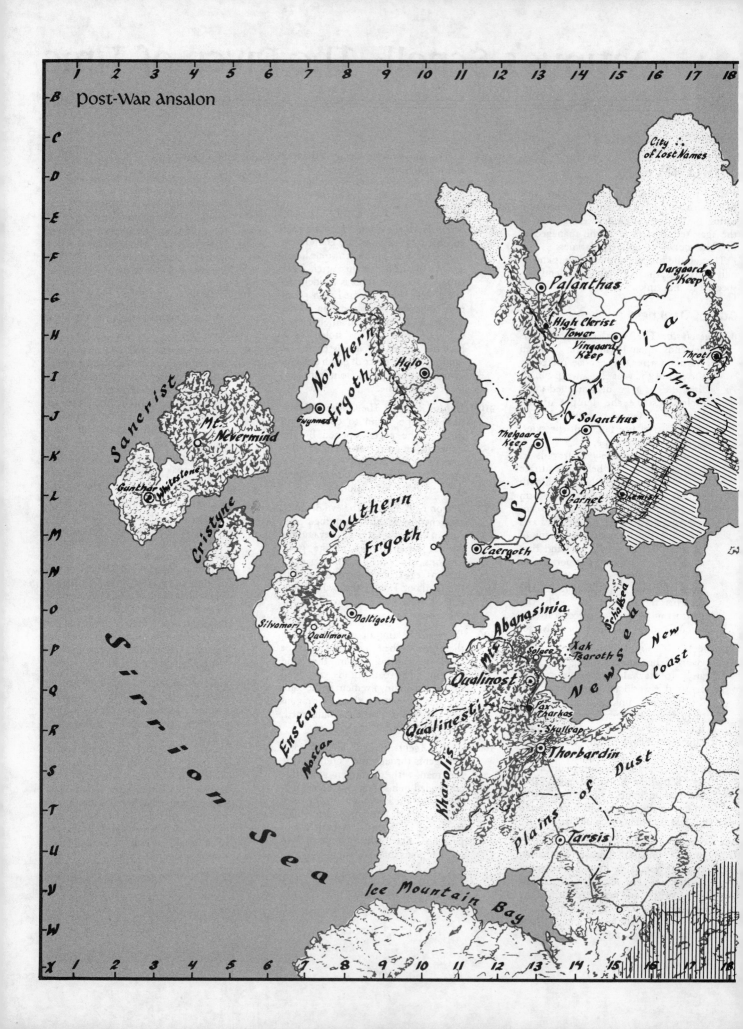

Post-War Ansalon

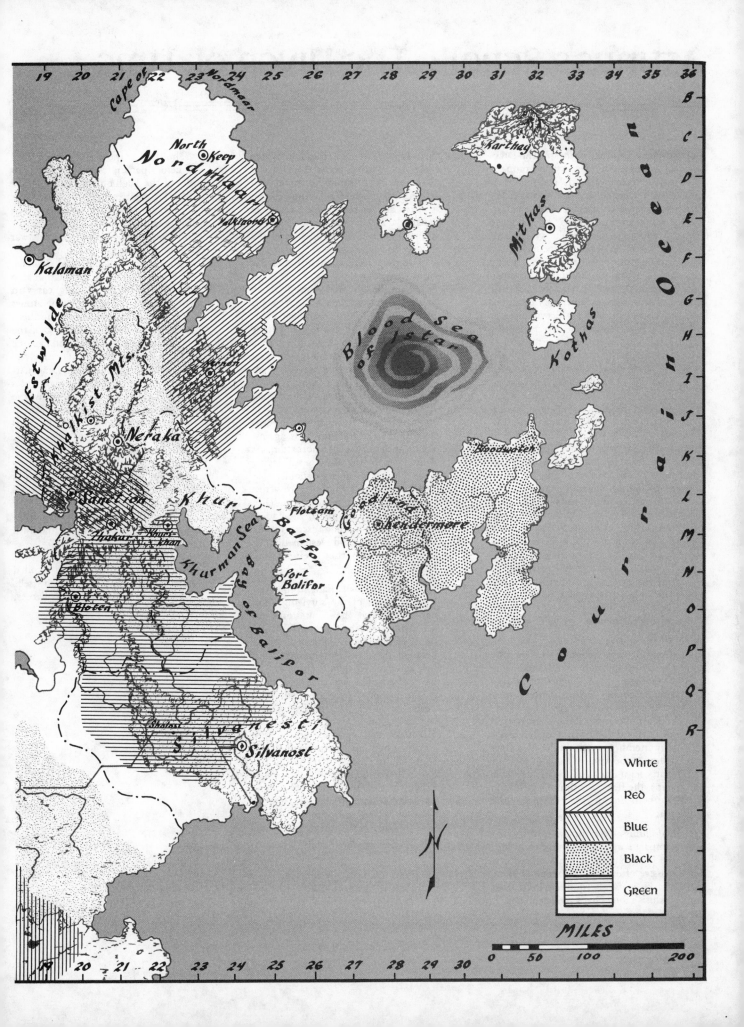

349 *Takhisis Turns to Silvanesti:* The Drag-onarmies commence a three-pronged attack into Silvanesti, utilizing their effective air and land combination. The elves, however, resist much more effec-tively than the humans and kender to the north. Losses are heavy on both sides, but the Dragonarmies make little progress into the dense forest. Using magic, discipline, and intimate knowl-edge of the terrain, the elves lure the Dragonarmies into a series of ambushes that seriously deplete the evil forces.

Takhisis sends her two remaining Dragonarmies to reinforce the attack, laying waste to the once-beautiful for-est and slowly advancing toward Silvanost. Although they fight coura-geously, the elves are decimated by the war, and the dragons set about system-atically destroying the elven food stock-piles. In autumn, the capital is evacuated with many refugees. The elven fleet sets out on the dangerous journey to Southern Ergoth, while many fighters remain behind.

On the last day of the year, the Drag-onarmies close upon Silvanost, and the elves realize that the war is lost. In a desperate effort to turn the tide, King Lorac attempts to use an *Orb of Dra-gonkind* to work the destruction of the evil armies. The perfidious orb seizes control of Lorac instead, plunging the land into a living nightmare and dis-persing the remaining elven fighters in chaos.

350 *Rearming Evil:* Seriously weakened by the costly invasion of Silvanesti, the Dragonarmies spend a year rebuilding and retraining. Takhisis's troops now control all of eastern Ansalon.

The minotaurs of Mithas and Kothas are recruited to the evil cause and belat-edly attempt to intercept the elven fleet sailing to the west. Although a series of sharp skirmishes cost each side some ships, the fleet sails through, reaching Southern Ergoth near the end of the year.

351 *Evil Turns West:* Again starting the campaign with the coming of spring, the Dragonarmies surge westward in a massive offensive. The scope of these attacks is far beyond anything that Takhisis's forces have yet attempted.

A huge force, spearheaded by the Blue Army, strikes across the Plains of Solamnia, overrunning Kalaman, Vin-gaard, and much of Solanthus. Disor-ganized and bickering, the Knights of Solamnia are slow to respond to the threat. Lemish sides with the evil forces, but the dwarves of Kaolyn pro-vide a strong linchpin on the right flank of the defenders.

Meanwhile, the Red Army leads an amphibious attack across the New Sea to the Plain of Abanasinia. The barbar-ian tribes of the plain are swiftly absorbed by the onslaught, which soon brings the Dragonarmies to the borders of Qualinesti. Knowing that they can-not withstand the might arrayed against them, the elves evacuate their homeland, fleeing westward to join their cousins on Southern Ergoth. Finally, the Dragonarmy rolls against the dwarven fortress of Thorbardin. As winter sets in, the army is still laying siege to the dwarven stronghold.

Additional evil troops strike across the Tarsian Plain from Silvanesti. They reach and occupy Tarsis by the end of the year. All of Ansalon, except for the western coastline and western islands, now lies under the heels of the Highlords.

352 *Whitestone Council:* Early in the year, representatives of the surviving good nations meet at the Whitestone, on Sancrist Isle, for the Council of White-stone. Here an uneasy alliance is forged between the elves and humans, and they agree to save their fighting for the forces of evil. The council is decided by the arrival of Theros Ironfeld, who wears the *Silver Arm of Ergoth* and bears a *dragonlance.*

With the coming of spring, the Blue Dragonarmy hurls itself against the High Clerist Tower that blocks the mountain pass leading into Palanthus. Rallying at last, the Knights of Solam-nia make a heroic stand and, for the first time, a Dragonarmy retreats from a field of battle. The battle marks the first modern use of *dragonlances.*

Shortly after the battle, a small band of heroes penetrates the deepest tem-ples of the Highlords in Sanction and discovers the treachery being wrought on the good dragons' eggs. News is swiftly returned to the Isle of Dragons, and the good dragons join the war against evil with savage intensity.

With the aid of the good dragons, the Whitestone forces are at last able to take the offensive. Surging eastward with violence and purpose, the armies of good reclaim the entire northern Solamnic Plain during the rest of the year. Gunthar Uth Wistan and Laurana of Qualinesti lead armies of men, elves, and dwarves against the evil Dragonar-mies. Carrying mounted *dragonlances* on the backs of the good dragons, the Whitestone forces emerge victorious from every engagement they fight dur-ing the long summer.

The recapture of Kalaman spells the beginning of the end for the Dragonar-mies, but the Queen of Darkness is determined to pass through the portal of the Foundation Stone, with the legions of the Abyss behind her. Des-perately, her minions seek the man with the green gemstone.

Yet the armies of Whitestone close upon Neraka, and the Queen is foiled in her attempt. Evil turns upon itself, and the Dragonarmy alliance collapses. The War of the Lance Ends.

RATHE IS FROM
362 CALER QUALINOST
CITY and SOLACE CITY

ansalon after the war

areas of Control

The map of postwar Krynn displays the areas that are controlled by the various factions left at the conclusion of the War of the Lance. The areas shown as controlled by a faction are controlled solidly. There are no wars in these areas, unless your campaign considerations dictate otherwise. Isolated guerilla or bandit activity is possible, but these occur only rarely.

Each of the factions includes a veteran force of troops. These troops quickly quash any uprisings and maintain order. They may be occupied in fighting border wars or in garrison duties throughout the controlled territory. In areas where no controlling power is shown, the area is in a dangerous state of anarchy. Bandits are common there, and small cities are struggling to gain control of their immediate environs. Armed forces from nearby areas of control are often encountered here, as each faction attempts to expand its influence and combat the influence of its rivals.

If your campaign has created conditions that are not consistent with the setting presented here, by all means change the information to create the reality of your campaign. For example, if you played the Battle of Neraka in the campaign and the Blue Dragonarmy was completely destroyed and Kitiara killed, the area of Blue Army control does not exist. Instead, the regions controlled by the Red and Green Armies and the Knights of Solamnia expand to fill the void. Very possibly, much of the area is under no faction's control.

All of the factions have achieved some degree of law and order within their borders. Entry into towns and cities, and perhaps even villages, is observed by guards of the appropriate faction. Strangers are viewed suspiciously.

Conversely, war heroes are recognized readily by comrades in arms. Characters who have led units in combat are almost always recognized by troops from the same army, and heroes of note stand a 50% chance of being recognized by troops of their alignment.

factions

Control of Ansalon following the War of the Lance has fallen to nine powerful factions, each of which controls one or more tracts of territory. Areas outside the control of these factions are either independent city-states or neutral territory currently contested by several factions. The factions are listed below.

Faction	Align.	Allies
Red Dragonarmy	CE	Black Army
Blue Dragonarmy	LE	Green Army
White Dragonarmy	CE	None
Black Dragonarmy	CE	Red Army, Minotaurs
Green Dragonarmy	LE	Blue Army
Minotaurs	LE	Black Army
Knights of Solamnia	LG	Elves, Dwarves
Elves	CG	Knights
Dwarves	LG	Knights

Wherever factions of good and evil alignments control adjacent areas, border skirmishes are frequent. Troop movements and battles are also common here. No trade occurs through these areas.

Wherever factions of the same alignment that are not allies control adjacent areas, border guards are common. There is a 10% chance per month that the border erupts into skirmishing, although such fighting usually stays well below the level of all-out war.

Allies actively cooperate with each other in the pursuit of their objectives. If two allies share a border with a common enemy, troops of those allies fight side by side against that enemy. Even among allies, however, troops of one faction are never commanded by a leader from another faction.

General Conditions

As with any world that has just emerged from an all-consuming war, conditions on Krynn are far from idyllic. The remnants of the evil forces still control much of the landscape. These forces fight each other as readily as they battle the forces of good. With the defeat of the Dark Queen, most of the troops in the Whitestone armies returned home to plant crops or tend their shops and stores. Thus there is no concentration of good forces to systematically regain the lands held by the Dragonarmies. Wars fought in this period are small-scale, but may be very violent. Mercenaries are readily available to work for anyone who can pay. Many have spent most of their adult lives waging war and have no other skills or interests.

Communications between areas of control are primitive to nonexistent. Factions that are friendly to each other may send occasional (heavily guarded) caravans back and forth. Roads are watched by bandits, however, and accommodations for travelers are few and far between.

The borders of factions that are unfriendly toward each other are continuously patrolled, and intruders are accosted for questioning, or worse. Members of all factions worry about spies and do not hesitate to use persuasive methods to determine whether a traveler is who he claims to be.

Many of the cities of Ansalon have been devastated by the war. Only Palanthus, of all the great cities, escaped damage. Because of this good fortune, Palanthus is now the center of civilization upon Krynn. The Knights of Solamnia have set up their central headquarters there, and the Port of Palanthus still receives ships from all corners of Ansalon.

Climate

Some information on climate is necessary if you intend to run an extended campaign in the world of Krynn. The information given here should be considered a rough guideline; DMs who want a more exact procedure for determining weather are referred to the *Wilderness Survival Guide* hardback.

Ansalon is a continent in the southern hemisphere of Krynn. Consequently, its coldest region lies to the south. Icewall Glacier is a region of constantly freezing temperatures and frequent snowfall. During winter, the sun illuminates this area for only a few short hours every day, and blizzards roar across the ice fields.

The region ranging from Qualinesti to Silvanesti (including Tarsis) suffers severe winters that begin early in autumn and continue far into spring. The elven forests receive plenty of rain during spring and summer, while the Tarsian Plain is relatively dry most of the year.

The western islands of Sancrist, Southern Ergoth, and Northern Ergoth, are treated to relatively mild winters because of warm ocean currents that keep the temperatures not too far below freezing. These areas receive much snow in winter and suffer very rainy springs. They are subject to flooding several times a year.

The lands of Solamnia, as well as the Lundian peninsula of Eastern Ansalon, are the most pleasantly temperate on the continent. Winters are snowy, but not very long. Plentiful rainfall allows for a long growing season, and these regions consequently produce most of Ansalon's food.

The central plains, including Estwilde, Neraka, Kern, and the surrounding areas, is a dry and desolate region. Severe winter storms sweep across the area, yet little rain falls during the growing season.

105

The northern tip of the continent is the land of Nordmaar, which swelters through long and humid summers and rarely receives a snowfall in winter. Certain crops can be grown during the long summer season, but the temperature is often too hot for more temperate crops. The islands of Mithas and Kothas share this type of climate.

Beyond the Map

What lies beyond the horizons shown on the map? Sooner or later characters in an extended campaign will begin to wonder about this.

The answer is up to you.

The continent of Ansalon is only one of several land masses on the surface of Krynn. As the setting for the War of the Lance, Ansalon was the location for all of the adventures in the DRAGONLANCE® saga.

If your characters desire to travel beyond the boundaries of the maps, then you need to design the lands and locales that await them. Brief introductory descriptions are provided for the start of the journey:

South lies the icy vastness of Icewall Glacier. The glacier covers the south polar region for several hundred miles in all directions.

West, out to sea, lies a huge region of tempests and typhoons. Winds blow from the west with steady intensity, carrying one storm after another into the western shores of Ansalon. Travel by sailing ship in this direction is nearly impossible, since it involves moving into the teeth of these savage winds.

North lie the tropics. A scattering of pleasant islands can be encountered after many weeks of sailing time. These tropical islands include the Isle of Dragons, where the good dragons remained until freed from their Oath, as well as many other idyllic and enchanted settings. It is

in this direction that the fabled and much feared land of the Irda is said to exist.

East lies an ocean of unspeakable vastness. Strong winds aid sailors who wish to travel in this direction, but a voyage of many months is required before reaching land. The peoples and creatures of the lands to the east are very different from those encountered upon Ansalon.

The Lands of Ansalon

The racial makeup of each nation's population, the primary resources produced by that nation, and any special notes required to run that nation in a campaign context are presented on the following table.

The Nations of Ansalon

Name	Pop./Al	Products	Notes
Abanasinia	H/N	Fur, Corn	Many tribes of barbarians, stone buildings
Blode	O/CE	Nil	Raid caravans and commerce
Caergoth	H/LG	Ships, Timber	Deep port, Knight stronghold
Estwilde	H/N(E)	Goats	Barren, dry
Goodlund	K/N(G)	Maps, Coral	Vast forest, small villages
Hylo	K/N(G)	Carved wooden objects	Port city Hylo, largest kender community
Icereach	Thanoi(LE), H(LG)	Nil	Iceriggers for travel
Kalaman	H/N(G)	Ships, Navigators	Ravaged by war
Kaolyn	D/LG	Gems, Iron, Steel	Very loyal to Knights
Kern	O/CE	Nil	Mercenaries and bandits
Khur	H/N(E)	Horses	Warlike nomads
Kothas	M/LE	Ships	Pirates, stone castles
Lemish	H/N(E)	Timber, Small ships	Hunters and sailors
Mithas	M/LE	Ships	Pirates, stone castles
Neraka	H/N(E)	Sheep, Wool	Small bands of nomads
Nordmar	H/N(G)	Horses, Chariots	Small tribes, central king
N. Ergoth	H/N(G)	Copper, Brass	Many ruins of ancient Ergoth
Palanthus	H/N	Ships, Books	Largest city on Ansalon, center of good religions
Qualinesti	E/CG	Fruits, Leather	Devastated in war—slowly rebuilding
Sancrist	H/LG	Gold, Silver, Platinum	Largest gnome community, traditional home of Knights
Sanction	H/N	Ships, Pirates	City rapidly eroding from lava flow
Silvanesti	E/CG	Nil	Forest twisted by king's nightmares during war—slowly recovering
Solanthus	H/LG	Grain, Cattle	Occupied during war—towns burned, people slowly returning
S. Ergoth	E/CG	Nil	Different elven cultures slowly melding
Tarsis	H/N	Furs, Horses, Wagons	Road to coast started
Thorbardin	D/N(G)	Steel, Gems, Weapons	Beginning to trade w/humans and elves
Throtyl	Hob/LE	Nil	Hobgoblin race retreated here and is entrenched
Vingaard	H/LG	Horses, Cattle	Reclaimed from evil, prospers
Zhakar	D/L(E)	Gems, Armor	Mysterious race of evil dwarves

Abbreviations:

Al = Alignment; D = Dwarf; E = Elf; Hob = Hobgoblin
H = Human; K = Kender; M = Minotaur; O = Ogre

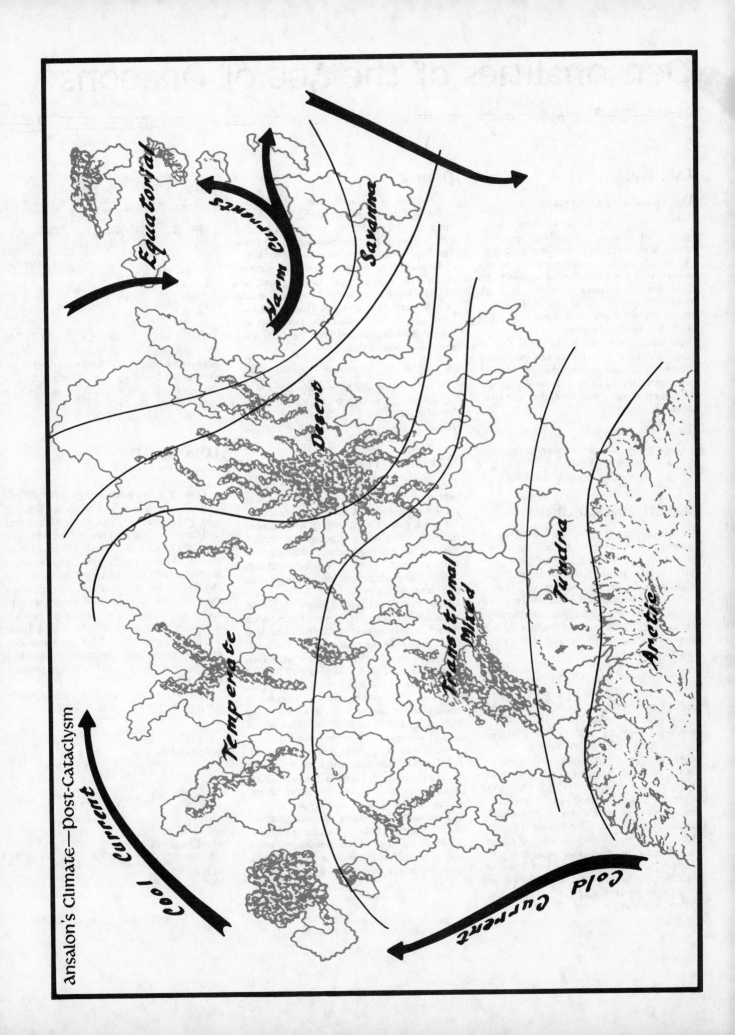

Ansalon's Climate—Post-Cataclysm

Cool Current

Cold Current

Warm Currents

Equatorial

Savanna

Desert

Temperate

Transitional Mixed

Tundra

Arctic

personalities of the age of dragons

Takhisis

The Queen of Darkness

The Dark Queen can take any form—male, female, or dragon—depending upon her needs. She can appear as the Dark Temptress, the most beautiful, desirable woman a man has ever seen in his life. She can appear as the Dark Warrior, a fearsome warrior in black armor with eyes of fire and a sword of flame or she can transform into her favored shape, that of the five-headed dragon.

No matter what form the Dark Queen takes, all those in her presence (including those of good alignment) feel her power and experience a sense of awe and reverence. Even though she is evil, she is one of the three creators of the world.

Game statistics for Takhisis can be found in the section on Krynn's gods (page 46).

Fizban the Fabulous

Fizban appears as a gray-bearded old wizard in mouse-colored robes with a beat-up, pointed wizard's hat that is off his head more than it is on it. He carries a plain wooden staff that appears to do nothing whatsoever, plus a shabby spell book in which he can never find the spell he is searching for (generally to everyone's relief!). Pouches hang from his belt, but these are just as likely to contain his dirty socks as spell components.

Descriptions of Paladine and his statistics can be found in the section on Krynn's gods.

The beloved, befuddled old wizard is a wonderful character who can have players gasping with laughter even while they're ready to wring his neck. Since he is a god (Paladine), Fizban is interested in people learning about themselves and developing their true potential. When Fizban tries to help characters out of a fix, it often seems as if he is simply making the situation worse instead of better. Fizban always allows others freedom of choice and does not interfere with their decisions. Fizban's purpose is to restore the balance of good and evil to the world, not to make one triumph over the other. DMs should keep this in mind when playing this character.

Pyrite

Fizban often has an ancient gold dragon known as Pyrite as his companion. Deaf, half-blind, irascible, and senile, the golden dragon spends most of his time sleeping in the sun. The dragon's great days were during the time of Huma (which he remembers much more clearly than recent times). Consequently he will fight when called upon, but only if he can be convinced he is going to Huma's rescue. Pyrite has all the spell-casting powers of an ancient gold dragon and on a good day can remember most of them.

Pyrite is an ancient huge gold dragon. Use the statistics for such creatures from the *Monster Manual*.

Raistlin Majere

Raistlin seems frail, but one is never really certain whether this frailty is real or feigned to lull his enemies into a false sense of security. He still speaks in a whispering voice, having discovered that this gets people's attention. Raistlin has one consuming ambition—he wants to become a god. He will use any means to gain this goal; he will let nothing and no one stand in his way.

Raistlin does not love Crysania. He desires her and feels natural feelings of protectiveness toward her but that is all. Raistlin has deep feelings for only one person on this world and that is his twin brother, Caramon. Any feelings of affection for Caramon are all tangled up with hatred and jealousy, but real love for his twin lives beneath. Raistlin is cunning enough and strong enough, however, to use his feelings and those of others to his advantage by manipulating his twin and Crysania.

Raistlin has a charisma that is very powerful. Thus Dalamar stays with him, even at the peril of his own life. Crysania is drawn to him, though she can't explain why. He can be very charming, when it suits his purpose.

Raistlin will not, under any circumstances, return to the Red Robes, much less the White. Raistlin is truly evil. He chose to be evil, and it is only because of his final sacrifice that he is rewarded by the salvation of peace in death.

Raistlin
(20th-Level Human Black Robe Wizard)

STR	INT	WIS	DEX	CON	CHR
10	17	14	16	10	15

THAC0: 9
AL: Chaotic Evil
HP: 44
AC: −2

DMs who are running campaigns based on the DRAGONLANCE® *Legends* books need to make Raistlin an NPC character since he has gone beyond 18th level. Raistlin is a complex character and this information should help you play him effectively.

Lord Soth
(Knight of the Black Rose)

Though a death knight (see the *FIEND FOLIO*® tome), Lord Soth wears the armor of a Knight of the Rose. This armor is blackened and charred as if it had been in a fire. He wears the helm of a Knight as well. All that can be seen of his face is two flaming orange eyes. He is a frightening apparition who can even make the fearless kender "feel a bit queer" when they are in his presence. Soth's voice is deep, seeming to come from far underground. Although thoroughly evil, he is proud and will fight an enemy honorably. His admiration and respect for Kitiara becomes, eventually, a dark passion that will lead him into plotting her death.

Lord Soth's tragic history is told in part in the history of the Knights of Solamnia.

Lord Soth
(Solamnic Deathknight)

STR	INT	WIS	DEX	CON	CHR
18/99	10	9	14	17	17

THAC0: 12
AL: Chaotic Evil
HP: 59
AC: 0

Kitiara

Since her dreams of conquering the world under the banner of the Dark Queen have been crushed, Kitiara is frustrated and raging beneath her calm exterior. She has never admitted defeat and, in fact, has managed to make Sanction a haven that not even the Knights with their good dragons feel ready to attack.

She hopes Raistlin will help her gain her ambition; his plans to challenge the Dark Queen anger and scare Kitiara. Kitiara has a respect for the Queen born of fear and she is terrified that, if Raistlin fails, he will drag her down with him as well. Kitiara also has become enamored of the dark elf, Dalamar. Her plans to rule the world include the dark elf ruling at her side.

Kitiara is a gambler with fate. Having considered the odds, she has decided to put her money on the Dark Queen instead of her half-brother, Raistlin. It is a pretty good bet, since she undoubtedly believes she could worm her way back into Raistlin's favor should he succeed. What she has not counted upon is Lord Soth.

Kitiara

(15th-Level Human Fighter)

STR	INT	WIS	DEX	CON	CHR
14	13	7	18	14	14

THACO: 6
AL: Lawful Evil
HP: 68
AC: −3

Duncan

(King of the Dwarves of Thorbardin)

Approximately two hundred years old when he died, Duncan was still in the prime of life for a dwarf. He was stoutly built with iron grey hair and a grey beard that he wore in long, flowing curls according to the fashion of the mountain dwarves. Quick-tempered, blunt, and gruff, Duncan was a shrewd old dwarf who held his position as king tenaciously despite the various dwarven factions that wanted to overthrow him. He accomplished this with wisdom, diplomacy, and common sense.

Duncan waged the Dwarfgate Wars because he knew that he could not open the gates of Thorbardin to the hill dwarves and plainsmen or all would perish of famine. He had not foreseen the terrible loss of life that would occur when Fistandantilus's magic wiped out almost all members of both armies. Duncan's sons died in this battle and their father did not long outlive them, dying of a broken heart in the arms of his young friend, Kharas.

Duncan

(10th-Level Mountain Dwarf Fighter)

STR	INT	WIS	DEX	CON	CHR
17	10	13	10	15	10

THACO: 12
AL: Chaotic Good
HP: 48
AC: −1

Kharas

(Dwarven Hero)

Taller than average for a dwarf, Kharas was a handsome dwarf of serious, solemn mein. He had dark hair and a luxurious beard worn in long curls according to the style of his people, the mountain dwarves. When Kharas was young, in the days before the Cataclysm, he fought with the Knights of Solamnia in the Goblin Wars. The Knights were impressed with Kharas's skill and valor as well as his nobility and honor. They named him "Kharas" which means knight in Solamnic. This is one of the highest honors the Knights can bestow on a member of another race.

Kharas wielded a huge hammer that he made himself, some say with the help of the god Reorx. (see page 96 for more info on the hammer). If the players meet Kharas during the time of the Dwarfgate Wars, he will have shaved his beard—a shocking act for a dwarf. Such a thing is done only to those dwarves who have performed a disgraceful act. Since he was opposed to warring against his kinsmen, the idealistic Kharas shaved his beard as a sign that he fought this war only because his king ordered him to do so and that he went forward to kill his fellow dwarves in bitter shame.

Kharas fled the final battle when he saw his kinsmen slaughtering each other for no purpose except hatred. With him he carried the bodies of the king's sons. Thus Kharas escaped the devastating blast that leveled the battle-field and wiped out both dwarven armies. He returned to King Duncan, who—shocked and horrified by Kharas's report—shut himself up in his home and refused to eat or drink, weakening and eventually dying in Kharas's arms.

The Thanes all fought to gain the kingship, each seeking out Kharas and vying for his support. Sickened by the greed and political back-stabbing of his people, Kharas took the body of his king and his magical *hammer* and carried them to a secret burial ground, where he died. Before he left, he foretold that the dwarves would never be united until one arose brave enough to seek out the *Hammer* and return it to the dwarves of Thorbardin.

Kharas

(14th-Level Mountain Dwarf Fighter)

STR	INT	WIS	DEX	CON	CHR
18/56	12	17	14	16	10

THACO: 7
AL: Lawful Good
HP: 78
AC: 2

Reghar Fireforge

Reghar was the elderly hill dwarf (Flint's grandfather) who led his people during the Dwarfgate Wars. Hale and hearty, Reghar was stubborn and fiercely proud. He had gray hair and a gray beard that he wore plaited and tucked into his belt in the fashion of the hill dwarves. He went to war against his cousins because he was convinced that the mountain dwarves had great wealth and stores of food hidden beneath the mountain that they refused to share with those in need. Although this is not true, nothing anyone said convinced Reghar otherwise. He believed in this for too long and, besides, it was the hill dwarves' only hope for survival.

Reghar had one son who lived to adulthood (Flint's father). His other son died of heart disease (the same affliction that killed Flint). Reghar himself died in the Dwarfgate Wars, killed in the blast of magic that destroyed nearly everyone in both dwarven armies.

Reghar fireforge

(9th-Level Hill Dwarf Fighter)

STR	INT	WIS	DEX	CON	CHR
17	10	8	12	14	12

THACO: 12
AL: Chaotic Good
HP: 52
AC: 4

amothus palanthus

(Lord of Palanthus)

As his name implies, the family of Amothus Palanthus has ruled the city of Palanthus for hundreds of years. Rulership of Palanthus was always passed on to the eldest son, while the younger sons generally served in the Knights of Solamnia. Amothus is an only child, however, and is unmarried—a situation that many mothers of daughters in Palanthus hope to remedy. In his early forties, Amothus is much like the people of Palanthus themselves—appearing weak, shallow, and foppish, but with a core of steel beneath.

amothus palanthus

(7th-Level Human Fighter)

STR	INT	WIS	DEX	CON	CHR
11	14	12	16	11	15

THACO: 14
AL: Lawful Good
HP: 41
AC: 6

Elistan

(Cleric of Paladine)

Elistan is the prophet of Paladine on Krynn. During the Dragonlance Wars he brought the knowledge of the true gods back to the greater world. Now, however, he is gravely ill. Elistan refuses to allow any to pray to Paladine in an attempt to heal him, saying that the god had granted him life once and his work here is complete. He has brought back knowledge of the true gods and built a beautiful Temple in Palanthus. He now wants only to die in peace.

Elistan's greatest concern is for the church and for Crysania. He has been given knowledge from Paladine that if Crysania succeeds in her quest, she will be a great leader—a powerful cleric, ruling over the church with wisdom and compassion. Thus Elistan will do what he can to counsel Crysania, but will not attempt to dissuade her (or any other player character) from seeking her own destiny.

Elistan

(18th-Level Human Cleric of Paladine)

STR	INT	WIS	DEX	CON	CHR
13	14	17	12	12	16

THACO: 10
AL: Lawful Good
HP: 61
AC: −1

The character of Elistan before and during the War of the Lance has been described in the modules. Those who meet Elistan after the war find the cleric dying of a wasting illness.

Par-Salian

(Head of the Conclave)

A powerful wizard of the White Robes, Par-Salian is an elderly human male, probably in his early 70s at the end of the War of the Lance. The archmage has long white hair and his white beard is straight and inclined to be wispy. His robes are snow white and are not adorned with runes of any type. He appears frail, but his eyes are a bright, glittering blue. His face is like that of a fierce old eagle.

Par-Salian is not a wizard of action, preferring to spend his time in study. It was primarily because of his vast knowledge of magic that he obtained his high rank. It was he who made the important decision to allow the young mage, Raistlin Majere, to take the Test at an age earlier than most. Some wizards believed that it was because of this decision that Fistandantilus was able to seal a bargain with the young mage and thus lead him into paths of evil.

Par-Salian is aware, however, that without Raistlin's skill and power, the War of the Lance would never have been won. He knows that Raistlin chose for himself the path he walks. At this point in his life, Par-Salian would like very much to give up the burden of heading the Conclave, but he cannot while Raistlin's

threat to the world exists. Under no circumstances will Par-Salian leave the Tower of Wayreth.

Par-Salian

(18th-Level Human White Robe Wizard)

STR	INT	WIS	DEX	CON	CHR
10	18	15	17	9	12

THACO: 13
AL: Lawful Good
HP: 47
AC: 0

Justarius

(Head of the Order of Red Robes)

A human male in his late 40s, Justarius is considered by many to be next in line as Head of the Conclave when Par-Salian retires. A big, robust man with an open, honest face, Justarius walks with a pronounced limp. His left leg was crippled during the magical Test. How or why no one knows, but it is rumored that Justarius was exceptionally proud of his physical prowess when young and that his Test forced him to choose between physical strength or his magic.

Justarius likes and admires Par-Salian. He respects Ladonna, his nearest competitor for the Head of the Conclave. The Red-Robed wizard is ambitious, but he knows that he can bide his time. He is in no hurry to take over the responsibilities as Head of the Conclave. Justarius enjoys adventure and might be persuaded by an adventuring party to accompany them on a quest—particularly if they can make it worth his while by offering the possibility of a magical artifact, spell book, or other unusual item.

Although an honest man, Justarius is neutral in all things and is not overly compassionate. He is secretive and not inclined to trust anyone. He has many magical means of compensating for his handicap, some of which can be extremely startling and surprising. His red robes are made of plain material decorated with runes of warding and protection.

Justarius

(17th-Level Human Red Robe Wizard)

STR	INT	WIS	DEX	CON	CHR
14	17	14	16	13	12

THACO: 12
AL: Lawful Neutral
HP: 48
AC: −2

Ladonna

(Head of the Order of Black Robes)

An extraordinarily beautiful human female in her 60s, Ladonna is a powerful wizardress who rules over the Black Robes only because Raistlin has never challenged her. Just why he has not done so is uncertain; possibly because he considers it beneath him. Ladonna is well aware that if Raistlin did challenge her to the ritual magical contest to gain control of the Order, he would not hesitate to kill her. Because of this, Ladonna hates and fears Raistlin more than any other member of the Conclave. She will do everything in her power, sacrifice anyone or anything, to stop him—as long as she herself is protected. She will not attack him directly.

Despite her age—which she scorns to hide by means of magical arts—Ladonna is still a woman of striking appearance. She has iron gray hair that she wears woven in the most intricate designs upon her head. Her black robes are rich and luxurious, glittering with runes of protection stitched in silver. She wears many jewels, some of which are magical and others not, for Ladonna has a weakness for fine jewelry. In their youth, Ladonna and Par-Salian were lovers and there is still a kind of affection and understanding between them.

Ladonna

(17th-Level Human Black Robe Wizardress)

STR	INT	WIS	DEX	CON	CHR
9	18	16	18	12	18

THACO: 12
AL: Lawful Evil
HP: 49
AC: −3

Maquesta Kar-thon

(Pirate)

A very attractive black woman in her late 20s, Maquesta has short curly hair and the lithe, strong body of an athlete. Owner of the doomed ship *Perechon*, Maquesta comes from the seafaring race of humans in Northern Ergoth. Her father, a sailor, left Maquesta the *Perechon* and a pile of debts. He had trusted in a friend who betrayed him. Before he died, Maq's father enjoined her never to trust anyone and to do whatever she had to in order to make money—wealth being the only thing worthwhile in this world.

Bitter at the betrayal of her father, Maq follows his instructions to the letter. The only person she even considers trusting is Koraf, her minotaur first mate. Maq and Koraf met on the Isle of Mithas, where Maq was being held prisoner by the minotaurs for encroaching on their territory. Koraf was also a prisoner, under a sentence of death. He saved Maq's life and helped her escape. Maq still has nightmares about what she saw in the minotaur prison.

Maq is fond of men, but loves them and leaves them. She prefers handsome men with few brains; she has a guy in every port. But, deep in her heart, Maq truly loves the ugly, bestial-looking Koraf, although it takes a lot for her to admit this even to herself.

Maquesta Kar-thon

(8th-Level Half-Elf Fighter-Thief)

STR	INT	WIS	DEX	CON	CHR
15	11	13	18	16	13

THACO: 14
AL: Neutral
HP: 58
AC: 4

Bas-Ohn Koraf

(Minotaur First Mate to Maquesta)

Although his face is bestial and ugly, the tall Koraf has the superb, muscular body of a human in his late 20s. Koraf was sentenced to death in his homeland for killing another minotaur in a fit of rage. (Killing another minotaur is sanctioned only in the Games, which are held to determine superiority.) Koraf's death would not have been pleasant

and he saw escape as the only alternative.

Koraf met Maquesta in prison. She was scheduled to die after having seen most of the rest of her crew being tortured to death. He helped her escape, she saved his life, and the two became fast friends. Despite the fact that Koraf at first thought Maq one of the ugliest females he had ever seen (minotaurs feel that way about all humans), he has lived among humans long enough to believe that she is beautiful and that he himself is hideous. A truly noble being, if somewhat quick-tempered and savage, Koraf is deeply in love with Maquesta, but believes that his love is hopeless since he is so ugly.

Bas-Ohn Koraf

(10th-Level Minotaur Fighter)

STR	INT	WIS	DEX	CON	CHR
18/90	8	6	10	14	6

THACO: 10
AL: Neutral (Evil)
HP: 55
AC: 6

Player Characters from the DRAGONLANCE® Legends Books

The *Legends* series are stories about people who are being tested. Some are being tested in their love, some in their faith. Each has a lesson to learn in life and sometimes the learning is very difficult and dangerous. DMs devising campaigns based on the Legends series should keep this in mind. Once again, we urge DMs and players to read the novels for ideas and descriptions of places and people.

Dalamar

(Dark Elf Wizard)

At the beginning of the *Legends* books, Dalamar is a young dark elf of 90 years, which figures out to about 25 in human years. Dalamar is a very handsome elf with long, flowing brown hair, brown eyes, and an extremely charming and winning personality. He is in

excellent health and condition, well-built and muscular.

A skilled young wizard, Dalamar has just completed his Test. His first task as an apprentice is to serve Raistlin, the Master of the Tower of High Sorcery in Palanthus.

The Conclave of Wizards fears Raistlin more than any other threat in the history of their Orders. In a secret meeting, they asked for a volunteer to serve as Raistlin's apprentice and to spy on him for the Conclave. Dalamar volunteered without hesitation.

The dark elf was originally from Silvanesti. A member of a low caste, he would have been allowed to proceed only so far in his magical arts and then forbidden by law to gain further power. Ambitious, hungering for knowledge and the power that magic conferred, Dalamar turned from the White Robes that all elves wear and chose to wear the Black. He continued his studies in secret, hiding himself away from his people. But eventually he was discovered and was cast out of his race by Porthios, then the new Speaker of the Sun and Stars. Thus Dalamar became a dark elf, one who is cast out of the light.

Bound hand and foot and blind-folded, Dalamar was driven in a cart to the borders of Silvanesti and there thrown out. This was about one year after the end of the War of the Lance. Dalamar made his way to the Tower of High Sorcery at Wayreth, where he took the Test and completed it successfully. The Test for Dalamar involved his lingering love and longing for his elven homeland and people—a matter he had to resolve within himself before he could be free to devote himself to magic.

Dalamar's first love and loyalty is to his magic and to the Conclave. He admires Raistlin, however, and is fascinated by the power of the archmage. Thus he willingly risks his life to study with him and serve as his apprentice. But Dalamar is smart enough to know that man was not meant to challenge the gods and that only destruction can result from such vast ambition.

The dark elf has a high Wisdom, which gives him the understanding that balance and order must be maintained in the world. Thus he respects Elistan as a cleric of Paladine. He fears Raistlin as a renegade who would topple balance and order and throw the world into chaos. Dalamar's admiration and fascination with his dark master, however, have led him more than once to seriously question whether he could truly destroy Raistlin if he had to do so.

Like so many other men before him, Dalamar is highly attracted to Kitiara. Dalamar is being tested in his devotion to his art and his ability to sacrifice worldly ambition and perhaps even his life for it.

Dalamar

(13th-Level Dark-Elf Black Robe Wizard)

STR	INT	WIS	DEX	CON	CHR
16	17	16	16	12	14

THACO: 16
AL: Chaotic Evil
HP: 41
AC: 0

Crysania

(Cleric of Paladine)

An attractive young woman in her late 20s, Crysania has black hair, white skin, and grey eyes. Her face, in fact, appears colorless and cold to those who first meet her. She is a Revered Daughter of Paladine, a dedicated cleric. Her first and only love is her church.

The daughter of an ancient, noble family of Palanthus, Crysania is cultured and extremely well-educated. She could have had her choice of husbands, not only because of her manners and attractiveness, but also because of her family's wealth, to which Crysania is the only heir. The young woman wants something more from life, however, than settling down and raising children. She knows that she has been destined for greatness and in her early youth was frustrated and unable to find her calling in life. When she met Elistan, she discovered her destiny. One of the cleric's earliest converts, Crysania left home and wealth and dedicated her life to her faith.

Crysania is devout, but she is also ambitious. She knows that she has within her the strength and the ability to lead the church when Elistan is gone. What she does not yet understand is that she must also have compassion, humility, and tolerance or she will follow in the footsteps of the Kingpriest.

In much the same way as magic-users must pass a Test in their arcane arts, so clerics are tested by their gods. These are tests of life, however, and may come at any time, even when the cleric appears to be well-established. (The Kingpriest, for example, was tested and failed, thus precipitating the Cataclysm.) Crysania's journey through time and entering the Abyss with Raistlin is a test of her faith.

Crysania

(14th-Level Human Cleric of Paladine)

STR	INT	WIS	DEX	CON	CHR
10	13	12	11	16	16

THACO: 14
AL: Lawful Good
HP: 63
AC: 2

Caramon Majere

Twenty-eight years old and 50 pounds overweight at the beginning of the *Legends* series, Caramon is in terrible physical condition and an alcoholic. He is a sodden wreck of a man, fluctuating between self-pity and self-indulgence. Caramon's testing is the most demanding of all the characters, since it is physical, mental, and spiritual. The trials Caramon undergoes are meant to teach him that he has value as a person and that he must live his own life.

Following the War of the Lance, Caramon came home a hero. He married Tika and should have lived happily ever after. Unfortunately, once the war had ended and life for people was returning to normal, no one needed Caramon. Even Tika had developed her own life, managing the Inn of the Last Home.

Caramon had devoted his life solely to his brother, appearing noble and self-sacrificing in giving way to his twin's every whim. The truth was, of course, that Caramon didn't view himself as a person of worth. He needed Raistlin to feel needed himself. Caramon has so little self-esteem that he doesn't really know how to love anyone.

Caramon's learning experience should involve three goals: he must free himself of his addiction to dwarven spirits and get himself in physical shape once more; he must learn that he is intelligent, a leader of men, and has ideas that are of value and worth; he must accept the fact that his twin is truly evil, that Raistlin chose to be evil, and that Caramon cannot change him.

Caramon Majere

(12th-Level Human Fighter)

STR	INT	WIS	DEX	CON	CHR
18/63	12	10	11	17	15

THACO: 10
AL: Lawful Good
HP: 95
AC: −1

Caramon's problem is one of will power and self-esteem, coupled with the disease of alcoholism. It will take a great deal to get him out of this slump.

Caramon has a Willpower statistic in addition to his other statistics. This starts at 1. Each time Caramon passes a bar or any location at which drink is offered, he must roll 1d10. If the result is greater than his willpower he will stop and get drunk. If it is equal to or less than his willpower, then he steels himself and passes by the bar. When drunk, he suffers a −10 penalty to hit and has an AC of 8 regardless of his armor or other protections.

As long as Caramon gets drunk at least once in three days, he suffers a −5 penalty to hit and a −5 penalty to his Armor Class. He is either noisy and rude or sulky and blubbery. He cannot travel farther than two miles in a day before collapsing.

Should he go more than three days without getting drunk, things get worse for him. He becomes violently ill and attacks anyone who stands between him and getting drunk. He is unable to travel more than one mile and is incapable of defending himself or engaging in any combat whatsoever. This condition lasts for one day.

After this period, he returns to his −5 penalty to hit and −5 penalty to his Armor Class. For every week thereafter that he remains sober, his penalties to hit and Armor Class drop by one and his Willpower increases by one. His Willpower will eventually reach 10, but if he ever takes another drink it will immediately drop by three.

Tasslehoff Burrfoot

Even the merry-hearted kender is tested in the *Legends* books. Due to his experiences in the War, particularly in losing two people he truly loved—Flint and Sturm—Tasslehoff is probably a bit more serious-minded than most kender (which isn't saying a lot). Certainly Tas has great insight into character,

although generally he doesn't know what to do with it.

Primarily, the thoughtless, heedless kender must learn to accept responsibility for his actions. He needs to learn that there is a serious side to life that must (on occasion) be faced. Finally, he should learn that evil isn't exciting and interesting. It is often ugly, hurtful, and destructive.

Tas is an interesting character, however, in that he teaches as well as learns. His natural buoyancy and good humor carry him through many predicaments, as does his caring, compassion, and loyalty for his friends. Tasslehoff's sheer joy and pleasure in living from day to day, in viewing each day as an exciting new adventure, make him a fun companion.

Tasslehoff Burrfoot

(12th-Level Kender Thief...er...Handler)

STR	INT	WIS	DEX	CON	CHR
13	9	12	16	14	11

THACO: 16
AL: Neutral
HP: 44
AC: 1

Tika Waylan Majere

Tika is a lovely young woman in her early 20s. A heroine celebrated in legend and song throughout Krynn, Tika could have had her choice of men. She has loved Caramon since she was a girl and her love for him grew deeper during their adventures and perils together. Unfortunately, Tika never fully understood Caramon's relationship with his twin and his dependency on Raistlin. Tika hurried Caramon into marriage following the war, assuming that she could take Raistlin's place in Caramon's heart.

But, though Tika loves Caramon dearly, the independent, strong-willed young woman can never need Caramon the way Raistlin needed him. Although she can't express it, Tika is wise enough to know that this type of relationship is poison anyway. Tika blames herself, however, for Caramon's slow descent into the bottle. She is ashamed of him and of herself and tries to hide his worsening condition from their friends. Tika realizes, finally, that Caramon will die unless he changes and therefore she throws him out, telling him not to return to her as husband or friend until he knows himself.

Tika Waylan Majere

(10th-Level Human Fighter)

STR	INT	WIS	DEX	CON	CHR
14	9	12	16	13	14

THACO: 12
AL: Neutral Good
HP: 60
AC: 0

Tanis Half-Elven

Although Tanis remains in the present in the *Legends* novels, he may return to the past—either with Caramon or on his own. He might also accompany Tika in a search for Caramon and Lady Crysania.

Tanis is married to Laurana and is basically living happily ever after. Their love grows daily. Both are extremely busy—Laurana serving as a diplomat for the Knights of Solamnia, Tanis accompanying her as advisor, guide, and bodyguard. Both are highly respected and admired throughout Ansalon.

If there is any hint of dissatisfaction in Tanis's life, it is that the demands of being famous have forced him to give up much of his beloved privacy and independence. Laurana, being the daughter of royalty, is accustomed to life in the public eye. Tanis isn't, and he resents the loss of his freedom. There is also a great deal of pressure on Tanis to try to "put the world back together." He doesn't really feel adequate for the task, but he is doing the best he can.

There is always in the back of Tanis's mind the fantasy of Kitiara—just as Kit knew there would be when she aided his escape from the Temple at Neraka. Much as Crysania is in love with an ideal of Raistlin that can never possibly be, so Tanis is in love with an ideal of Kitiara. He still doesn't truly know her.

Tanis

(12th-Level Half-Elf Fighter)

STR	INT	WIS	DEX	CON	CHR
16	12	13	16	12	15

THACO: 10
AL: Neutral Good
HP: 79
AC: −3

Character Alignment Tracking Chart

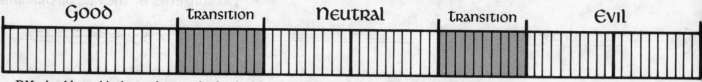

| Good | Transition | Neutral | Transition | Evil |

DMs should use this chart to keep track of each player character's alignment as determined by his actions.

A player character's initial position on this chart is the midpoint of his professed alignment.

Actions that are contrary to the character's professed alignment shift the character's position on this chart in the appropriate direction (toward good, evil, or neutrality). Most shifts involve moves of one to four boxes. The DM must determine the number of boxes to shift in each case.

The grey areas labeled "Transition" are passed through when a character's actions dictate a change in alignment. The penalties the character suffers while his alignment is in a grey area are given on page 13.

Races of Krynn

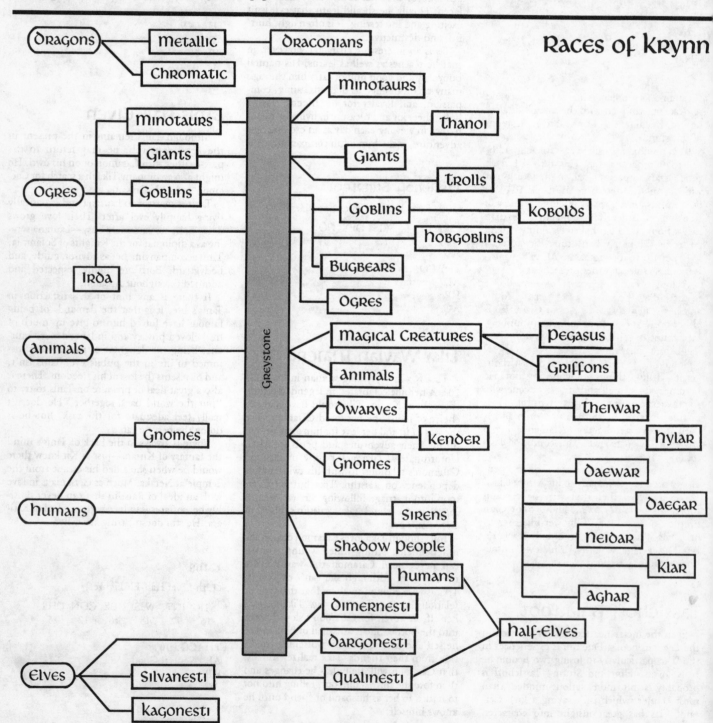

Unified Ansalon Monster Chart

Name	AC	MV	HD	hp	#AT	Dmg	SA	SD	AL	THACO	Book
Bat	8	1"/24"	1/4	2	1	1	yes	no	N	20	M2-15
Carrion Crawler	3/7	12"	3+1	18	8	Paralyze	yes	no	N	16	M-13
Centaur	5(4)	18"	4	21	2	1d6/1d6	no	no	CG	15	dl1-31
Centipede, Giant	9	15"	1/4	1	1	poison(−4)	yes	no	N	20	dl2-30
Crayfish, Giant	4	6"//12"	4+4	24	2	1d12/1d12	no	no	N	15	M-15
Crocodile, Giant	4	6"//12"	7	35	2	3d6/2d10 or 2d20	no	no	N	15	M-15
Draconian:											
Aurak	0	15"	8	42	2	(1d8+2)x2	yes	yes	LE	12	DL-73
Baaz	4	6"/15"/18"	2	12	1	1d8	no	yes	LE(C)	16	DL-74
Bozak	2	6"/15"/18"	4	22	1	1d8	yes	yes	LE	15	DL-74
Kapak	4	6"/15"/18"	3	17	1	1d4	yes	yes	LE	16	DL-74
Sivak		16"/15"/18"	6	31	3	1d6/1d6/2d6	no	yes	NE	13	DL-75
Dragon (hatchling):											
Black	3	12"/24"	6	6	3	1d4/1d4/3d6	yes	no	CE	16	dl1-31
Dragon (average adult):											
Black	3	12"/24"	7	35	3	1d4/1d4/3d6	yes	no	CE	12	M-31
Blue	2	9"/24"	9	45	3	1d6/1d6/3d8	yes	no	LE	10	M-31
Green		29"/24"	8	40	3	1d6/1d6/2d10	yes	no	LE	12	M-33
Red	-1	9"/24"	10	50	3	1d8/1d8/3d10	yes	no	CE	9	M-33
White	3	12"/30"	6	30	3	1d4/1d4/2d8	yes	no	CE	13	M-34
Dragon (huge ancient):											
Black (Khisanth)	3	12"/24"	8	64	3	1d4/1d4/3d6	yes	yes	CE	8	dl1-26
Red	-1	9"/24"	11	88	3	1d8/1d8/3d10	yes	yes	CE	7	M-33
Dryad	9	12"	2	9	1	1d4	yes	yes	N	16	dl1-9
Dog, Wild	7	15"	1+1	8	1	1d4	no	no	N	18	dl2-30
Elk	8	18"	3	15	1	1d4	no	no	N	16	dl2-30
Elf, Qualinesti											
Border Patrol	5	12"	2+2	17	1	1d8+1 or 1d6	no	no	LG	19	dl1-8
Fighter	4	12"	3	20	1	1d8+2 or 1d6+1	no	no	LG	17	dl2-12
Magic-User	8	12"	5	13	1	1d4	yes	no	LG	20	dl2-12
Warriors	5	12"	1+1	7	1	1d8+1 or 1d6	no	no	LG	19	dl2-12
Frog, Giant	7	3"//9"	3	16	1	2d4	yes	no	N	16	M-41
Froghemoth	2/4/6	2"//8"	1	69	5	15d10	yes	yes	N	7	M2-67
Fungus, Violet	7	1"	3	17	12d4	Rot	yes	no	N	16	M-42
Gelatinous Cube	8	6"	4	21	1	2d4	yes	no	N	15	M-43
Ghast	4	15"	4	22	3	1d4/1d4/1d8	yes	yes	CE	15	M-43
Ghoul	6	9"	2	11	3	1d3/1d3/1d6	yes	yes	CE	16	M-43
Giant, Hill	4	12"	8+2	45	1	2d8	yes	no	CE	12	M-45
Goblin	6	6"	1-1	3	1	1d6	no	no	LE	20	dl2-30

Book Notes:
M-X = *Monster Manual*, page X
M2-X = *Monster Manual II*, page X
FF-X = *FIEND FOLIO®* tome, page X
DL-X = *DRAGONLANCE® Adventures*, page X
dlY-X = DRAGONLANCE Module #Y, page X

Unified Ansalon Monster Chart

Name	AC	MV	HD	hp	#AT	Dmg	SA	SD	AL	THAC0	Book
Gorzaug											
(Type V Demon)	-7/-5	12"	7+7	41	7	1d8	yes	yes	CE	12	M-19
Green Slime	9	0"	2	10	0	Rot	yes	yes	N	16	M-49
Groaning Spirit	0	15"	7	36	1	1d8	yes	yes	CE	13	M-50
Gully Dwarf	8	12"	4	14	1	1d6	no	yes	N	15	DL-67
Hobgoblin	5	9"	1+1	5	1	1d8	no	no	LE	18	dl1-4
Leech, Giant	9	3"	4	18	1	1d4	yes	no	N	1 5	M-60
Kender	5	9"	3	12	1	1d4	yes	no	C G	20	DL-51
Man											
Freedom Fighter	7	12"	3	18	1	1d8	no	no	NG	18	dl-14
Gladiator	4	9"	2	11	3	1d3/1d3/1d6	yes	yes	CE	16??	dl-14
Guard, City	8	12"	2	8	1	1d6	no	no	var	20	dl1-10
Guard, Holy	4	12"	4	25	1	1d8	no	no	CG	18	dl1-7
Laborer	9	12"	1	4	1	1d6	no	no	N	20	dl-14
Mercenary	6	9"	2	10	1	1d8	no	no	NE	20	dl-14
Merchant	10	12"	1	5	1	1d4	no	no	N	20	dl-14
Officer	3	9"	7	37	1	1d8+2	no	no	LE	12	dl-14
Refugees	8-10	12"	0-3	var	1	1d4	no	no	var	var	dl1-7
Slave	10	12"	1	3	1	1d4	no	no	N	20	dl-14
Townsperson	10	12"	1	5	1	1d4	no	no	var	20	dl1-5
Trollop	9	12"	1	4	1	1d6	no	no	N	20	dl-14
Minotaur	6	12"	6+3	33	1	1d10	no	yes	CE	13	DL-69
Mobat	7	3"/15"	4	19	1	2d4	yes	yes	NE	15	M2-15
Mold, Brown	9	0"	na	na	0	0	yes	yes	N	na	M-71
Mold, Yellow	9	0"	na	na	1	1d8	yes	yes	N	Spc	M-71
Ogre	5	9"	4+1	26	1	1d10	no	no	CE	15	M-75
Pedipalp, Huge	4	9"	2+2	14	3	1d6/1d6/1d8	yes	no	N	16	M2-100
Pegasus	6	24"/48"	4	18	3	1d8/1d8/1-3	no	no	CG	16	dl1-9
Rat, Giant	7	12"//6"	1/2	3	1	1d3	yes	no	N	20	M-81
Skeleton	7	12"	1	5	1	1d6	no	yes	N	19	M-87
Slug, Giant	8	6"	12	58	1	1d12	yes	no	N	9	dl2-20
Snake											
Giant Constrictor	5	9"	6+1	31	2	1d4/2d4	yes	no	N	13	M-88
Poisonous	6	15"	2+1	10	1	1 + poison (3d4)	yes	no	N	16	M2-111
Spectral Minion											
Reveler	2	30"	5	22	1	1d4 + revel	yes	yes	CE	15	DL-70
Guardian	2	30"	10	46	1	1d10	no	yes	LG	10	DL-70
Warrior	2	30"	9	40	1	1d10	no	yes	var	12	DL-70
Berserker	2	30"	10	48	2	1d10/1d10	no	yes	CE	10	DL-70
Philosopher	2	30"	17 4		na	na	no	yes	var	na	DL-70
Searcher	2	30"	6	30	na	na	no	yes	LE	na	DL-70
Spider, Huge	6	18"	2+2	11	1	1d6 + poison	yes	no	N	16	M-90
Stag, White	-5	24"	10	77	3	1d12/1d6/1d6	no	yes	LG	10	dl1-6
Troll	4	12"	6+6	37	3	5-8/5-8/2d6	yes	yes	CE	13	M-97
Unicorn (Forestmaster)	2	24"	10	60	3	1d8/1d8/1d20	no	no	CG	10	dl1-9
Vampire	1	12"/18"	8+3	42	1	1d6+4	yes	yes	CE	12	M-99
Wight	5	12"	4+3	27	1	1d4	yes	yes	LE	15	M-100
Witherweed	8	0"	3	16	1d12+12	Spc	yes	yes	N	16	FF-95
Wraith	4	12"/24"	5+3	26	1	1d6	yes	yes	LE	15	M-102
Wyvern	3	6"/24"	7+7	43	2	2d8/1d6 + poison	yes	no	NE	12	dl2-30
Yellow Musk Creeper	7	0"	3	15	2d6	Spc	yes	yes	N	16	FF-97
Zombie	8	6"	2	11	1	1d8	no	no	N	16	M-103

Character Class Master Statistics Range Table

Character Class	STR	INT	WIS	DEX	CON	CHA	Proficiencies Initial	Added	Book
CAVALIER (CV)	15/-	10/-	10/-	15/-	15/-	-/-	3/2	1/1 per 2	Unearthed Arcana
Paladin (P)	15/-	10/-	13/-	15/-	15/-	17/-	3/2	1/1 per 2	Unearthed Arcana
Knights of the Crown (KC)	10/-	7/-	10/-	8/-	10/-	-/-	3/2	1/1 per 2	DL Adventures
Knights of the Sword (KS)	12/-	9/-	13/-	9/-	10/-	-/-	3/2*	1/1 per 2	DL Adventures
Knights of the Rose (KR)	15/-	10/-	13/-	12/-	15/-	-/-	3/2*	2/ 1 per 2	DL Adventures
FIGHTER (F)	9/15	-/-	-/-	-/-	7/-	-/-	4/2	1/1 per 3	Player's Handbook
Barbarian (B)	15/-	-/-	(16)/-	14/-	15/-	-/-	6/3	1/1 per 2	Unearthed Arcana
Ranger (R)	13/15	13/15	14/15	-/-	14/-	-/-	3/2	1/ 1 per 3	Player's Handbook
MAGIC-USER (RENEGADE) (MU)	-/-	9/16	-/-	6/-	-/-	-/-	1/3	1/2 per 6	Player's Handbook
Illusionist (Renegade) (I)	-/-	15/-	-/-	16/-	-/-	-/-	1/3	1/2 per 6	Player's Handbook
Wizard of High Sorcery (W)	-/-	9/16	-/-	6/-	-/-	-/-	1/3‡	1/2 per 5	DL Adventures
THIEF (T)	-/-	-/-	-/-	9/15	-/-	-/-	2/3	1/1 per 4	Player's Handbook
Thief/Acrobat (A)	15/16	-/-	-/-	16/-	-/-	-/-	2/3	1/1 per 4	Unearthed Arcana
CLERIC (HEATHEN) (CL)	-/-	-/-	9/15	-/-	-/-	-/-	2/3	1/1 per 4	Player's Handbook
Druid (Heathen) (D)	-/-	-/-	12/16	-/-	-/-	15/16	2/3	1/1 per 5	Player's Handbook
Holy Orders of the Stars (H)	-/-	-/-	9/15	-/-	-/-	-/-	3/4	1/2 per 5	DL Adventures
TINKER GNOMES (TG)	6/-	10/15	(12)/-	12/-	8/-	-/-	2/3	1/2 per 3	DL Adventures

Character Racial Minimum & Maximum Table

Character Race	STR	INT	WIS	DEX	CON	CHA	Accepted Classes	Book
Human	-/-	-/-	-/-	-/-	-/-	-/-	Any*	Player's Handbook
Kender	6/16	6/-	3/16	8/-	10/-	6/-	F,B,R, T,A,H	DL Adventures
Gnomes (Mad)	6/-	7/-	-/-	-/-	8/-	-/-	CL,F,I,T,A	Player's Handbook
Tinker Gnomes	6/-	8/-	-/12	8/-	8/-	-/-	TG	DL Adventures
Elves (Dark)	-/-	-/-	-/-	7/-	6/-	8/-	CL,D,F,R,MU, W,T,A	Player's Handbook
Qualinesti	7/-	8/-	6/-	7/-	7/-	8/-	C,F,W,T,A,H R	DL Adventures
Silvanesti	-/-	10/-	6/-	7/-	6/-	12/-	P,M,W,H,F	DL Adventures
Kagonesti	8/-	-/12	8/-	8/-	8/-	8/-	F,B,R,T,A,H	DL Adventures
Dimernesti	-/-	8/-	8/-	10/-	-/-	8/-	C,P,F,W,H	DL Adventures
Half Elves	-/-	4/-	-/-	6/-	6/-	-/-	C,P,KC,KS,F,R,W,T,A,H	DL Adventures
Dwarves (Fatherless)	8/-	-/-	-/-	-/17	12/-	-/16	F,B,R,T,A,H	Player's Handbook
Hill Dwarves	9/-	-/-	-/-	-/17	14/-	-/16	F,B,R,T, A,H	DL Adventures
Mountain Dwarves	8/-	-/-	-/-	-/17	12/-	-/16	C,P,F,T,A,H	DL Adventures
Gully Dwarves	6/-	-/9	-/9	6/-	-/12	-/9	F,B,T,A,H	DL Adventures
Irda	12/-	5/15	10/-	8/-	15/-	15/-	C,P,F, R,W,T,A,H	DL Adventures
Minotaurs	12/-	5/-	-/12	8/-	12/-	-/12	F, B,R,W,H	DL Adventures

* Except tinkers—only gnomes can become tinkers.

Gnome Device Complexity Level

Complexity	Size	A Damage/ Protection	B Move Vertical*	C Move Horizontal*	D Sound	Temperature†	E Environment Atmosphere‡	Light	F Communication Information	G Alter Object**
1	Small Sack	1hp/AC 10	4'	8'	Silence	+1°	Normal Air	Darkness	Cams/Ruler	Perfect Optics
2	Knife	1d4/AC 9	8'	16'	Whisper	+5°	Slight Odor	Starlight	Protractor	Pipes & Wire
3	Sword/Pouch	1d6/AC 8	12'	24'	Low Voices	+10°	Tainted/Odor	Moonlight	Compass/Magnetic Measure	Springs & Gears
4	Crossbow	1d8/AC 7	16'	32'	Talking	+20°	Stink	Candlelight	Abacus	Tools
5	Backpack	1d10/AC 6	20'	40'	Shouting	Freeze Water/ +30°	Strench	Lamplight	Theodolite	Steel
6	Chest	2d6/AC 5	24'	48'	Yelling	+50°	5,000' alt.‡	Daylight	Air Pressure Measure	Steel/Processed Food
7	Couch	2d8 or 1d20/AC 4	40'	80'	Noisy	+100°	10,000' alt.‡	Desert Sun	Clockwork Sequencer	Iron
8	Small Cabinet/Man	2d10/AC 3	120'	160'	Loud	+200°	—	Lightning	Inertial Measure	Glass
9	Large Cabinet	2d20/AC 2	160'	400'	Roar	+300°	Tear Gas	Blinding Flash	Sound Recording	Polished Wood/ Cooked Food
10	Large Wagon	3d10/AC 1	200'	800'	Deafening	—/Burning Wood	—	—	Programmable Sequencer	Refined Ore
11	Small Cottage	3d20/AC 0	600'	1,600'	—	Liquid to Gas	Sickening	—	Picture Recording	Tooled Wood
12	Large Cottage	1d100/AC -1	800'	2,400'	—	Solid to Liquid	Vacuum‡	—	Automated Calculator	Cut Wood Pieces
13	Mansion	2d100/AC -2	1,000'	3,200'	—	Liquid to Solid	Poisonous	—	Light Measure	Plowed Field
14	Tower (3 Stories)	3d100/AC -3	2,000'	1 mile	—	Solid to Gas	—	—	Direct Sound	Raw Ore/Raw Food
15	Tower (6 Stories)	—	5,000'	5 miles	—	Gas to Liquid	—	—	Direct Wire Control	Broken Ground
16	Tower (10 Stories)	—	5 miles	20 miles	—	Gas to Solid	—	—	Direct Picture	Broken or Cut Trees
17	Small Keep	—	20 miles	100 miles	—	—	—	—	Indirect Sound Transmission	Cleared Raw Ground
18	Castle	—	space	500 miles	—	—	—	—	Indirect Remote Control	Raw Wooded Ground
19	Township	—	—	Forward in Time	—	Transmutation	—	—	Indirect Picture Transmission	Broken Stone
20	Mountain	—	—	Back in Time	—	—	—	—	—	Raw Stone

* This represents the distance an object is moved in one round. For increased duration of such a flight, use the duration modifiers chart for increasing the length of the effect over a period of time. This also assumes that the object being moved is size 1 (equal to complexity 1). If the object being moved is larger than size 1, add 1 for every 2 sizes larger to the size and complexity of the machine.

† The degrees are degrees of change from its present state to its new state. If two entries are separated by a slash, the first indicates temperature shifts toward cold, while the second indicates temperature shifts toward hot. The changing of elements from one state to another is not permanent, except as modified by duration factors. Transmutation is always permanent and deals with changing the basic properties of an item (lead to gold for example). Note also that this column does not take into account any secondary effects as a result of the heat or cold involved. For example, the heating of sand to melt it into glass is figured on the Alter Object column rather than this one.

‡ Not only does this column deal with the state of the atmosphere, but with differences in air pressure as well. Note that hypoxia (drunken condition due to lack of sufficient oxygen) occurs at altitudes over 10,000 feet.

** This column is used somewhat differently than other columns: to determine the size/complexity number of the end state of the device. First, find both the *initial state* of the object being modified and the *end state* desired. Second, subtract the complexity of the end state from that of the initial state. The result is the size/complexity number required. If you are trying to take a more finely crafted object and make it rougher (e.g., reduce a polished table to the state of broken wood) then subtract the lower number from the higher number and subtract an additional 4. It is always easier to make something less finished than to take something raw and make it beautiful.

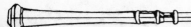

Gnome Mishap Table

Note: The effect level or damage caused by a device is often equated with its complexity. To find the magnitude of the specific effect involved, look on the Gnome Device Complexity Level Table. Examples: Complexity 5 damage is 1d10. If a complexity 8 temperature (200°) may be reduced by 1d6, and the die roll result is 3, then it would become a complexity 5 temperature (or +30°).

1-8 Needs Another Part: The device requires another device to be built before it can function properly. The new part *must* be a useful device on its own and have a demonstrated use other than in conjunction with fixing this device. Example: a gnome who gets this result while attempting to construct a catapult now may declare that he must first build an automated can opener before he can finish the catapult. This second device must be built using the same rules as any other device. Of course, if a mishap occurs while building the can opener that requires yet another device be built....

9 Communication Glitch: If the device was designed to communicate, it will function in unexpected ways at the discretion of the DM. If the device was not meant to communicate, it will do so in one of the following bad ways at a level 1d4 below its current complexity. Options include: sends message directly to foes and enemies with perfect clarity; randomly changes messages in such a way that their true intent is never trustworthy; only sends every second or third word.

10-11 Improper Alteration: If designed to alter an object, the machine will do it improperly. If it is not designed to alter an object, it will do so badly at a level 1d4 below its current complexity. Options include: does the reverse of its intention (takes knitted sweaters and turns them into yarn); creates something absolutely useless in the current situation; reduces finished goods to their base elements.

12 Unexpected Glow: The machine suddenly begins to glow so brightly that the operator and anyone within 10′ times the size of the machine is blinded for 10 rounds. No other functions occur.

13 Olfactory Malfunction: If the device was designed to change the state of the surrounding atmosphere, it will have the reverse effect (machines to clear air will pollute it, machines to obscure air will cleanse it). If not so designed, it will create a complexity 9 *tear gas* effect in a number of 10-foot cubic areas equal to its size. All in the area must make a successful Constitution Check or flee the area at once. Any who remain suffer a −5 attack penalty and a +5 Armor Class penalty until the area is cleared. Any Dexterity Checks are at a +3 penalty. The gas remains as long as the machine continues to function + 1d6 rounds thereafter.

14 Unbearable Temperature Changes: If designed to create a certain temperature the machine will have the opposite effect (ovens will refrigerate, for example). If not, then the device will get hot (50%) or cold (50%)to a degree equal to its complexity. This may result in the destruction of the machine itself should the temperature reach the point to burn it or even change the state of its components (solid to liquid).

15 Horrendous Sound: The device makes a horrible complexity 10 noise *(deafening)* in a number of 10-foot cubic areas equal to its size. All in the area must make a successful Constitution Check or flee the area at once. Any who remain suffer a −5 attack penalty and a +5 Armor Class penalty until the area is cleared. Any Dexterity Checks are at a +3 penalty. The noise continues as long as the machine continues to function + 1d6 rounds thereafter.

16 Moves Uncontrollably Downward: Regardless of the intentions for the device, it suddenly takes off on its own. If the device was designed to move downward, then substitute result #17 below for this result. Otherwise, the device digs (or submerges) straight down a distance equal to its complexity. It does so in one turn. The device continues to move down as it is running. No directional control is possible.

17 Moves Uncontrollably Upward: Regardless of the intentions for the device, it heads for the sky. If the device was designed to fly, substitute result #16 for this result. The device flies upward a distance equal to its complexity rating and remains there until turned off. Turning the device off results in a fall from that height.

18 Reverse Direction, with Damage: The device inflicts damage equal to its complexity and then fails. The machine must be repaired before it can be used again.

19 Machine Pursuit: The device attacks its operator for damage equal to its complexity and unerringly chases the operator for five + 1d6 melee rounds or until it is shut off, whichever comes first. The operator of the device must make a Dexterity Check to turn off the device. The machine rolls to hit as though it were a monster with hit dice equal to its complexity.

20 Explosion!: The machine explodes, doing damage equal to its complexity over a number of 10-foot cubes equal to its complexity. The machine is then broken and must be fixed before it can be used again.

Spheres of Influence—The Gods of Good

SPHERE/SPELL	BOOK	Lvl	Pal	Maj	Ki-Jo	Mish	Habb	Bran
All								
Atonement	PH	5	A	A	A	A	A	A
Ceremony	*UA	1	A	A	A	A	A	A
Combine	UA	1	A	A	A	A	A	A
Holy Symbol	UA	2	A	A	A	A	A	A
Purify Food and Water	PH	1R	True	True	True	True	True	True
Animal								
Animal Friendship	*PH	1	—	—	—	Add	A	—
Animal Growth	*PH	5R	—	—	—	—	A	—
Animal Summoning I	*PH	4	—	—	—	—	A	—
Animal Summoning II	*PH	5	—	—	—	—	A	—
Animal Summoning III	*PH	6	—	—	—	—	A	—
Anti-Animal Shell	*PH	6	—	—	—	—	A	—
Call Woodland Beings	*PH	4	—	—	—	—	A	—
Charm Person or Mammal	*PH	2	—	Spc	—	A	A	—
Creeping Doom	*PH	7	—	Add	—	—	A	—
Giant Insect	UA	4R	—	—	—	—	A	—
Hold Animal	*PH	3	—	—	—	—	A	—
Invis. to Animals	*PH	1	—	—	—	—	A	—
Messenger	UA	2	—	—	—	—	A	—
Repel Insects	*PH	4	—	Add	—	—	A	—
Reincarnate	*PH	7	—	—	—	—	A	—
Snake Charm	PH	2	—	—	—	—	A	—
Speak with Animals	*PH	1	—	—	—	—	A	—
Summon Insects	*PH	3	—	Spc	—	—	A	—
Astral								
Astral Spell	PH	7	A	A	A	A	—	—
Plane Shift	PH	5	A	A	A	A	—	—
Charm								
Charm Person or Mammal	*PH	2	A	A	—	A	—	—
Cloak of Fear/Bravery	UA	4R	A	A	Add	A	—	—
Command	PH	1	A	A	—	A	—	—
Confusion	*PH	7	A	A	—	A	—	—
Enthrall	UA	2	A	A	—	A	—	—
Feeblemind	*PH	6	A	A	—	A	—	—
Hold Person	PH	2	A	A	—	A	—	—
Imbue with Spell Ability	UA	4	A	A	—	A	—	—
Quest	PH	5	A	A	Add	A	—	Add
Remove/Cause Fear	PH	1R	A	A	—	True	—	—
Combat								
Bless/Curse	PH	1R	Add	—	A	Add	—	—
Chant—	PH	2	—	—	A	Add	—	—
Flame Strike	PH	5	Add	—	A	—	—	—
Holy/Unholy Word	PH	7R	True	—	True	True	—	—
Insect Plague	*PH	5	—	Add	A	—	—	—
Magic Stone	UA	1	—	—	A	—	—	—
Prayer	PH	3	—	—	A	Spc	—	—
Spiritual Hammer	PH	2	—	—	A	Spc	—	—
Create								
Animate Object	PH	6	—	—	—	A	—	—
Create Food and Water	PH	3	—	—	Spc	A	Add	Add
Heroes' Feast	UA	6	—	—	Add	A	Add	Add
Divination								
Augury	PH	2	Add	A	—	A	—	—
Commune	PH	6	—	A	—	A	—	—
Commune with Nature	*PH	5	—	A	—	A	Add	—
Detect Balance	*UA	1	Spc	A	—	A	—	—
Detect/Obscure Charm	PH	1R	—	A	—	A	—	—
Detect Evil/Good	PH	1R	—	A	—	A	—	—
Detect/Undetectable Lie	PH	1R	—	True	—	True	—	—
Detect Life	UA	2	—	A	—	A	Spc	Spc
Detect Magic	*PH	1	—	A	Spc	A	—	—
Detect Poison	*UA	1	—	A	—	A	—	—
Detect Snares and Pits	*PH	1	—	A	Add	A	—	Add
Divination	PH	4	—	A	—	A	—	—
Find/Obscure the Path	PH	6R	—	A	—	A	—	—
Find Traps	PH	2	—	A	Add	A	—	—
Know/Obscure Alignment	*UA	3R	—	A	—	A	—	—
Locate Animal	*PH	1	—	A	—	A	Spc	—
Locate/Obscure Object	PH	3R	—	A	—	A	—	—
Locate Plants	*PH	2	—	A	—	A	—	Spc
Magic Font	UA	5	—	A	—	A	—	—
Penetrate Disguise	UA	1	—	A	Add	A	—	—
Portent	UA	1	—	A	—	A	—	—
Reflecting Pool	*UA	2	Spc	A	—	A	—	—
Speak with Monsters	PH	6	—	A	—	A	Add	—
Tongues/Confuse Tongues	PH	4R	—	A	—	A	—	—
True/False Seeing	PH	5R	—	True	—	True	—	—
Elemental								
Air Walk	UA	5	—	—	—	—	A	—
Animate Rock	*PH	7	—	—	—	—	A	—
Chariot of Sustarre	*PH	7	—	—	—	—	A	—
Conjure/Dis. Earth Elem.	*PH	7R	—	—	—	—	A	—
Conjure/Dis. Fire Elem	*PH	6R	—	—	—	—	A	—
Create/Destroy Water	*PH	1/2R	—	—	—	—	A	—
Dust Devil	UA	2	—	—	—	—	A	—
Earthquake	PH	7	—	—	—	—	A	—
Fire Storm/Quench	*PH	7R	—	—	—	—	A	—
Fire Trap	*PH	2	—	—	—	—	A	—
Flame Blade	*UA	2	—	—	—	—	A	—
Heat/Chill Metal	*PH	2R	—	—	Add	—	A	—
Lower/Raise Water	PH	4R	—	—	—	—	A	—
Meld into Stone	UA	3	—	—	—	—	A	—
Part Water	PH	6	—	—	—	—	A	—
Produce Fire	*PH	4	—	—	—	—	A	—
Produce Flame	*PH	2	—	—	—	—	A	—
Purify/Contaminate Water	*PH	1R	—	—	—	—	True	—
Pyrotechnics	*PH	3	—	—	—	—	A	—
Spike Stones	*UA	5	—	—	—	—	A	—
Stone Shape	*PH	3	—	—	Add	—	A	—
Stone Tell	PH	6	—	—	—	—	A	—
Transmute Metal to Wood	*PH	7	—	—	—	—	A	—
Transmute Rock to Mud	*PH	5	—	—	—	—	A	—
Transmute Water to Dust	*UA	6R	—	—	—	—	A	—
Wall of Fire	*PH	5	—	—	—	—	A	—
Water Breathing	*PH	3	—	—	—	—	A	—
Water Walk	UA	3	—	—	—	Add	A	—
Wind Walk	PH	7	—	—	—	—	A	—
Guardian								
Blade Barrier	PH	6	A	—	A	—	—	—
Glyph of Warding	PH	3	A	—	A	—	—	—
Silence 15' r.	PH	2	A	Spc	A	Add	—	—
Symbol	PH	6/7	A	—	A	—	—	—
Wyvern Watch	UA	2	A	—	A	—	—	—

Abbreviations:

R (after spell level #) = reversible; * = druidical; A = castable in any form; Add = additional spell cleric can cast even though it is out of his deity's spheres of influence; Spc = special power, a spell the deity grants in addition to the cleric's normal allotment of spells; X = excluded, clerics of this god cannot use this spell; True = reverse of spell cannot be cast; Rev = only reversed spell can be cast.

Spheres of Influence—the Gods of Good

SPHERE/SPELL	BOOK	Lvl	Pal	Maj	Ki-Jo	Mish	Habb	Bran
Healing								
Cure/Cause Blindness	PH	3R	—	—	Rev	A	—	—
Cure/Cause Critical Wnds	*PH	5/6R	—	—	Rev	A	—	—
Cure/Cause Disease	*PH	3R	—	—	Rev	A	—	—
Cure/Cause Light Wnds	*PH	1R	True	—	Rev	A	—	—
Cure/Cause Serious Wnds	*PH	4R	—	—	Rev	A	—	—
Heal/Harm	PH	6R	—	—	Rev	A	—	—
Neutralize/Poison	*PH	4/3R	—	—	X	True	—	Add
Remove/Cause Paralysis	UA	3R	—	—	Rev	A	—	—
Slow Poison	*PH	2	—	—	X	A	—	Add
Necromantic								
Aid	UA	2	—	—	—	A	—	—
Animate Dead	PH	3	—	—	—	A	—	—
Animate Dead Monsters	UA	5	—	—	—	A	—	—
Death's Door	UA	3	—	—	Add	A	—	—
Feign Death	*PH	3/2	—	—	—	A	—	—
Finger of Death	*PH	7	—	—	Add	A	—	—
Invis to Undead	UA	1	—	—	—	A	—	—
Raise Dead/Slay Living	PH	5R	—	—	Rev	A	—	—
Regeneration/Wither	PH	7R	—	—	Rev	A	—	—
Restoration/Energy Drain	PH	7R	—	—	Rev	A	—	—
Resurrection/Destruction	PH	7R	—	—	Rev	A	—	—
Speak with Dead	PH	3	—	—	—	A	—	—
Plant								
Anti-Plant Shell 10' r.	*PH	5	—	—	—	—	—	A
Barkskin	*PH	2	—	—	—	—	—	A
Changestaff	*UA	7	—	—	—	—	—	A
Entangle	*PH	1	—	—	—	—	—	A
Fire Seeds	*PH	6	—	—	—	—	—	A
Goodberry/Badberry	*UA	2R	—	—	—	—	—	A
Hallucinatory Forest	*PH	4R	—	—	—	—	—	A
Hold Plant	*PH	4	—	—	—	—	—	A
Liveoak	*UA	6	—	—	—	—	—	A
Pass Plant	*PH	5	—	—	—	—	—	A
Pass Without Trace	*PH	1	—	—	—	—	—	A
Plant Door	*PH	4	—	—	—	—	—	A
Plant Growth	*PH	3	—	—	—	—	—	A
Shillelagh	*PH	1	—	—	—	—	—	Add
Snare	*PH	3	—	—	—	—	—	A
Speak with Plants	*PH	4	—	—	—	—	—	A
Spike Growth	*UA	4	—	—	—	—	—	A
Sticks to Snakes	*PH	4/5R	—	—	—	—	—	A
Transport via Plants	*PH	4	—	—	—	—	—	A
Tree	*PH	3	—	—	—	—	—	A
Trip	*PH	2	—	—	—	—	—	A
Turn Wood	*PH	6	—	—	—	—	—	A
Wall of Thorns	*PH	6	—	—	—	—	—	A
Warp Wood	*PH	2	—	—	—	—	—	A

SPHERE/SPELL	BOOK	Lvl	Pal	Maj	Ki-Jo	Mish	Habb	Bran
Protection								
Dispel Magic	*PH	3/4	A	—	—	—	—	—
Endure/Dispel Cold/Heat	UA	1R	A	—	—	Add	—	—
Flame Walk	UA	3	A	—	—	—	—	—
Forbiddance	UA	6	A	—	—	—	Add	—
Magical Vestment	UA	3	A	—	Add	—	—	—
Negative Plane Protection	UA	3	A	—	—	—	—	—
Protection from Evil/Good	PH	1R	True	True	True	True	True	True
Prot. from Evil/Good 10' r.	PH	4R	True	True	True	True	True	True
Protection from Fire	*PH	3	A	—	—	—	—	—
Protection from Lightning	*PH	4	A	—	—	—	—	—
Remove/Bestow Curse	PH	3R	A	—	—	Spc	—	—
Resist Cold	PH	1	A	—	—	Add	—	—
Resist Fire	PH	2	A	—	—	—	—	—
Sanctuary	PH	1	A	—	—	—	—	—
Spell Immunity	UA	4	A	—	—	—	—	—
Withdraw	UA	2	A	—	—	—	—	—
Stellar								
Continual Light/Dark	PH	3R	A	Add	Add	True	Add	Add
Light/Darkness	PH	1R	A	Add	Add	True	Add	Add
Moonbeam	*UA	5	A	—	—	A	—	A
Starshine	*UA	3	A	—	—	A	—	A
Sunray	*UA	7	A	—	—	A	—	A
Summoning								
Abjure/Implore	UA	4R	—	A	—	—	—	—
Aerial Servant	PH	6	—	A	—	—	—	Add
Conjure Animals	PH	6	—	A	—	—	Add	—
Dispel Evil/Good	PH	5R	—	True	—	—	—	—
Exaction	UA	7	—	A	—	—	—	—
Exorcise	PH	4	—	A	—	—	—	—
Gate	PH	7	—	A	—	—	—	—
Golem	UA	5	—	A	—	—	—	—
Succor	PH	6	—	A	—	—	—	—
Word of Recall	PH	6	—	A	—	—	—	—
Weather								
Call Lightning	*PH	3	—	—	—	—	—	A
Cloudburst	*UA	3	—	—	—	—	—	A
Control Temperature	*PH	4	—	—	—	—	—	A
Control Weather	*PH	7	—	—	—	—	—	A
Control Winds	*PH	5	—	—	—	—	—	A
Faerie Fire	*PH	1	—	—	—	—	—	A
Obscurement	*PH	2	—	—	—	—	—	A
Precipitation	*UA	1	—	—	—	—	—	A
Predict Weather	*PH	1	—	—	Add	—	—	A
Rainbow	UA	5	—	—	—	—	—	A
Weather Summoning	*PH	6	—	—	—	—	—	A

Abbreviations:

R (after spell level #) = reversible; * = druidical; A = castable in any form; Add = additional spell cleric can cast even though it is out of his deity's spheres of influence; Spc = special power, a spell the deity grants in addition to the cleric's normal allotment of spells; X = excluded, clerics of this god cannot use this spell; True = reverse of spell cannot be cast; Rev = only reversed spell can be cast.

Spheres of Influence—The Gods of Neutrality

SPHERE/SPELL	BOOK	Lvl	Gil	Sirr	Reorx	Chislev	Zivil	Shin
All								
Atonement	PH	5	A	A	A	A	A	A
Ceremony	*UA	1	A	A	A	A	A	A
Combine	UA	1	A	A	A	A	A	A
Holy Symbol	UA	2	A	A	A	A	A	A
Purify Food and Water	PH	1R	True	True	True	True	True	True
Animal								
Animal Friendship	*PH	1	—	—	—	A	—	—
Animal Growth	*PH	5R	—	—	—	—	A	—
Animal Summoning I	*PH	4	—	—	—	A	—	—
Animal Summoning II	*PH	5	—	—	—	A	—	—
Animal Summoning III	*PH	6	—	—	—	A	—	—
Anti-Animal Shell	*PH	6	—	—	—	A	—	—
Call Woodland Beings	*PH	4	—	—	—	A	—	—
Charm Person or Mammal	*PH	2	—	—	—	A	—	—
Creeping Doom	*PH	7	—	—	—	A	—	—
Giant Insect	UA	4R	—	—	—	A	—	—
Hold Animal	*PH	3	—	—	—	A	—	—
Invis. to Animals	*PH	1	—	—	—	A	—	—
Messenger	UA	2	Add	—	—	A	—	—
Repel Insects	*PH	4	—	—	—	A	—	—
Reincarnate	*PH	7	—	—	—	A	—	—
Snake Charm	PH	2	—	—	—	A	—	—
Speak with Animals	*PH	1	Add	—	—	A	—	—
Summon Insects	*PH	3	—	—	—	A	—	—
Astral								
Astral Spell	PH	7	A	—	—	—	A	—
Plane Shift	PH	5	A	—	—	—	A	—
Charm								
Charm Person or Mammal	*PH	2	—	—	—	—	—	A
Cloak of Fear/Bravery	UA	4R	—	—	—	—	—	A
Command	PH	1	—	—	—	—	—	A
Confusion	*PH	7	Add	—	—	—	—	A
Enthrall	UA	2	—	—	—	—	—	A
Feeblemind	*PH	6	Add	—	—	—	—	A
Hold Person	PH	2	—	—	—	—	—	A
Imbue with Spell Ability	UA	4	—	—	—	—	—	A
Quest	PH	5	—	—	—	—	—	A
Remove/Cause Fear	PH	1R	—	—	—	—	—	A
Combat								
Bless/Curse	PH	1R	—	A	A	—	—	—
Chant—	PH	2	Add	A	—	A	—	—
Flame Strike	PH	5	—	A	—	A	—	—
Holy/Unholy Word	PH	7R	—	A	A	—	—	—
Insect Plague	*PH	5	—	A	A	—	—	—
Magic Stone	UA	1	—	A	A	—	—	—
Prayer	PH	3	Add	A	A	—	—	—
Spiritual Hammer	PH	2	—	A	A	—	—	—
Create								
Animate Object	PH	6	A	—	A	—	—	A
Create Food and Water	PH	3	A	—	A	—	—	A
Heroes' Feast	UA	6	A	—	A	—	—	A
Divination								
Augury	PH	2	A	—	—	—	A	—
Commune	PH	6	A	—	—	—	A	—
Commune with Nature	*PH	5	A	—	—	—	A	—
Detect Balance	*UA	1	A	—	—	—	A	—
Detect/Obscure Charm	PH	1R	A	—	—	—	A	—
Detect Evil/Good	PH	1R	A	—	—	—	A	—
Detect/Undetectable Lie	PH	1R	A	—	—	—	A	—
Detect Life	UA	2	A	—	—	A	—	—
Detect Magic	*PH	1	A	—	—	—	A	—
Detect Poison	*UA	1	A	—	—	—	A	—
Detect Snares and Pits	*PH	1	A	—	—	—	A	—
Divination	PH	4	A	—	—	—	A	—
Find/Obscure the Path	PH	6R	A	—	—	—	A	—
Find Traps	PH	2	A	—	—	—	A	—
Know/Obscure Alignment	*UA	3R	A	—	—	—	A	—
Locate Animal	*PH	1	A	—	—	—	A	—
Locate/Obscure Object	PH	3R	A	—	—	—	A	Spc
Locate Plants	*PH	2	A	—	—	—	—	—
Magic Font	UA	5	A	—	—	—	A	—
Penetrate Disguise	UA	1	A	—	—	—	A	—
Portent	UA	1	A	—	—	—	A	—
Reflecting Pool	*UA	2	A	—	—	—	A	—
Speak with Monsters	PH	6	A	—	—	—	A	—
Tongues/Confuse Tongues	PH	4R	A	—	—	—	A	—
True/False Seeing	PH	5R	A	—	—	—	A	—
Elemental								
Air Walk	UA	5	—	—	A	—	—	—
Animate Rock	*PH	7	—	—	A	—	—	—
Chariot of Sustarre	*PH	7	—	—	A	—	—	—
Conjure/Dis. Earth Elem.	*PH	7R	—	—	A	—	—	—
Conjure/Dis. Fire Elem	*PH	6R	—	—	A	—	—	—
Create/Destroy Water	*PH	1/2R	—	—	A	—	—	—
Dust Devil	UA	2	—	—	A	—	—	—
Earthquake	PH	7	—	—	A	—	—	—
Fire Storm/Quench	*PH	7R	—	—	A	—	—	—
Fire Trap	*PH	2	—	—	A	—	—	—
Flame Blade	*UA	2	—	—	A	—	—	—
Heat/Chill Metal	*PH	2R	—	—	A	—	—	—
Lower/Raise Water	PH	4R	—	—	A	—	—	—
Meld into Stone	UA	3	—	—	A	—	—	—
Part Water	PH	6	—	—	A	—	—	—
Produce Fire	*PH	4	—	—	A	—	—	—
Produce Flame	*PH	2	—	—	A	—	—	—
Purify/Contaminate Water	*PH	1R	—	—	A	—	—	—
Pyrotechnics	*PH	3	—	—	A	—	—	—
Spike Stones	*UA	5	—	—	A	—	—	—
Stone Shape	*PH	3	—	—	A	—	—	—
Stone Tell	PH	6	—	—	A	—	—	—
Transmute Metal to Wood	*PH	7	—	—	A	—	—	—
Transmute Rock to Mud	*PH	5	—	—	A	—	—	—
Transmute Water to Dust	*UA	6R	—	—	A	—	—	—
Wall of Fire	*PH	5	—	—	A	—	—	—
Water Breathing	*PH	3	—	—	A	—	—	—
Water Walk	UA	3	—	—	A	—	—	—
Wind Walk	PH	7	—	—	A	—	—	—
Guardian								
Blade Barrier	PH	6	—	A	—	—	—	A
Glyph of Warding	PH	3	—	A	—	—	—	A
Silence 15' r.	PH	2	—	A	—	—	—	A
Symbol	PH	6/7	—	A	—	—	—	—
Wyvern Watch	UA	2	—	A	—	—	—	A

Abbreviations:

R (after spell level #) = reversible; * = druidical; A = castable in any form; Add = additional spell cleric can cast even though it is out of his deity's spheres of influence; Spc = special power, a spell the deity grants in addition to the cleric's normal allotment of spells; X = excluded, clerics of this god cannot use this spell; True = reverse of spell cannot be cast; Rev = only reversed spell can be cast.

Spheres of Influence—The Gods of Neutrality

SPHERE/SPELL	BOOK	Lvl	Gil	Sirr	Reorx	Chislev	Zivil	Shin
Healing								
Cure/Cause Blindness	PH	3R	—	A	—	A	—	—
Cure/Cause Critical Wnds	*PH	5/6R	—	A	—	A	—	—
Cure/Cause Disease	*PH	3R	—	A	—	A	—	—
Cure/Cause Light Wnds	*PH	1R	Add	A	—	A	—	—
Cure/Cause Serious Wnds	*PH	4R	Add	A	—	A	—	—
Heal/Harm	PH	6R	—	A	—	A	—	—
Neutralize/Poison	*PH	4/3R	—	A	—	A	—	—
Remove/Cause Paralysis	UA	3R	—	A	—	A	—	—
Slow Poison	*PH	2	—	A	—	A	—	—
Necromantic								
Aid	UA	2	—	—	—	—	A	—
Animate Dead	PH	3	—	—	—	—	A	—
Animate Dead Monsters	UA	5	—	—	—	—	A	—
Death's Door	UA	3	—	—	—	—	A	—
Feign Death	*PH	3/2	—	—	—	—	A	—
Finger of Death	*PH	7	—	—	—	—	A	—
Invis to Undead	UA	1	—	—	—	—	A	—
Raise Dead/Slay Living	PH	5R	—	—	—	—	A	—
Regeneration/Wither	PH	7R	—	—	—	—	A	—
Restoration/Energy Drain	PH	7R	—	—	—	—	A	—
Resurrection/Destruction	PH	7R	—	—	—	—	A	—
Speak with Dead	PH	3	—	—	—	—	A	—
Plant								
Anti-Plant Shell 10' r.	*PH	5	—	—	—	—	A	—
Barkskin	*PH	2	A	—	—	—	—	A
Changestaff	*UA	7	—	—	—	—	A	—
Entangle	*PH	1	—	—	—	—	A	—
Fire Seeds	*PH	6	—	—	—	—	A	—
Goodberry/Badberry	*UA	2R	—	—	—	—	A	—
Hallucinatory Forest	*PH	4R	—	—	—	—	A	—
Hold Plant	*PH	4	—	—	—	—	A	—
Liveoak	*UA	6	—	—	—	—	A	—
Pass Plant	*PH	5	—	—	—	—	A	—
Pass Without Trace	*PH	1	—	—	—	—	A	—
Plant Door	*PH	4	—	—	—	—	A	—
Plant Growth	*PH	3	—	—	—	—	A	—
Shillelagh	*PH	1	—	—	—	—	A	—
Snare	*PH	3	—	—	—	—	A	—
Speak with Plants	*PH	4	—	—	—	—	A	—
Spike Growth	*UA	4	—	—	—	—	A	—
Sticks to Snakes	*PH	4/5R	—	—	—	—	A	—
Transport via Plants	*PH	4	—	—	—	—	A	—
Tree	*PH	3	—	—	—	—	A	—
Trip	*PH	2	—	—	—	—	A	—
Turn Wood	*PH	6	—	—	—	—	A	—
Wall of Thorns	*PH	6	—	—	—	—	A	—
Warp Wood	*PH	2	—	—	—	—	A	—

SPHERE/SPELL	BOOK	Lvl	Gil	Sirr	Reorx	Chislev	Zivil	Shin
Protection								
Dispel Magic	*PH	3/4	A	—	—	—	—	A
Endure/Dispel Cold/Heat	UA	1R	A	—	—	—	—	A
Flame Walk	UA	3	A	—	—	—	—	A
Forbiddance	UA	6	A	—	—	—	—	A
Magical Vestment	UA	3	A	—	—	—	—	A
Negative Plane Protection	UA	3	A	—	—	—	—	A
Protection from Evil/Good	PH	1R	A	A	A	A	A	A
Prot. from Evil/Good 10' r.	PH	4R	A	A	A	A	A	A
Protection from Fire	*PH	3	A	—	—	—	—	A
Protection from Lightning	*PH	4	A	—	—	—	—	A
Remove/Bestow Curse	PH	3R	A	—	—	—	—	A
Resist Cold	PH	1	A	—	—	—	—	A
Resist Fire	PH	2	A	—	—	—	—	A
Sanctuary	PH	1	A	—	—	—	—	A
Spell Immunity	UA	4	A	—	—	—	—	A
Withdraw	UA	2	A	—	—	—	—	A
Stellar								
Continual Light/Dark	PH	3R	A	A	A	A	A	A
Light/Darkness	PH	1R	A	A	A	A	A	A
Moonbeam	*UA	5	—	—	A	—	—	—
Starshine	*UA	3	—	—	A	—	—	—
Sunray	*UA	7	—	—	A	—	—	—
Summoning								
Abjure/Implore	UA	4R	—	A	—	—	—	—
Aerial Servant	PH	6	—	A	—	—	—	—
Conjure Animals	PH	6	—	A	—	—	—	—
Dispel Evil/Good	PH	5R	—	A	—	—	—	—
Exaction	UA	7	—	A	—	—	—	—
Exorcise	PH	4	—	A	—	—	—	—
Gate	PH	7	—	A	—	—	—	—
Golem	UA	5	—	A	—	—	—	—
Succor	PH	6	—	A	—	—	—	—
Word of Recall	PH	6	—	A	—	—	—	—
Weather								
Call Lightning	*PH	3	—	—	—	A	—	—
Cloudburst	*UA	3	—	—	—	A	—	—
Control Temperature	*PH	4	—	—	—	A	—	—
Control Weather	*PH	7	—	—	—	A	—	—
Control Winds	*PH	5	—	—	—	A	—	—
Faerie Fire	*PH	1	—	—	—	A	—	—
Obscurement	*PH	2	—	—	—	A	—	—
Precipitation	*UA	1	—	—	—	A	—	—
Predict Weather	*PH	1	—	—	—	A	—	—
Rainbow	UA	5	—	—	—	A	—	—
Weather Summoning	*PH	6	—	—	—	A	—	—

Abbreviations:

R (after spell level #) = reversible; * = druidical; A = castable in any form; Add = additional spell cleric can cast even though it is out of his deity's spheres of influence; Spc = special power, a spell the deity grants in addition to the cleric's normal allotment of spells; X = excluded, clerics of this god cannot use this spell; True = reverse of spell cannot be cast; Rev = only reversed spell can be cast.

Spheres of Influence—the Gods of Evil

SPHERE/SPELL	BOOK	Lvl	Tak	Sarg	Morg	Chem	Zeb	Hidd
All								
Atonement	PH	5	A	A	A	A	A	A
Ceremony	*UA	1	A	A	A	A	A	A
Combine	UA	1	A	A	A	A	A	A
Holy Symbol	UA	2	A	A	A	A	A	A
Purify Food and Water	PH	1R	A	A	A	A	A	A
Animal								
Animal Friendship	*PH	1	—	—	—	—	A	—
Animal Growth	*PH	5R	—	—	—	—	A	—
Animal Summoning I	*PH	4	—	—	—	—	A	—
Animal Summoning II	*PH	5	—	—	—	—	A	—
Animal Summoning III	*PH	6	—	—	—	—	A	—
Anti-Animal Shell	*PH	6	—	—	—	—	A	—
Call Woodland Beings	*PH	4	—	—	—	—	A	—
Charm Person or Mammal	*PH	2	—	—	—	—	A	—
Creeping Doom	*PH	7	—	—	—	—	A	—
Giant Insect	UA	4R	—	—	—	—	A	—
Hold Animal	*PH	3	—	—	—	—	A	—
Invis. to Animals	*PH	1	—	—	—	—	A	—
Messenger	UA	2	—	—	—	—	A	—
Repel Insects	*PH	4	—	—	—	—	A	—
Reincarnate	*PH	7	—	—	—	—	A	—
Snake Charm	PH	2	—	—	—	—	A	—
Speak with Animals	*PH	1	—	—	—	—	A	—
Summon Insects	*PH	3	—	—	—	—	A	—
Astral								
Astral Spell	PH	7	A	A	A	A	—	—
Plane Shift	PH	5	A	A	A	A	—	—
Charm								
Charm Person or Mammal	*PH	2	—	A	—	—	—	—
Cloak of Fear/Bravery	UA	4R	—	True	—	—	—	—
Command	PH	1	—	A	—	—	—	—
Confusion	*PH	7	—	A	—	—	—	—
Enthrall	UA	2	—	A	—	—	—	—
Feeblemind	*PH	6	—	A	—	—	—	—
Hold Person	PH	2	—	A	—	—	—	—
Imbue with Spell Ability	UA	4	—	A	—	—	—	—
Quest	PH	5	—	A	—	—	—	—
Remove/Cause Fear	PH	1R	—	Rev	—	—	—	—
Combat								
Bless/Curse	PH	1R	—	Rev	—	Rev	—	—
Chant	PH	2	—	A	—	A	—	—
Flame Strike	PH	5	Add	A	—	A	—	—
Holy/Unholy Word	PH	7R	Rev	Rev	—	Rev	—	—
Insect Plague	*PH	5	—	A	—	A	—	—
Magic Stone	UA	1	—	A	—	A	—	—
Prayer	PH	3	—	A	—	A	—	—
Spiritual Hammer	PH	2	Add	A	—	A	—	—
Create								
Animate Object	PH	6	Spc	Add	—	Add	Add	—
Create Food and Water	PH	3	Add	—	Add	—	Add	—
Heroes' Feast	UA	6	—	—	—	—	—	—

SPHERE/SPELL	BOOK	Lvl	Tak	Sarg	Morg	Chem	Zeb	Hidd
Divination								
Augury	PH	2	—	—	—	—	—	A
Commune	PH	6	—	—	—	—	—	A
Commune with Nature	*PH	5	—	—	—	—	—	A
Detect Balance	*UA	1	—	—	—	—	—	A
Detect/Obscure Charm	PH	1R	—	—	—	—	—	A
Detect Evil/Good	PH	1R	—	—	—	—	—	A
Detect/Undetectable Lie	PH	1R	—	—	—	—	—	A
Detect Life	UA	2	—	—	—	—	—	A
Detect Magic	*PH	1	—	—	—	—	—	A
Detect Poison	*UA	1	—	—	—	—	—	A
Detect Snares and Pits	*PH	1	—	—	—	—	—	A
Divination	PH	4	—	—	—	—	—	A
Find/Obscure the Path	PH	6R	—	—	—	—	—	A
Find Traps	PH	2	—	—	—	—	—	A
Know/Obscure Alignment	*UA	3R	—	Spc	—	—	—	A
Locate Animal	*PH	1	—	—	—	—	—	A
Locate/Obscure Object	PH	3R	—	—	—	—	—	A
Locate Plants	*PH	2	—	—	—	—	—	A
Magic Font	UA	5	—	—	—	—	—	A
Penetrate Disguise	UA	1	—	—	—	—	—	A
Portent	UA	1	—	—	—	—	—	A
Reflecting Pool	*UA	2	—	—	—	—	—	A
Speak with Monsters	PH	6	—	—	—	—	—	A
Tongues/Confuse Tongues	PH	4R	—	—	—	—	—	A
True/False Seeing	PH	5R	—	—	—	—	—	A
Elemental								
Air Walk	UA	5	—	—	—	—	A	—
Animate Rock	*PH	7	—	—	—	—	A	—
Chariot of Sustarre	*PH	7	—	—	—	—	A	—
Conjure/Dis. Earth Elem.	*PH	7R	—	—	—	—	A	—
Conjure/Dis. Fire Elem	*PH	6R	—	—	—	—	A	—
Create/Destroy Water	*PH	1/2R	—	—	—	—	A	—
Dust Devil	UA	2	—	—	—	—	A	—
Earthquake	PH	7	—	—	—	—	A	—
Fire Storm/Quench	*PH	7R	—	—	—	—	A	—
Fire Trap	*PH	2	—	—	—	—	A	—
Flame Blade	*UA	2	—	—	—	—	A	—
Heat/Chill Metal	*PH	2R	—	—	—	—	A	—
Lower/Raise Water	PH	4R	—	—	—	—	A	—
Meld into Stone	UA	3	—	—	—	—	A	—
Part Water	PH	6	—	—	—	—	A	—
Produce Fire	*PH	4	—	—	—	—	A	—
Produce Flame	*PH	2	—	—	—	—	A	—
Purify/Contaminate Water	*PH	1R	—	—	—	—	A	—
Pyrotechnics	*PH	3	—	—	—	—	A	—
Spike Stones	*UA	5	—	—	—	—	A	—
Stone Shape	*PH	3	—	—	—	—	A	—
Stone Tell	PH	6	—	—	—	—	A	—
Transmute Metal to Wood	*PH	7	—	—	—	—	A	—
Transmute Rock to Mud	*PH	5	—	—	—	—	A	—
Transmute Water to Dust	*UA	6R	—	—	—	—	A	—
Wall of Fire	*PH	5	—	—	—	—	A	—
Water Breathing	*PH	3	—	—	—	—	A	—
Water Walk	UA	3	—	—	—	—	A	—
Wind Walk	PH	7	—	—	—	—	A	—
Guardian								
Blade Barrier	PH	6	A	—	—	—	—	A
Glyph of Warding	PH	3	A	—	—	—	—	A
Silence 15' r.	PH	2	A	—	—	—	—	A
Symbol	PH	6/7	A	—	—	—	—	A
Wyvern Watch	UA	2	A	—	—	—	—	A

Abbreviations:

R (after spell level #) = reversible; * = druidical; A = castable in any form; Add = additional spell cleric can cast even though it is out of his deity's spheres of influence; Spc = special power, a spell the deity grants in addition to the cleric's normal allotment of spells; X = excluded, clerics of this god cannot use this spell; True = reverse of spell cannot be cast; Rev = only reversed spell can be cast.

Spheres of Influence—the Gods of Evil

SPHERE/SPELL	BOOK	Lvl	Tak	Sarg	Morg	Chem	Zeb	Hidd
Healing								
Cure/Cause Blindness	PH	3R	—	A	A	—	—	—
Cure/Cause Critical Wnds	*PH	5/6R	—	Rev	Rev	—	—	—
Cure/Cause Disease	*PH	3R	—	Rev	Rev	—	—	—
Cure/Cause Light Wnds	*PH	1R	—	A	A	—	—	—
Cure/Cause Serious Wnds	*PH	4R	—	Rev	Rev	—	—	—
Heal/Harm	PH	6R	—	A	A	—	—	—
Neutralize/Poison	*PH	4/3R	—	A	A	—	—	—
Remove/Cause Paralysis	UA	3R	—	Rev	Rev	—	—	—
Slow Poison	*PH	2	—	A	A	—	—	—
Necromantic								
Aid	UA	2	—	—	—	A	—	—
Animate Dead	PH	3	—	—	—	A	—	—
Animate Dead Monsters	UA	5	—	—	—	A	—	—
Death's Door	UA	3	—	—	—	A	—	—
Feign Death	*PH	3/2	—	—	—	A	—	—
Finger of Death	*PH	7	—	—	—	A	—	—
Invis to Undead	UA	1	—	—	—	A	—	—
Raise Dead/Slay Living	PH	5R	—	—	—	Rev	—	—
Regeneration/Wither	PH	7R	—	—	—	Rev	—	—
Restoration/Energy Drain	PH	7R	—	—	—	Rev	—	—
Resurrection/Destruction	PH	7R	—	—	—	Rev	—	—
Speak with Dead	PH	3	—	—	—	A	—	—
Plant								
Anti-Plant Shell 10' r.	*PH	5	—	—	A	—	—	—
Barkskin	*PH	2	A	—	—	—	—	—
Changestaff	*UA	7	—	—	A	—	—	—
Entangle	*PH	1	—	—	A	—	—	—
Fire Seeds	*PH	6	—	—	A	—	—	—
Goodberry/Badberry	*UA	2R	—	—	A	—	—	—
Hallucinatory Forest	*PH	4R	—	—	A	—	—	—
Hold Plant	*PH	4	—	—	A	—	—	—
Liveoak	*UA	6	—	—	A	—	—	—
Pass Plant	*PH	5	—	—	A	—	—	—
Pass Without Trace	*PH	1	—	—	A	—	—	—
Plant Door	*PH	4	—	—	A	—	—	—
Plant Growth	*PH	3	—	—	—	A	—	—
Shillelagh	*PH	1	—	—	—	A	—	—
Snare	*PH	3	—	—	A	—	—	—
Speak with Plants	*PH	4	—	—	A	—	—	—
Spike Growth	*UA	4	—	—	A	—	—	—
Sticks to Snakes	*PH	4/5R	—	—	A	—	—	—
Transport via Plants	*PH	4	—	—	A	—	—	—
Tree	*PH	3	—	—	A	—	—	—
Trip	*PH	2	—	—	A	—	—	—
Turn Wood	*PH	6	—	—	A	—	—	—
Wall of Thorns	*PH	6	—	—	A	—	—	—
Warp Wood	*PH	2	—	—	A	—	—	—

SPHERE/SPELL	BOOK	Lvl	Tak	Sarg	Morg	Chem	Zeb	Hidd
Protection								
Dispel Magic	*PH	3/4	A	—	—	—	—	—
Endure/Dispel Cold/Heat	UA	1R	A	—	—	—	—	—
Flame Walk	UA	3	A	—	—	—	—	—
Forbiddance	UA	6	A	—	—	—	—	—
Magical Vestment	UA	3	A	—	—	—	—	—
Negative Plane Protection	UA	3	A	—	—	—	—	—
Protection from Evil/Good	PH	1R	A	—	—	—	—	—
Prot. from Evil/Good 10' r.	PH	4R	Rev	—	—	—	—	—
Protection from Fire	*PH	3	A	Add	—	—	—	—
Protection from Lightning	*PH	4	A	—	—	—	—	—
Remove/Bestow Curse	PH	3R	Rev	—	—	—	—	—
Resist Cold	PH	1	A	—	—	—	—	—
Resist Fire	PH	2	A	Spc	—	—	—	—
Sanctuary	PH	1	A	—	—	—	—	—
Spell Immunity	UA	4	A	—	—	—	—	—
Withdraw	UA	2	A	—	—	—	—	—
Stellar								
Continual Light/Dark	PH	3R	Rev	Rev	Rev	Rev	Rev	Rev
Light/Darkness	PH	1R	Rev	Rev	Rev	Rev	Rev	Rev
Moonbeam	*U—	5	—	—	—	—	—	—
Starshine	*U—	3	—	—	—	—	—	—
Sunray	*U—	7	—	—	—	—	—	—
Summoning								
Abjure/Implore	UA	4R	A	A	—	—	—	A
Aerial Servant	PH	6	A	A	—	—	—	A
Conjure Animals	PH	6	A	A	—	—	—	A
Dispel Evil/Good	PH	5R	A	A	—	—	—	A
Exaction	UA	7	A	A	—	—	—	A
Exorcise	PH	4	A	A	—	—	—	A
Gate	PH	7	A	A	—	—	—	A
Golem	UA	5	A	A	—	—	—	A
Succor	PH	6	A	A	—	—	—	A
Word of Recall	PH	6	A	A	—	—	—	A
Weather								
Call Lightning	*PH	3	—	—	—	—	A	—
Cloudburst	*UA	3	—	—	—	—	A	—
Control Temperature	*PH	4	—	—	—	—	A	—
Control Weather	*PH	7	—	—	—	—	A	—
Control Winds	*PH	5	—	—	—	—	A	—
Faerie Fire	*PH	1	—	—	—	—	A	—
Obscurement	*PH	2	—	—	—	—	A	—
Precipitation	*UA	1	—	—	—	—	A	—
Predict Weather	*PH	1	—	—	—	—	A	—
Rainbow	UA	5	—	—	—	—	A	—
Weather Summoning	*PH	6	—	—	—	—	A	—

Abbreviations:

R (after spell level #) = reversible; * = druidical; A = castable in any form; Add = additional spell cleric can cast even though it is out of his deity's spheres of influence; Spc = special power, a spell the deity grants in addition to the cleric's normal allotment of spells; X = excluded, clerics of this god cannot use this spell; True = reverse of spell cannot be cast; Rev = only reversed spell can be cast.

 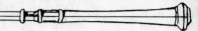

Spell Summary

In the following spell lists, the first entry is a somewhat abbreviated version of the spell name, the second entry is the level and magical type of the spell (C = Cleric, D = Druid, I = Illusionist, M = Magic-User). Combination spells have parenthetical third entries that list the other spell type involved, as follows: A = Alteration; Ab = Abjuration; C = Conjuration, Ch = Charm; D = Divination; E = Evocation; En = Enchantment; I = Invocation; Il = Illusion; N = Necromantic; P = Phantasm; S = Summoning.

Conjuration / Summoning

Bee	PC	(S only)
Bluelight	PC	(C only)
Bug	PC	(S only)
Gnats	PC	(S only)
Mouse	PC	(S only)
Spider	PC	(S only)
Tweak	PC	(C only)
Unlock	PC	(C only)
Armor	1M	(C only)
Beckon	5M	(Rev Avoidance)
Cacodemon	7M	
Conjure Elem	5M	
Death Spell	6M	
Drawmij's Ins Sum	7M	
Enchant An Item	6M	
Ensnarement	6M	
Evard's Blck Tent	4M	
Find Familiar	1M	
Flame Arrow	3M	
Gate	9M	
Invis Stalker	6M	
Leomund's Chest	5M	(Ab)
Limited Wish	7M	
Magic Jar	5M	
Material	3M	(C & E)
Maze	8M	
Monster Sum I	3M	
Monster Sum II	4M	
Monster Sum III	5M	
Monster Sum IV	6M	
Monster Sum V	7M	
Monster Sum VI	8M	
Monster Sum VII	9M	
Mord's Hound	5M	
Mord's Mansion	7M	
Mount	1M	
Power Wd Blind	8M	
Power Wd Kill	9M	
Power Wd Stun	7M	
Prismatic Sphere	9M	(Ab)
Push	1M	
Sepia Snake Symb	3M	
Symbol	8M	
Trap the Soul	8M	
Unseen Servant	1M	
Wish	9M	
Alter Reality	7I	(Il/P)
Conjure Animals	6I	
Maze	5I	
Prismatic Spray	7I	(Ab)
Prismatic Wall	7I	(Ab)
Summon Shadow	5I	

Invocation / Evocation

Belch	PA
Blink	PA
Chill	UC
Color	UC
Cough	PA
Dampen	UC
Dirty	RC
Dusty	RC
Nod	PA

Salt	UC	
Scratch	PA	
Sour	RC	
Sneeze	PA	
Spice	UC	
Sweeten	UC	
Twitch	PA	
Warm	UC	
Yawn	PA	
Alarm	1M	
Astral Spell	9M	
Banishment	7M	(Ab)
Bigby's Clench Fist	8M	
Bigby's Crush Hand	9M	
Bigby's Force Hand	6M	
Bigby's Grspg Hand	7M	
Bigby's Inter Hand	5M	
Binding	8M	(En)
Chain Lightning	6M	
Cloudkill	5M	
Cone of Cold	5M	
Contingency	6M	
Delay Blast Fball	7M	
Demand	8M	(En/charm)
Dig	4M	
Energy Drain	9M	
Fireball	3M	
Fire Shield	4M	(A)
Fire Trap	4M	
Flaming Sphere	2M	
Force Cage	7M	
Grease	1M	
Guards & Wards	6M	(A & En/Ch)
Ice Storm	4M	
Incendiary Cloud	8M	(A)
Leomund's Belab	5M	(En)
Lightning Bolt	3M	
Magic Missile	1M	
Material	3M	(C)
Melf's Acid Arrow	2M	
Meteor Swarm	9M	
Morden's Sword	7M	
Otiluke's Frzg Sph	6M	(A)
Otiluke's Res Sphere	4M	(A)
Otiluke's Tele Sph	8M	(A)
Sending	5M	
Shield	1M	
Shout	4M	
Spiritwrack	6M	(Ab)
Stinking Cloud	2M	
Tasha's Laughter	2M	
Tenser's Transf	6M	(A)
Torment	7M	(A)
Wall of Fire	4M	
Wall of Force	5M	
Wall of Ice	4M	
Wall of Iron	5M	
Wall of Stone	5M	
Web	2M	
Whip	2M	
Write	1M	
Zephyr	2M	
Chromatic Orb	1I	(A)
Death Fog	6I	(A)

Weird	7I	(Il/P)

Enchantment / Charm

Creak	HC	
Curdle	RC	
Distract	LC	
Flavor	UC	
Freshen	UC	
Smokepuff	PC	
Tap	HC	
Whistle	HC	
Wilt	RC	
Wink	PAC	
Anti/Sympathy	8M	
Bind	2M	(En & A)
Binding	8M	(En & E)
Charm Monster	4M	
Charm Person	1M	
Charm Plants	7M	
Confusion	4M	
Deeppockets	2M	(En & A)
Demand	8M	(En/Ch & E)
Dolor	4M	
Eyebite	5M	(En/Charm & Il/P)
Fabricate	5M	(En & A)
Feeblemind	5M	
Fire Charm	4M	
Forget	2M	
Friends	1M	
Fumble	4M	
Geas	5M	
Guards & Wards	5M	(En/Ch & A, E)
Hold Monster	5M	
Hold Person	3M	
Leomund's Belab	5M	(E)
Leomund's Shelter	4M	(En & A)
Magic Mirror	4M	(En & Conjuration)
Mass Charm	8M	
Mord's Disjunct	9M	(En & A)
Otiluke's Irr Dance	8M	
Ray of Enfeeb	2M	
Run	1M	(En only)
Scare	2M	
Sink	8M	(En & A)
Sleep	1M	
Succor	9M	(En & A)
Suggestion	3M	
Taunt	1M	(En only)
Truename	7M	(En & A)
Chaos	5I	
Confusion	4I	
Emotion	4I	
Hypnotism	1I	
Magic Mirror	5I	(En & D)
Mass Suggestion	6I	
Shadow Walk	7I	(En & Il)
Suggestion	3I	

Alteration

Change	LC
Fire Finger	PC
Gather	UC
Hairy	RC

Knot	RC	
Mute	LC	
Polish	UC	
Present	LC	
Ravel	RC	
Shine	UC	
Spill	RC	
Sprout	UC	
Stitch	UC	
Tangle	RC	
Tarnish	RC	
Tie	UC	
Untie	RC	
Wrap	UC	
Aff Norm Fires	1M	
Airy Water	5M	
Animal Growth	5M	
Avoidance	5M	(Ab)
Bind	2M	(En)
Blink	3M	
Burning Hands	1M	
Cloudburst	3M	
Comp Languages	1M	
Cont Light	2M	
Control Weather	6M	
Crystalbrittle	9M	
Dancing Lights	1M	
Darkness 15' r	2M	
Deeppockets	2M	(En)
Dimension Door	4M	
Disintegrate	6M	
Distance Distort	5M	
Duo-Dimension	7M	
Enchanted Weapon	4M	
Enlarge	1M	
Erase	1M	
Explosive Runes	3M	
Extension I	4M	
Extension II	5M	
Extension III	6M	
Fabricate	5M	(En)
Feather Fall	1M	
Fire Shield	4M	(E)
Firewater	1M	
Flaming Sphere	2M	(E)
Fly	3M	
Fools Gold	2M	
Glassee	6M	
Glassteel	8M	
Guards & Wards	6M	(E & En/Ch)
Gust of Wind	3M	
Haste	3M	
Hold Portal	1M	
Incendiary Cloud	8M	(E)
Infravision	3M	
Irritation	2M	
Item	3M	
Jump	1M	
Knock	2M	
Leomund's Chest	5M	(C/S)
Leomund's Hut	3M	
Leomund's Shelter	4M	(En)
Levitate	2M	
Light	1M	

126

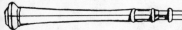

Spell Summary

Lower Water	6M		
Magic Mouth	2M		
Melf's Meteors	3M	(E)	
Melt	1M		
Mending	1M		
Message	1M		
Mord's Disjunct	9M	(En)	
Mord's Mansion	7M	(C)	
Move Earth	6M		
Otiluke's Frzg Sph	6M	(E)	
Otiluke's Res Sph	4M	(E)	
Otiluke's Tele Sph	8M	(E)	
Part Water	6M		
Passwall	5M		
Permanency	8M		
Plant Growth	4M		
Phase Door	7M		
Polymorph Any Obj	8M		
Polymorph Other	4M		
Polymorph Self	4M		
Project Image	6M	(Il/P)	
Precipitation	1M		
Pyrotechnics	2M		
Rary's Mnem Enhan	4M		
Reverse Gravity	7M		
Rope Trick	2M		
Serten's Sp Immun	8M		
Secret Page	3M		
Shape Change	9M		
Shatter	2M		
Shocking Grasp	1M		
Sink	8M	(En)	
Slow	3M		
Spider Climb	1M		
Statue	7M		
Stone Shape	5M		
Stone to Flesh	6M		
Stoneskin	4M		
Strength	2M		
Succor	9M	(En)	
Telekinesis	5M		
Teleport	5M		
Temporal Stasis	9M		
Tenser's Transf	6M	(E)	
Time Stop	9M		
Tongues	3M		
Trans Rock/Mud	5M		
Trans Water/Dust	6M		
Truename	7M	(En)	
Ultravision	4M		
Vanish	7M		
Vocalize	2M		
Water Breathing	3M		
Wind Walk	3M		
Wizard Eye	4M		
Wizard Mark	1M		
Wizard Lock	2M		

Colored Lights	MIC		
Dim	MIC		
Haze	MIC		
Rainbow	MIC		
Chromatic Orb	1I	(E)	
Color Spray	1I		
Cont Darkness	3I		
Cont Light	3I		
Dancing Lights	1I		
Darkness	1I		
Death Fog	6I	(E)	
Delude	3I		
Dream	5I	(Il/P)	
Fog Cloud	2I		
Gaze Reflection	1I		
Light	1I		
Magic Mouth	2I		
Major Creation	5I		
Minor Creation	4I		
Phantom Armor	1I	(Il)	
Phantom Wind	3I	(P)	
Project Image	5I	(Il/P)	
Rainbow Pattern	4I	(P)	
Rope Trick	3I		
Solid Fog	4I		
Ultravision	2I		
Vacancy	4I	(P)	
Wall of Fog	1I		
Wraithform	3I	(Il)	
Whispering Wind	2I	(P)	

Necromantic

Animate Dead	5M	
Clone	8M	
Feign Death	3M	
Reincarnate	6M	

Divination

Clairaudience	3M	
Clairvoyance	3M	
Cont Other Plane	5M	
Detect Evil	2M	
Detect Illusion	3M	
Detect Invis	2M	
Detect Magic	1M	
ESP	2M	
Identify	1M	
Know Alignment	2M	
Legend Lore	6M	
Locate Object	2M	
Read Magic	1M	
Detect Illusion	1I	
Detect Invis	1I	
Detect Magic	2I	
Read Illus Magic	1I	
True Sight	6I	
Vision	7I	

Illusion/Phantasms

Footfall	HC	(Il only)	
Groan	HC	(Il only)	
Hide	LC	(Il only)	
Moan	HC	(Il only)	
Palm	LC	(Il only)	
Rattle	HC	(Il only)	
Thump	HC	(Il only)	
Audible Glamer	2M		
Eyebite	6M	(En/Ch)	
Fear	4M		
Halluc Terrain	4M		
Invisibility	2M		
Invis 10' r	3M		
Leomund's Trap	2M		
Mass Invis	7M		
Massmorph	4M		
Mirror Image	2M		
Nystul's Mag Aura	1M		
Phantasmal Force	3M		
Project Image	6M	(A)	
Sequester	7M	(Ab)	
Simulacrum	7M		
Ventriloquism	1M		
Mask	MIC	(Il only)	
Mirage	MIC	(Il only)	
Noise	MIC	(Il only)	
Two-D Illusn	MIC	(Il only)	
Advanced Illusn	5I		
Alter Realty	7I	(C/S)	
Alter Self	2I	(Il only & A)	
Audible Glamer	1I		
Blindness	2I		
Blur	2I		
Change Self	1I		
Deafness	2I		
Demi-Shadow Mon	5I		
Demi-Shadow Magic	6I		
Dispel Exhaust	4I		
Fascinate	2I		
Fear	3I		
Halluc Terrain	3I		
Hypnotic Pattern	2I		
Illusion Script	3I		
Improved Invis	4I		
Impr Phan Force	2I		
Invis 10' r	3I		
Dream	5I	(A)	
Invisible	2I		
Massmorph	4I		
Mirage Arcane	6I		
Mirror Image	2I		
Misdirection	2I		
Mislead	6I		
Paralyzation	3I		
Permanent Illusn	6I		

Phantasmagoria	6I		
Phantasmal Force	1I		
Phantasmal Killer	4I		
Phantom Armor	1I	(Il only & A)	
Phantom Steed	3I	(P & C)	
Phantom Wind	3I	(P & A)	
Programmed Illusn	6I		
Project Image	5I	(A)	
Rainbow Pattern	4I	(P & A)	
Shades	6I		
Shadow Door	5I		
Shadow Magic	5I		
Shadow Monsters	4I		
Shadow Walk	7I	(Il, & En)	
Spectral Force	3I		
Spook	1I		
Tempus Fugit	5I		
Vacancy	4I	(P & A)	
Veil	6I		
Ventriloquism	2I		
Weird	7I	(E)	
Whispering Wind	2I	(P & A)	
Wraithform	3I	(Il & A)	

Abjurations

Clean	UC		
Dry	UC		
Dust	UC		
Exterminate	UC		
Anti-Magic Shell	6M		
Avoidance	5M	(A)	
Banishment	7M	(E)	
Dismissal	5M		
Dispel Illusion	4M		
Dispel Magic	3M		
Globe of Invuln	6M		
Imprisonment	9M		
Mind Blank	8M		
Minor Globe Invuln	4M		
Preserve	2M		
Prismatic Sphere	9M		
Prot/Cantrips	1M		
Prot/Evil	1M		
Prot/Evil 10' r	3M		
Prot/Normal Miss	3M		
Remove Curse	4M		
Repulsion	6M		
Spiritwrack	6M	(E)	
Sequester	7M	(Il/P)	
Volley	7M		
Dispel Illusion	3I		
Dispel Magic	4I		
Non-Detection	3I		
Prismatic Spray	7I	(C/S)	
Prismatic Wall	7I	(C/S)	

knights circle table

1d6 + modifier	Coin*	Equipment	Healing	Ranking Authority
1 or less	n/a	n/a	n/a	No Circle Present
2	1d4 stl	dagger/none	n/a	Knight of the Crown (Crown 3rd)
3	1d6 stl	spear/none	n/a	Knight of the Crown (Crown 3rd)
4	1d8 stl	quarter staff/none	1/-/-	Knight of the Crown (Crown 3rd)
5	2d4 stl	short sword/leather	2/-/-	Knight of the Sword (Sword 4th)
6	1d10 stl	morning star/leather & shield	3/1/-	Knight of the Crown (Crown 3rd)
7	1d12 stl	battle axe/ring	4/1/-	Knight of the Sword (Sword 4th)
8	1d20 stl	short bow/ring & shield	5/2/-	Knight of the Heart (Rose 5th)
9	2d10 stl	long bow/chain	6/2/1	Shield Knight (Crown 5th)
10	2d20 stl	long sword/chain & shield	7/3/1	Bladeknight (Sword 5th)
11	1d100 stl	crossbow/banded	8/3/1	Knight of the Rose (Rose 6th)
12	3d20 stl	halberd/banded & shield	9/4/1	Lord of Shields (Crown 7th)
13	4d20 stl	lance (light)/plate	10/4/2	Elder of Sword (Sword 8th)
14	5d20 stl	lance (heavy)/plate & shield	11/5/2	Keeper of the Rose (Rose 9th)
15	2d100 stl	*sword +1*/Solamnic armor	12/5/3	Lord Warrior (Crown 10th)
16	3d100 stl	*sword +2*/Solamnic armor	13/5/3	Master Clerist (Sword 11th)
17	4d100 stl	*sword +3*/Solamnic armor	14/6/3	Lord of Roses (Rose 12th)
18	5d100 stl	single artifact†/*plate +1*	15/6/4	Lord Warrior (Crown 10th)
19	6d100 stl	*Dragonlance‡*/*plate +2*	17/7/5	Lord Clerist (Sword 12th)
20 or above	10d100 stl	*Dragonlance*/*plate +3*	18/8/6	Lord of Justice (Rose 14th)

* This represents the amount of coin available to the Knight from that location on a given day. It does not represent how much money the Knight may draw from the Circle. Knights may draw from any Circle no more than the amount listed for their level. For example: a 10th-level Knight of Solamnia could draw no more than 20 stl from a given Circle on a given day. If that same Knight is going to a Circle that can only pay 2d4 stl because of its small size, then 2d4 stl is all he will receive. If he is attending a large Circle (with modifiers the Circle turns out to be an 18) then he would still only be able to draw 20 stl from the Circle even though the amount listed is 5d100 stl. *Stl* stands for steel pieces, the universal equivalent of gold pieces in Krynn.

† This artifact is a weapon or magical device of combat value found either in the *Dungeon Masters Guide* or in this *DRAGONLANCE*® Adventures book. The exact device is up to the DM, who should exercise discretion.

‡ The type of lance is determined by a roll of 1d6. It would be a footman's lance (1-4) or a mounted lance (5-6). The quality of the lance is determined by a roll of 1d12. This could be made without the use of either the *Hammer of Kharas* or the *Silver Arm* (1-9); made with one of the artifacts (10-11) or with both from ancient times (12).

knights circle modifiers

Description	Modifier	Description	Modifier
Community Size		Society	
Village, Small	−2	Capital of Region	+2
Village, Medium	−1	Major Constructions	
Village, Large	none	Small Keep present	+1
Town, Small	+1	Large Keep present	+2
Town, Medium	+2	Small Castle present	+2
Town, Large	+3	Large Castle present	+3
City, Small	+4	Major Fortifications	+1
City, Medium	+5	Inside traditional Solamnia borders*	+4
City, Large	+6	Inside areas controlled by Dragon Highlords‡	−10

* This would include mainland Solamnia and Sancrist.

‡ Circles in these areas, when they are present, are maintained and operated clandestinely by the Knights. Merely finding and getting in touch with such Circles can often be difficult or impossible.